final

blood
urine
digestive
metabolism
- few from physio
chem

INTEGRATE

the benjamin cummings custom laboratory program
for anatomy & physiology

Biology 2020
Human Anatomy & Physiology II

1 inch - 2.54 cm
1 yd - 191
1 mi -

Pearson Learning Solutions

New York Boston San Francisco
London Toronto Sydney Tokyo Singapore Madrid
Mexico City Munich Paris Cape Town Hong Kong Montreal

Senior Vice President, Editorial and Marketing: Patrick F. Boles
Senior Sponsoring Editor: Natalie Danner
Development Editor: Annette Fantasia
Editorial Assistant: Jill Johnson
Executive Marketing Manager: Nathan L. Wilbur
Operations Manager: Eric M. Kenney
Production Manager: Jennifer Berry
Art Director: Renée Sartell
Cover Designer: Kristen Kiley

Cover Art: Courtesy of DK Images and Prentice-Hall, Inc.

This special edition published in cooperation with Pearson Learning Solutions.

Printed in the United States of America.

Please visit our web site at *www.pearsoncustom.com.*

Attention bookstores: For permission to return unused stock, contact us at *pe-uscustomreturns@pearson.com.*

Pearson Learning Solutions, 501 Boylston Street, Suite 900, Boston, MA 02116
A Pearson Education Company
www.pearsoned.com

2 3 4 5 6 V0ZU 14 13 12 11 10

PEARSON

ISBN 10: 0-558-27772-1
ISBN 13: 978-0-558-27772-7

Contents

The Metric System

Measurement	Unit and abbreviation	Metric equivalent	Metric to English conversion factor	English to metric conversion factor
Length	1 kilometer (km)	= 1000 (10^3) meters	1 km = 0.62 mile	1 mile = 1.61 km
	1 meter (m)	= 100 (10^2) centimeters = 1000 millimeters	1 m = 1.09 yards 1 m = 3.28 feet 1 m = 39.37 inches	1 yard = 0.914 m 1 foot = 0.305 m
	1 centimeter (cm)	= 0.01 (10^{-2}) meter	1 cm = 0.394 inch	1 foot = 30.5 cm 1 inch = 2.54 cm
	1 millimeter (mm)	= 0.001 (10^{-3}) meter	1 mm = 0.039 inch	
	1 micrometer (μm) [formerly micron (μ)]	= 0.000001 (10^{-6}) meter		
	1 nanometer (nm) [formerly millimicron (mμ)]	= 0.000000001 (10^{-9}) meter		
	1 angstrom (Å)	= 0.0000000001 (10^{-10}) meter		
Area	1 square meter (m^2)	= 10,000 square centimeters	1 m^2 = 1.1960 square yards 1 m^2 = 10.764 square feet	1 square yard = 0.8361 m^2 1 square foot = 0.0929 m^2
	1 square centimeter (cm^2)	= 100 square millimeters	1 cm^2 = 0.155 square inch	1 square inch = 6.4516 cm^2
Mass	1 metric ton (t)	= 1000 kilograms	1 t = 1.103 ton	1 ton = 0.907 t
	1 kilogram (kg)	= 1000 grams	1 kg = 2.205 pounds	1 pound = 0.4536 kg
	1 gram (g)	= 1000 milligrams	1 g = 0.0353 ounce 1 g = 15.432 grains	1 ounce = 28.35 g
	1 milligram (mg)	= 0.001 gram	1 mg = approx. 0.015 grain	
	1 microgram (μg)	= 0.000001 gram		
Volume (solids)	1 cubic meter (m^3)	= 1,000,000 cubic centimeters	1 m^3 = 1.3080 cubic yards 1 m^3 = 35.315 cubic feet	1 cubic yard = 0.7646 m^3 1 cubic foot = 0.0283 m^3
	1 cubic centimeter (cm^3 or cc)	= 0.000001 cubic meter = 1 milliliter	1 cm^3 = 0.0610 cubic inch	1 cubic inch = 16.387 cm^3
	1 cubic millimeter (mm^3)	= 0.000000001 cubic meter		
Volume (liquids and gases)	1 kiloliter (kl or kL)	= 1000 liters	1 kL = 264.17 gallons	1 gallon = 3.785 L 1 quart = 0.946 L
	1 liter (l or L)	= 1000 milliliters	1 L = 0.264 gallons 1 L = 1.057 quarts	
	1 milliliter (ml or mL)	= 0.001 liter = 1 cubic centimeter	1 ml = 0.034 fluid ounce 1 ml = approx. $\frac{1}{4}$ teaspoon 1 ml = approx. 15–16 drops (gtt.)	1 quart = 946 ml 1 pint = 473 ml 1 fluid ounce = 29.57 ml 1 teaspoon = approx. 5 ml
	1 microliter (μl or μL)	= 0.000001 liter		
Time	1 second (s or sec)	= $\frac{1}{60}$ minute		
	1 millisecond (ms or msec)	= 0.001 second		
Temperature	Degrees Celsius (°C)		°F = $\frac{9}{5}$(°C) + 32	°C = $\frac{5}{9}$(°F − 32)

PHYSIOLOGICAL CHEMISTRY

An understanding of some simple chemical principles is essential to the understanding of many physiological processes, e.g. acid-base balance, kidney function, and respiration. The goal of Labs 1 and 2 is to acquaint (or re-acquaint) you with some basic concepts in physiological chemistry.

DEFINITIONS

(1) **Element**: a substance composed of atoms of the same atomic number

(2) **Compound**: a substance composed of two or more elements

(3) **Molecule**: the smallest particle into which an element or compound may be divided without losing its chemical characteristics; further division of a molecule results in altered chemical properties.

(4) **Solution**: a mixture in which a solid (= solute) is dissolved in a fluid or gas (= solvent), so that the dissolved substances cannot be distinguished from the fluid or gas (i.e., a homogenous mixture).

(5) **Solute**: the dissolved portion of a solution, e.g. in a sodium chloride solution, sodium chloride is the solute

(6) **Solvent**: the portion of a solution in which the solute is dissolved and is usually present in larger amounts than the solute, e.g. in a sodium chloride solution, water is the solvent

(7) **Mole (mol)**: Avagadro's number (= 6.02×10^{23}) molecules or atoms

(8) **Molecular weight**: the weight in grams of one mole of any substance

(9) **Molar (M)**: an expression of a solution's concentration, it is the number of moles of solute per liter of solution

(10) **Millimolar (mM)**: number of millimoles (or 1/1000 mol) per liter of solution

(11) **Osmole (osmol)**: the amount of a substance (solute) that dissociates in solution to form one mole of osmotically active particles, e.g. 1 mol of glucose, which does not dissociate in water, forms 1 osmole of solute; 1 mol of sodium chloride forms 2 osmoles of solute, because sodium chloride dissociates into Na^+ and Cl^- in water osm = M × #particles it breaks up into

(12) **Osmolar (Osm)**: another expression of a solution's concentration, it is the number of osmoles of solute per liter of solution

(13) **Milliosmolar (mOsm)**: number of milliosmoles (or 1/1000 osm) per liter of solution

(14) % **Solution**: grams solute per 100 ml of solution

(15) **Osmosis**: the diffusion of water across a semipermeable membrane from a region of high *water* (lower solute) concentration to one of lower *water* (higher solute) concentration

WAYS OF EXPRESSING SOLUTION CONCENTRATIONS

Although there are many ways of expressing the concentration of a solution, we will be discussing three main methods.

MOLAR SOLUTIONS

The molarity of a solution is expressed as Molar (M), the number of moles of a substance dissolved in each liter of solution.

$$M = \frac{\text{moles solute}}{\text{L solution}}$$

Note: 1 L = 1 liter = 1,000 milliliters (ml)

For water: 1 cubic centimeter (cm3) = 1 ml = 1 gram (g)

A liter of 1.0 M NaCl (sodium chloride) solution would be made by dissolving 1.0 mol of NaCl in enough distilled water to make 1 L of total solution. You can determine how much 1.0 mol of NaCl is by calculating the molecular weight of NaCl, done by adding the atomic weights of Na (sodium) and Cl (chloride) from the Periodic Table of the Elements:

Atom	Atomic Weight (g)
Na	22.98
Cl	35.45

Molecular weight of NaCl = 58.43 g

So, 1 mole of NaCl contains 58.4 g of NaCl (or, 6.02×10^{23} particles of NaCl weighs 58.4 g). Therefore, one liter of a 1.0M NaCl solution is made by adding 58.4 g of NaCl to enough pure water to make exactly one liter of the *solution.* Keep in mind that this is *NOT* the same as adding 58.4 g of NaCl to one liter of pure water.

Now that you know how to calculate molecular weights, you can calculate how much pure sulfuric acid (H_2SO_4) there is in a liter of 0.1M H_2SO_4.

Atom	Atomic Weight (g)		# Atoms in Compound
H	1	x	2
S	32	x	1
O	16	x	4

Molecular weight of H_2SO_4= 2(1) + 1(32) + 4(16) = 98 g in one mole or 98 g/mol

Now, let's go back and determine the amount of H_2SO_4 in 1 L of a 0.1M H_2SO_4 solution. Using unit conversion methods:

$$\frac{98\ g\ H_2SO_4}{mol\ H_2SO_4} \times \frac{0.1\ mol\ H_2SO_4}{L\ solution} = \frac{9.8\ g\ H_2SO_4}{L\ solution}$$

In biology, expressing concentrations in molar (M) units is cumbersome, because most physiological solutions are very dilute. It is most common to find solution concentrations in the range of one-thousandth (1/1000) of a mol, or millimole (mmol) per liter solution. Accordingly, a smaller unit of expressing solution concentration, the millimolar unit (mM) is more frequently used.

$$mM = \frac{millimoles\ solute}{L\ solution}$$

OSMOLAR SOLUTIONS

The number of osmotically active particles in solution.

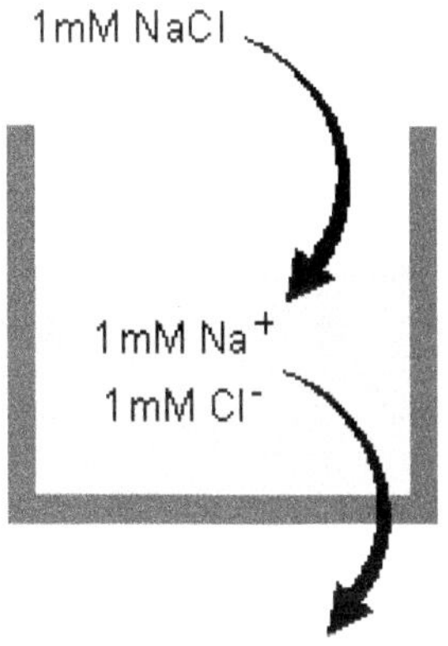
1mM NaCl
1 mM Na+
1 mM Cl-

total osmolarity = 2mOsM

Osmolarity is a measure of the osmotic pressure exerted by a solution across a perfect semi-permeable membrane (one which allows free passage of water and completely prevents movement of solute) compared to pure water. Osmolarity is dependent on the number of particles in solution. For example, 1 mol of glucose dissolved in 1 L of water has an osmolarity of 1 osmole (osm) per L. If 1 mol of NaCl were dissolved in 1 L of water, it would produce a 1 mol/l NaCl solution *with an osmolarity 2 osm/L,* because NaCl dissociates into Na^+ and Cl^- (two particles) in solution. This is true of all compounds that dissociate in solution. Na_2SO_4, which dissociates into Na^+, Na^+ and SO_4^{2-}, to give 3 particles per molecule produces 3 osm/L for every mole dissolved in 1 L. As in molar solutions, physiologically relevant units for osmolarity is in milliosmoles, or mOsm, and the osmolar concentration of a solution is expressed in mOsm/L or milliosmolar (mOsm).

mOsm = mM x number particles per molecule

PERCENT (%) SOLUTIONS

The term "percent" means "per 100." Used in the context of solutions, it means grams of solute per 100 milliliters of solution, or

$$\%\ Solution = \frac{g\ solute}{100\ ml\ solution}$$

This is also commonly known as the weight/volume %. To illustrate, a 10% NaCl solution has 10 g of NaCl dissolved in 100 ml of total solution. In medical practice, 5% glucose solutions are used in intravenous feedings.

How would you make 100 ml of a 5% glucose solution?

Calculations: ____

____

Procedure: ____

____

How would you make 100 ml of a 0.1 M glucose solution? The chemical formula for glucose is $C_6H_{12}O_6$. Show your calculations and describe how you would prepare this solution.

Calculations: ____

____

____

Procedure: ____

How would you make 100 ml of a 5 mM glucose solution?

Calculations: ____

____

Procedure: ____

What is the osmolarity of a 5 mM glucose solution?

____

LAB ACTIVITIES

(1) Do the 28 problems in the "*Chemical Calculations Problem Set*," copies of which are available at each station.

(2) Make up 25 ml of a 5% sucrose solution. Check with your instructor to make sure you have done it properly.

Calculations: ____

____

(3) Make up 50 ml of a 0.1 M sucrose solution. Is this more or less concentrated than the 5% sucrose solution you just made?

Calculations: ____

____

(4) Make up 25 ml of a 0.9% NaCl solution. (This concentration of NaCl is known as physiological saline.) What is the molarity of this solution? What is the osmolarity of this solution?

Calculations: ____

____

PHYSIOLOGICAL CHEMISTRY, Part II

IONIZATION REACTIONS

Certain compounds are made up of atoms having very different attractions for electrons. For example, NaCl is made up of sodium (Na) and chloride (Cl) atoms. The sodium atoms have a very weak attraction for one of its outermost electrons and will easily donate it to an atom having strong attraction for electrons. The chloride atoms in NaCl have an affinity for electrons and will accept them from sodium. Thus, in a crystal of NaCl the sodium atoms have a positive charge, and the chloride atoms have a negative charge; opposite charges attract one another, so Na is bound to Cl in what is known as an ionic bond. However, when the crystal is placed in water, it is attacked by water molecules. The attractive forces between water and sodium or chloride are stronger than those between sodium and chloride, so the Na is torn away from the Cl, and in the process, Cl leaves with one electron from Na. Thus, Na^+ and Cl^- ions are formed in solution. This process occurs with several other kinds of compounds in solution and is called ionization. Ionization is an extremely important process in living systems, in part because it determines how much H^+ (or acid) is in solution. Compounds capable of ionizing in solution are (1) salts, (2) acids, and (3) bases.

LAB ACTIVITY

Examine the conductivity apparatus: notice that there are two electrodes. After being plugged in, the bulb will light up *only* if a conductive medium is placed between the two electrodes. Test each of the solutions listed in the table below, and fill out the table with your results (no light, dim light, moderate light, or bright light) and the extent of ionization (none, small, moderate, or complete). Keep in mind that the extent of ionization = degree of dissociation of the components of a compound.

To test each solution for conductance, fill a 100 to 150 ml beaker with each of the solutions listed below to submerge the electrode tips under about 0.5 – 1 inch (or about 30-40 ml) of fluid. In between each solution test, rinse the electrodes with distilled water from the squirt bottle making sure to hold the large "waste" beaker under the electrodes to capture the rinse water, then dab the excess water off the electrodes using a Kimwipe. *CAUTION: NEVER TOUCH THE ELECTRODES WHEN THE APPARATUS IS PLUGGED IN!* All used solutions can be dumped down the sink under running tap water.

Solution	Result	Extent of Ionization
0.1M NaCl	bright	
0.1M Glucose	none	
0.1M Sucrose	none	
0.1M HCl	very bright	
* 0.1M NaOH	very, very bright	
0.1M Acetic Acid	none	
0.1M Sodium Acetate	weak	
0.1M Ammonium Hydroxide	none	

What causes the bulb to light up? What is conducting current between the two electrodes?

The dissociation of the ions

What is the relationship between extent of ionization of a substance and brightness of the bulb?

The ones That dissociate the most light up the most.

Why do some substances cause the bulb to light, while others do not?

Because some dissociate & others don't.

Why does the bulb light so dimly with acetic acid?

Because the ions dissociate weakly.

Why does sodium acetate give different results than acetic acid?

B/c they are chemically combined differently

DIFFUSION & OSMOSIS

Diffusion - the random movement of particles (solute) in solution from an area of higher concentration to one of lower concentration of particles (solute)

Osmosis - the diffusion of water across a semi-permeable membrane from an area of higher concentration of *water* to one of lower concentration of *water*

LAB ACTIVITY

1. *Diffusion*

Practical Application

Your instructor will show you how to place a puddle of food coloring on the bottom of the 3 beakers, half filled with tap water. Avoid stirring or agitating the solution. One beaker will be in ice, another on a hot plate and the last sitting at room temperature. Once the dye has been delivered to the beakers, turn on the hot plate. Note the results at intervals during the lab period. What is the effect of increasing or decreasing the temperature?

What is the effect of increased or decreased temperature on the rate of diffusion?

temperature speeds up diffusion

2. *Osmosis*

An osmometer experiment will be set up by your instructor to demonstrate the generation of osmotic pressure. Take note of the height of the meniscus in the tube at regular intervals from the start through the end of lab. You will observe one or all three of the following set-ups:

(a) A sucrose solution is placed inside a cellophane (dialysis) sac, and the sac is submerged in distilled water. A tube is placed inside the sac to measure its fluid volume (the height of the meniscus indicates sac volume, and as volume increases inside the sac, the height of the meniscus rises). The cellophane is selectively permeable, only allowing water to pass through (not sugar particles). In this case, the solution inside the sac is hyperosmotic (has a greater osmolarity, thus exerts a greater osmotic pressure) relative to the surrounding medium (distilled water).

(b) Distilled water is placed inside a cellophane sac, and the sac is submerged in a sucrose solution (the opposite of the previous arrangement). In this case, the solution inside the sac is hyposmotic (has lower osmolarity and low osmotic pressure) relative to the surrounding medium (sugar solution).

(c) Distilled water is placed inside a cellophane sac, and the sac is submerged in distilled water. In this case, both solutions are isosmotic (have the same osmolarity, same osmotic pressure).

What is the relationship of solute concentration to the final height to which the meniscus rises? bag

More concentrated the higher the meniscus

Is osmosis occurring? In which direction does water move in each of the set-ups?

Why does the meniscus stop rising?

The pressure equalizes as much as possible

What is "osmotic pressure"? ___

ACIDS, BASES, pH, and BUFFERS

Acid: any substance which liberates H^+ ion in solution

Base: any substance which liberates OH^- ion in solution, or has the ability to neutralize H^+ ion.

Buffer: a solution composed of a weak acid or base and its salt, which neutralizes excess acid or base over a certain range, thus preventing a marked change in the pH of the solution

Water makes up 50-95% of all living matter, so it is unquestionably a vital life component. As demonstrated previously, water is a substance that promotes the ionization of certain substances called *electrolytes*. Water itself can ionize, though to a very small extent. In pure water, there is predominantly undissociated H_2O, but there is also small amount of H^+ ion and OH^- which derive from the ionization of H_2O:

$$H_2O \rightarrow H^+ + OH^-$$

The concentration of H^+ in pure water is 10^{-7} moles per liter. If one were to write this hydrogen ion concentration in decimal form, it would be written as: 0.0000001 M (or 10^{-4} mM). This is of course a very small concentration of H^+, but it should be realized that similarly low concentrations are common in cells and in body fluids.

Obviously, such decimal expressions are awkward to work with, so a simpler method of writing hydrogen ion concentrations has been devised. It is based on logarithms, and is called the *pH* (potential of hydrogen) scale. pH is defined as the negative logarithm of hydrogen ion concentration.

$$pH = -\log [H^+]$$

In the following table, notice the relationship of H^+ and pH:

$[H^+]$ (decimal)	$[H^+]$ (exponential)	$pH = -\log [H^+]$
1 M	10^0	0
0.1 M	10^{-1}	1
0.000 01 M	10^{-5}	5
0.000 000 1 M	10^{-7}	7
0.000 000 01 M	10^{-8}	8
0.000 000 000 000 01 M	10^{-14}	14

There are several things you should notice from this table:

1. A change of one unit of pH represents a 10-fold change in H^+ concentration.
2. Increasing acid strength is indicated by decreasing pH values.
3. A pH of 7 represents a neutral solution.

The pH of blood is normally 7.35-7.45. The stomach contents may be as low as pH 1, a value over a million times more concentrated in acid than the blood!

Usually, pH is measured with a pH meter, though less accurate measurement with pH paper (paper impregnated with dyes which change color as pH changes) often suffices.

Weakly Dissociated Acids and Buffers

Most of the acids found in the body are not strong acids (with the exception of HCl) but are acids that only partially dissociate to release a small amount of H^+. Such acids are lactic acid (produced by exercising muscle) and carbonic acid (produced by a reaction of CO_2 with water).

To illustrate, a 1 M acetic acid solution has a pH of about 2.2 (recall that 1M HCl has a pH of 0), because it only slightly ionizes to release free hydrogen ion. Note: HAc = (acetic acid) & Ac^- = (acetate ion): $HAc \rightleftarrows H^+ + Ac^-$

When HAc and its salt NaAc (sodium acetate) are mixed in solution, we have what is called a *buffer*.

Buffer: A weak acid and its' salt

A buffer can resist changes in pH when either acid or base is added to the solution. The acid (HAc) neutralizes base:

$$HAc + OH^- \rightarrow H_2O + Ac^-$$

The salt absorbs the acid:

$$NaAc + H^+ \rightarrow HAc + Na^+$$

Note that both the weak acid and the salt (i.e., a buffer pair) are needed to have a buffer solution. Over a certain pH range, a buffer will maintain a reasonably stable pH even though acid or base is added to the solution. In physiological fluids buffers stabilize the pH so that regulation is possible. Blood is a buffer system, one that is well regulated and maintained at about pH 7.4. Blood buffers include carbonic acid/bicarbonate (H_2CO_3/HCO_3^-), proteins (especially hemoglobin), phosphate salts, and amino acids.

Clinically, various forms of acid-base disturbances are observed: respiratory, metabolic, diabetic, & renal acidosis; altitude, respiratory and metabolic alkalosis.

LAB ACTIVITY

1. Litmus paper is sensitive to acids and bases in solution.
What color does it turn in acid? red In basic solution? blue

2. Phenolphthalein is an indicator dye which changes color according to the pH of its environment. Add a drop of phenolphthale in to a basic solution and note its color: ________________________.
Repeat in acid solution, and note the color:________________________.

3. Put 20 ml. of acetic acid-sodium acetate buffer into one beaker, 20 ml. distilled H_2O into another. Use pH paper to measure pH as you add 0.1 M HCl one drop at a time to each beaker. Keep a count of the number of drops added; measure the pH after each drop and enter the data into the chart below. Repeat the comparison using 0.1M NaOH.

pH DATA

# of drops added	Addition of ACID		Addition of BASE	
	H_2O	*Buffer*	*H_2O*	*Buffer*
3	9	7	11	8
6	9	7	11.5	8
9	8.5	7	12	8
15	6.5	7	12	10
25	5	8	12	11

Predict the results if sodium chloride had been used rather than sodium acetate:

____

4. Add 5 drops of phenolphthalein to 100 ml. of distilled H_2O. Make the solution slightly basic by addition of a few drops of 0.1 M NaOH until a rose color appears and persists. Breathe into this solution with a straw.

What happens?

____

Explain the results:

____

Write a chemical equation describing the reaction:

---

5. Prepare two identical beakers of solution for a second trial by adding 0.1 M NaOH as above. Have one member of the group blow through a straw into the solution while another measures the time required for the color change of the solution. Measure the time required immediately after the subject has run in place for 2 minutes. Compare the times and explain any differences.

---

6. Can you suggest how anti-acid preparations, such as Alka-Seltzer and Tums work?

---

7. What happens when the buffering capacity of a buffer solution is exceeded?

Station #4 pH measurements

pH paper and forceps
2 50ml beakers
3 plastic pipettes marked with the solutions that will be used
1 M solutions of HCl and NaOH
Squeeze bottle with distilled water pH 7 buffer

Students will have 2 small beakers. They should be 50 ml in volume. One is labeled distilled water and the other pH 7 buffer. They will also have distilled water, pH paper, a strong acid (1M HCl) a strong base (1M NaOH) and a pH 7 buffer.
The students should follow this protocol.

1. Fill the beaker labeled distilled water with 20 ml of distilled water.
2. Fill the beaker labeled pH7 buffer with 20 ml of pH 7 buffer.
3. Measure the pH and record it on the table. **Tell the students to use short pieces of pH paper 1/2"**
4. Place 1 drop of acid (1M HCl) in both beakers.
5. Measure the pH of both beakers and record it on the table
6. Repeat 4 and 5 until you have added a total of 5 drops to both beakers.
7. **Wash both beakers**
8. Again fill the beaker labeled distilled water with 20ml of distilled water
9. Again fill the beaker labeled pH7 buffer with 20ml of pH 7 buffer

10. Measure the ph and record it on the table
11. Place 1 drop of base (1M NaOH) in both beakers
12. Measure the pH of both beakers and record it on the table
13. Repeat 11 and 12 until you have added a total of 5 drops to both beakers

14 **Wash the beakers and dispose of used pH paper**

Station #5 influence of breathing on pH
pH paper and forceps
Erlen flasks 125ml
phenolphthalein
straws
0.1M NaOH and 0.1 M HCl
distilled water
plastic pipette

1. Fill the Erlen flask 1/2 with distilled water
2. added 1 or 2 drops of 0.1M NaOH
3. Then you put 2 drops of Phenolphthalein indicator, (the indicator will turn pink which means the solution is a base.
4. Then using a straw, have a student blow into the solution.

What happens is the solution turns from pink to clear indicating that the pH has changed to below 7 (thus it has become an acid.) The reason for this is the CO2 mixes with water to form Hydrogen ions (by definition, an acid). This is a very important experiment that shows the bicarbonate buffering system in our bodies.

$CO_2+H_2O \longleftrightarrow H_2CO_3 \longleftrightarrow H^+ -HCO_3$

The reason why it is important is that it keeps the pH of our blood constant and depending on the way it is shifted, increases or decreases our drive to breath.
Dr. Symmons claims that he failed a student on his thesis defense when that student didn't know the formula.

MORE PRACTICE PROBLEMS

ELEMENT	ATOMIC WEIGHT (g)
H	1.0
O	16
C	12
Ca	40.1
Na	23
K	39.1
Cl	35.45

1. What is the molarity (M) of a 0.75% $CaCl_2$ (calcium chloride) solution? What is the millimolar (mM) concentration of this solution?

2. What is the osmolarity (Osm) of a 0.75% $CaCl_2$ solution? What is its milliosmolar (mOsm) concentration? *Hint: In solution, $CaCl_2$ will dissociate into one Ca^{+2} ion and two Cl^- ions.*

3. How much glucose (in grams) would you need to make 500 ml of a 1% glucose solution?

4. How much glucose (in grams) would you need to make 2 L of a 0.5M glucose solution? *Hint: glucose has the molecular formula $C_6H_{12}O_6$.*

5. What is the osmolarity of a 0.5M glucose solution?

6. Which solution is more concentrated: (a) a 2% HCl (hydrochloric acid) solution or (b) a 1 M HCl solution?

7. A 0.6 M NaCl solution is equivalent to a ______ mM NaCl solution and a _____ mOsm solution.

8. Mr. Green weighs 220 pounds, and his doctor has ordered treatment with Drug X. The prescribed dosage of Drug X is 100 mg/kg body weight. Drug X comes in vials containing the concentration of 75 mg/ml. What volume (in ml) of Drug X should be given to Mr. Green? *Hint: 1 kg = 2.2 lb.*

9. How much NaOH (sodium hydroxide) would you need (in grams) to make 125 ml of a 0.1 M NaOH solution?

10. How much NaOH would you need to make 1 L of a 3% NaOH solution?

11. How much KCl (potassium chloride) would you need to make 1.5 L of a 1.5% solution?

12. What would be the molarity (in M) of a solution containing 35 g of KCl in 1000 ml of solution? What is this solution's osmolarity (in Osm)?

ANSWERS (and Explanations)

1. **0.068 M; 68 mM**

   By definition, a % solution = g solute/100ml solution. So, a 0.75% $CaCl_2$ solution contains 0.75g $CaCl_2$/100ml solution. Now, you must take into account the molecular weight (MW) of $CaCl_2$, because the question is asking for solution *molarity*. From the given atomic weight chart, you can see that the MW of $CaCl_2$ = 40.1 + 2(35.45) = 111g. Remember that the MW of any substance is equivalent to 1 mol of that substance, or 111g $CaCl_2$/mol. Now, you want to set up your calculations so that you end up with M. Remember that M is always equivalent to mol/L. So…

   $$\frac{0.75\text{g}}{100\text{ml solution}} \times \frac{1000\text{ml}}{1\text{L}} \times \frac{\text{mol}}{111\text{g}} = 0.068\ \frac{\text{mol}}{\text{L}} \text{ or } \mathbf{0.068\ M}$$

   One millimolar (or mmol/L) is equivalent to 1/1000 molar, so multiply the above answer by 1000. You can show this dimensionally by the following:

   $$0.068\text{M} \times \frac{1000\text{mM}}{\text{M}} = \mathbf{68\ mM}$$

2. **0.204 Osm; 204 mOsm**

   Given that $CaCl_2$ dissociates into three parts when placed in solution, 1 M $CaCl_2$ = 3 Osm $CaCl_2$. So, for the same solution from Question 1, 0.068M x 3 = **0.204 Osm**. As explained above, 1 mOsm = 1/1000 Osm, so 0.204 Osm = **204 mOsm**.

3. **5 g**

   $$\frac{1\text{g glucose}}{100\text{ml solution}} \times 500\text{ml} = \mathbf{5\ g}$$

4. **180 g**

   Again, remember that M = mol/L. 1 mol glucose contains the MW of glucose, which is calculated using the given atomic weight chart: 6(12) + 12(1) + 6(16) = 180 g. Set up the calculation as follows:

   $$\frac{0.5\text{ mol}}{\text{L}} \times 2\text{L} \times \frac{180\text{ g}}{\text{mol}} = 180\text{ g}$$

5. **0.5 Osm**

   Glucose (as all sugars) do not dissociated in solution. So, 1 M glucose = 1 Osm glucose, and 0.5 M glucose = **0.5 Osm** glucose.

6. **1 M HCl is more concentrated.**

   2% HCl solution has $\frac{2\text{ g HCl}}{100\text{ ml}}$ or (making it a comparable volume to the other solution) $\frac{20\text{ g HCl}}{1\text{ L}}$.

   1 M HCl solution has $\frac{1\text{ mol HCl}}{\text{L}}$ or $\frac{36.45\text{ g HCl}}{\text{L}}$ (the MW of HCl is 1.0 + 35.45 = 36.45 g). So, this solution has more HCl in it per L and is therefore more concentrated.

7. **600; 1200**

   $$0.6\text{ M} = \frac{1000\text{ mM}}{\text{M}} \times 0.6\text{ M} = \mathbf{600\ mM}$$

   NaCl dissociates into Na^+ and Cl^- in solution, so 1 M = 2 Osm; likewise 1 mM = 2 mOsm, so 600 mM = 2(600) = **1200 mOsm**.

8. **133.33 ml of Drug X needed.**

   Convert Mr. Green's weight in lb. to kg: $220\text{ lb} \times \frac{\text{kg}}{\quad}$ = 100 kg. Next, calculate how much

Drug X he needs based on this weight: 100 kg of Mr. Green x $\frac{2.2 \text{ lb.}}{}$ $\frac{100 \text{ mg Drug}}{\text{kg}}$ = 10,000 mg Drug.

To determine the volume of Drug X he needs, incorporate the given Drug concentration: 10,000 mg Drug X x $\frac{\text{ml}}{75 \text{ mg}}$ = **133.33 ml Drug X.**

9. 0.5 g

MW of NaOH = 23 + 16 + 1 = 40 g. 0.1M NaOH = 0.1 mol/L NaOH. So…

$0.1 \frac{\text{mol}}{\text{L}} \times \frac{40 \text{ g NaOH}}{\text{mol}} \times 125 \text{ ml} \times \frac{1 \text{ L}}{1000 \text{ ml}}$ = **0.5 g**

10. 30 g

This one if fairly intuitive, because you know that 10 x 100 ml = 1L. However, to show the calculation: 3% solution is 3 g/100ml solution

$\frac{3 \text{ g}}{100 \text{ ml}} \times \frac{1000 \text{ ml}}{\text{L}}$ = **30 g in one liter solution**

11. 22.5 g

$\frac{1.5 \text{ g KCl}}{100 \text{ ml}} \times \frac{1000 \text{ ml}}{\text{L}} \times 1.5 \text{ L}$ = 22.5 g

12. 0.47 M; 0.94 Osm

MW of KCl = 39.1 + 35.45 = 74.55 g. So…

$35 \text{ g KCl} \times \frac{\text{mol}}{74.55 \text{ g KCl}} \times \frac{1000 \text{ ml}}{\text{L}}$ = 0.47 $\frac{\text{mol}}{\text{L}}$ = **0.47 M** KCl

Like NaCl, KCl dissociates into K^+ and Cl^- in solution, so 1 M KCl = 2 Osm KCl. Thus, 0.47 M = **0.94 Osm** KCl.

Classification of Tissues

MATERIALS

- ☐ Compound microscope
- ☐ Immersion oil
- ☐ Prepared slides of simple squamous, simple cuboidal, simple columnar, stratified squamous (nonkeratinized), stratified cuboidal, stratified columnar, pseudostratified ciliated columnar, and transitional epithelium
- ☐ Prepared slides of mesenchyme; of adipose, areolar, reticular, and dense (both regular and irregular connective tissues); of hyaline and elastic cartilage; of fibrocartilage; of bone (x.s.); and of blood
- ☐ Prepared slides of skeletal, cardiac, and smooth muscle (l.s.)
- ☐ Prepared slide of nervous tissue (spinal cord smear)
- **PEx** PhysioEx™ 7.0 Computer Simulation

OBJECTIVES

1. To name the four primary tissue types in the human body and the major subcategories of each.
2. To identify the tissue subcategories through microscopic inspection or inspection of an appropriate diagram or projected slide.
3. To state the location of the various tissue types in the body.
4. To list the general functions and structural characteristics of each of the four major tissue types.

The Cell: Anatomy and Division describes cells as the building blocks of life and the all-inclusive functional units of unicellular organisms. However, in higher organisms, cells do not usually operate as isolated, independent entities. In humans and other multicellular organisms, cells depend on one another and cooperate to maintain homeostasis in the body.

With a few exceptions, even the most complex animal starts out as a single cell, the fertilized egg, which divides almost endlessly. The trillions of cells that result become specialized for a particular function; some become supportive bone, others the transparent lens of the eye, still others skin cells, and so on. Thus a division of labor exists, with certain groups of cells highly specialized to perform functions that benefit the organism as a whole. Cell specialization carries with it certain hazards, because when a small specific group of cells is indispensable, any inability to function on its part can paralyze or destroy the entire body.

Groups of cells that are similar in structure and function are called **tissues.** The four primary tissue types—epithelium, connective tissue, nervous tissue, and muscle—have distinctive structures, patterns, and functions. The four primary tissues are further divided into subcategories, as described shortly.

To perform specific body functions, the tissues are organized into **organs** such as the heart, kidneys, and lungs. Most organs contain several representatives of the primary tissues, and the arrangement of these tissues determines the organ's structure and function. Thus **histology,** the study of tissues, complements a study of gross anatomy and provides the structural basis for a study of organ physiology.

The main objective of this exercise is to familiarize you with the major similarities and dissimilarities of the primary tissues, so that when the tissue composition of an organ is described, you will be able to more easily understand (and perhaps even predict) the organ's major function. Because epithelium and some types of connective tissue will not be considered again, they are emphasized more than muscle, nervous tissue, and bone (a connective tissue), which are covered in more depth in later exercises.

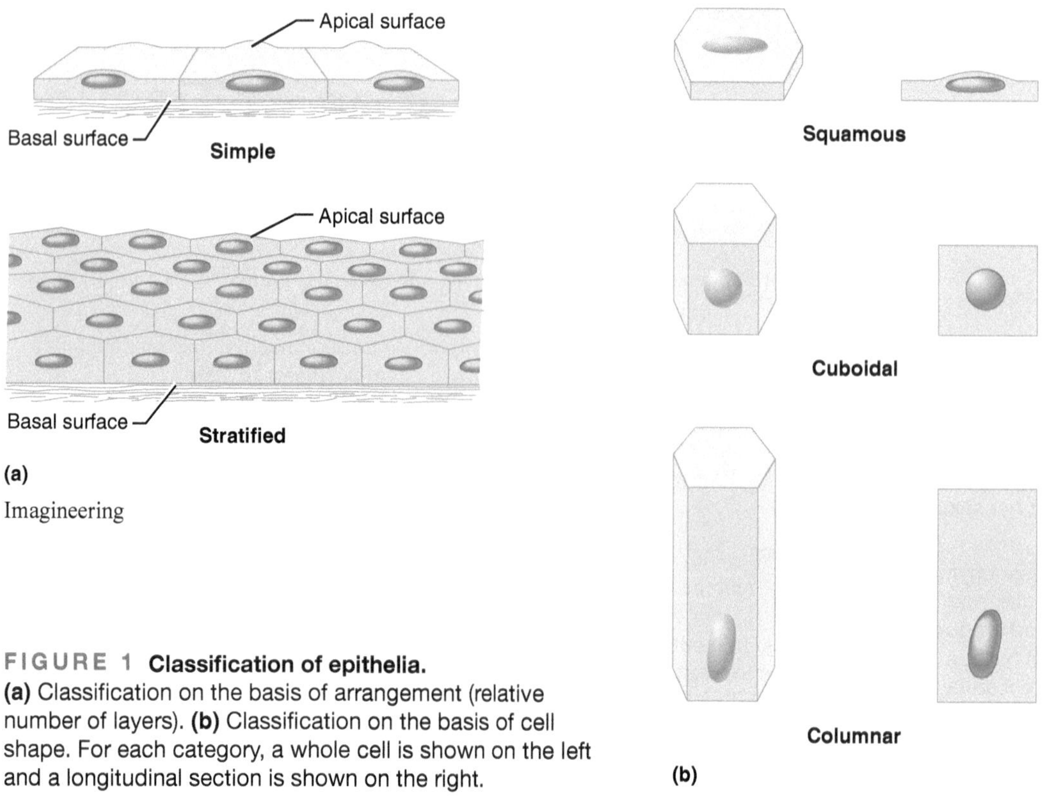

Imagineering

FIGURE 1 Classification of epithelia.
(a) Classification on the basis of arrangement (relative number of layers). **(b)** Classification on the basis of cell shape. For each category, a whole cell is shown on the left and a longitudinal section is shown on the right.

Epithelial Tissue

Epithelial tissue, or **epithelium,** covers surfaces. For example, epithelium covers the external body surface (as the epidermis), lines its cavities and tubules, and generally marks off our "insides" from our outsides. Since the various endocrine (hormone-producing) and exocrine glands of the body almost invariably develop from epithelial membranes, glands, too, are logically classed as epithelium.

Epithelial functions include protection, absorption, filtration, excretion, secretion, and sensory reception. For example, the epithelium covering the body surface protects against bacterial invasion and chemical damage; that lining the respiratory tract is ciliated to sweep dust and other foreign particles away from the lungs. Epithelium specialized to absorb substances lines the stomach and small intestine. In the kidney tubules, the epithelium absorbs, secretes, and filters. Secretion is a specialty of the glands.

The following characteristics distinguish epithelial tissues from other types:

- Polarity. The membranes always have one free surface, called the *apical surface,* and typically that surface is significantly different from the *basal surface.*
- Cellularity and specialized contacts. Cells fit closely together to form membranes, or sheets of cells, and are bound together by specialized junctions.
- Supported by connective tissue. The cells are attached to and supported by an adhesive **basement membrane,** which is an amorphous material secreted partly by the epithelial cells (*basal lamina*) and connective tissue cells (*reticular lamina*) that lie adjacent to each other.
- Avascularity. Epithelial tissues have no blood supply of their own (are avascular), but instead depend on diffusion of nutrients from the underlying connective tissue. (Glandular epithelia, however, are very vascular.)
- Regeneration. If well nourished, epithelial cells can easily regenerate themselves. This is an important characteristic because many epithelia are subjected to a good deal of friction.

The covering and lining epithelia are classified according to two criteria—arrangement or relative number of layers and cell shape (Figure 1). On the basis of arrangement, there are **simple** epithelia, consisting of one layer of cells attached to the basement membrane, and **stratified** epithelia, consisting of two or more layers of cells. The general types based on shape are **squamous** (scalelike), **cuboidal** (cubelike), and **columnar** (column-shaped) epithelial cells. The terms denoting shape and arrangement of the epithelial cells are combined to describe the epithelium fully. *Stratified epithelia are named according to the cells at the apical surface of the epithelial membrane,* not those resting on the basement membrane.

There are, in addition, two less easily categorized types of epithelia. **Pseudostratified epithelium** is actually a simple columnar epithelium (one layer of cells), but because its cells vary in height and the nuclei lie at different levels above the basement membrane, it gives the false appearance of being stratified. This epithelium is often ciliated. **Transitional**

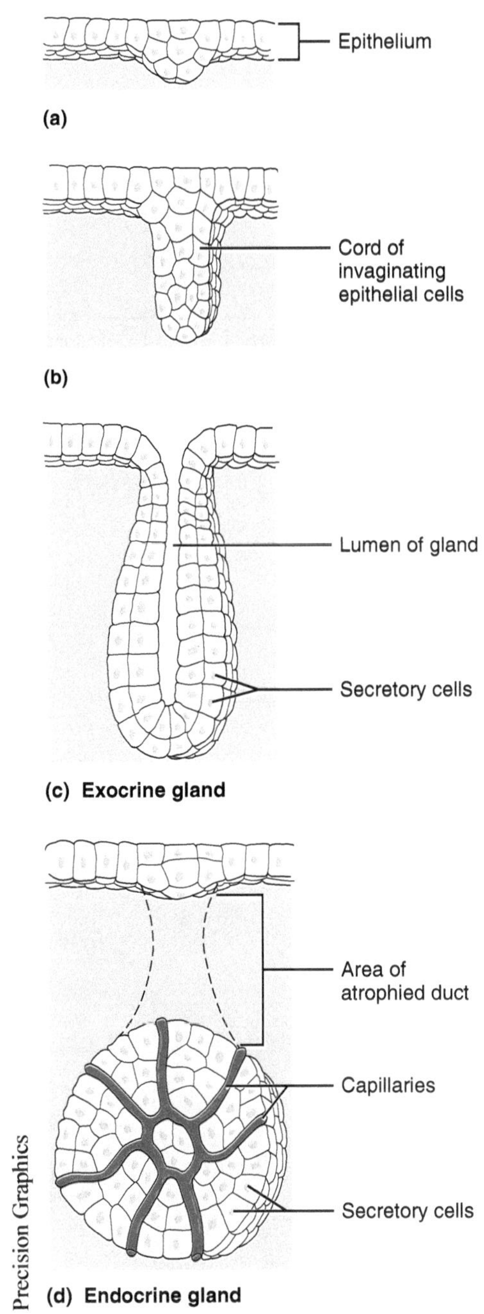
Epithelium
(a)
Cord of invaginating epithelial cells
(b)
Lumen of gland
Secretory cells
(c) Exocrine gland
Area of atrophied duct
Capillaries
Secretory cells
(d) Endocrine gland
Precision Graphics

FIGURE 2 Formation of endocrine and exocrine glands from epithelial sheets. (a) Epithelial cells grow and push into the underlying tissue. **(b)** A cord of epithelial cells forms. **(c)** In an exocrine gland, a lumen (cavity) forms. The inner cells form the duct, the outer cells produce the secretion. **(d)** In a forming endocrine gland, the connecting duct cells atrophy, leaving the secretory cells with no connection to the epithelial surface. However, they do become heavily invested with blood and lymphatic vessels that receive the secretions.

epithelium is a rather peculiar stratified squamous epithelium formed of rounded, or "plump," cells with the ability to slide over one another to allow the organ to be stretched. Transitional epithelium is found only in urinary system organs subjected to periodic distension, such as the bladder. The superficial cells are flattened (like true squamous cells) when the organ is distended and rounded when the organ is empty.

Epithelial cells forming glands are highly specialized to remove materials from the blood and to manufacture them into new materials, which they then secrete. There are two types of glands, as shown in Figure 2. **Endocrine glands** lose their surface connection (duct) as they develop; thus they are referred to as ductless glands. Their secretions (all hormones) are extruded directly into the blood or the lymphatic vessels that weave through the glands. **Exocrine glands** retain their ducts, and their secretions empty through these ducts to an epithelial surface. The exocrine glands—including the sweat and oil glands, liver, and pancreas—are both external and internal; they will be discussed in conjunction with the organ systems to which their products are functionally related.

The most common types of epithelia, their characteristic locations in the body, and their functions are described in Figure 3.

ACTIVITY 1

Examining Epithelial Tissue Under the Microscope

Obtain slides of simple squamous, simple cuboidal, simple columnar, stratified squamous (nonkeratinized), pseudostratified ciliated columnar, stratified cuboidal, stratified columnar, and transitional epithelia. Examine each carefully, and notice how the epithelial cells fit closely together to form intact sheets of cells, a necessity for a tissue that forms linings or covering membranes. Scan each epithelial type for modifications for specific functions, such as cilia (motile cell projections that help to move substances along the cell surface), and microvilli, which increase the surface area for absorption. Also be alert for goblet cells, which secrete lubricating mucus (see Plate of the Histology Atlas). Compare your observations with the descriptions and photomicrographs in Figure 3.

While working, check the questions in the Review Sheet. A number of the questions there refer to some of the observations you are asked to make during your microscopic study.

Text continues

(a) Simple squamous epithelium

Description: Single layer of flattened cells with disc-shaped central nuclei and sparse cytoplasm; the simplest of the epithelia.

Function: Allows passage of materials by diffusion and filtration in sites where protection is not important; secretes lubricating substances in serosae.

Location: Kidney glomeruli; air sacs of lungs; lining of heart, blood vessels, and lymphatic vessels; lining of ventral body cavity (serosae).

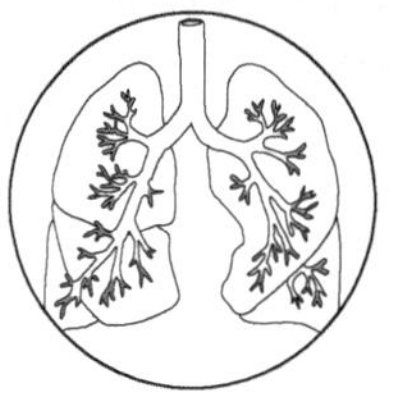

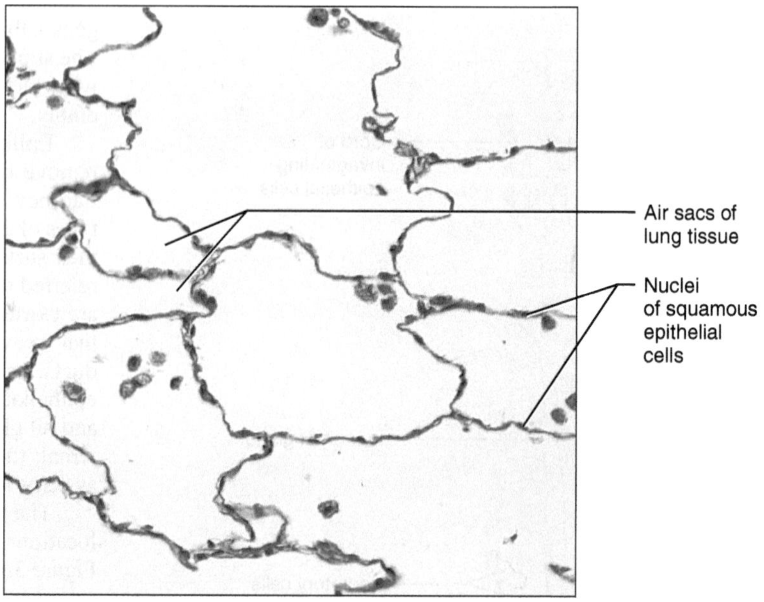
Air sacs of lung tissue
Nuclei of squamous epithelial cells

Photomicrograph: Simple squamous epithelium forming part of the alveolar (air sac) walls (400×).

(b) Simple cuboidal epithelium

Description: Single layer of cubelike cells with large, spherical central nuclei.

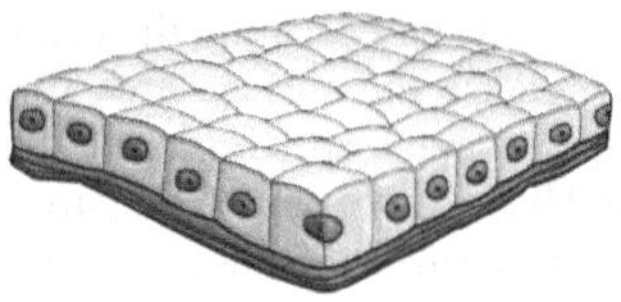

Function: Secretion and absorption.

Location: Kidney tubules; ducts and secretory portions of small glands; ovary surface.

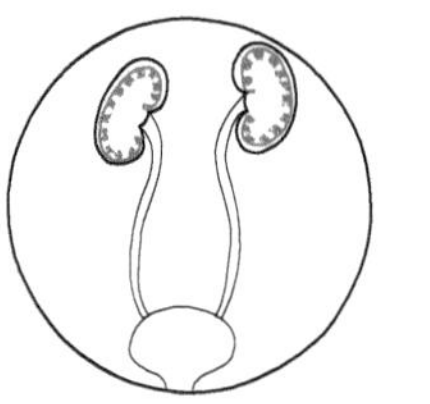

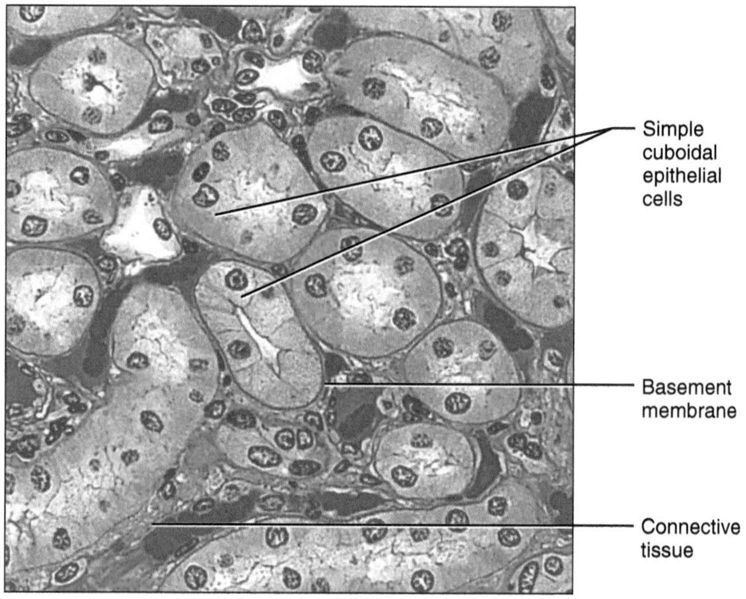
Simple cuboidal epithelial cells
Basement membrane
Connective tissue

Photomicrograph: Simple cuboidal epithelium in kidney tubules (400×).

FIGURE 3 **Epithelial tissues.** Simple epithelia **(a** and **b)**.

(c) Simple columnar epithelium

Description: Single layer of tall cells with *round* to *oval* nuclei; some cells bear cilia; layer may contain mucus-secreting unicellular glands (goblet cells).

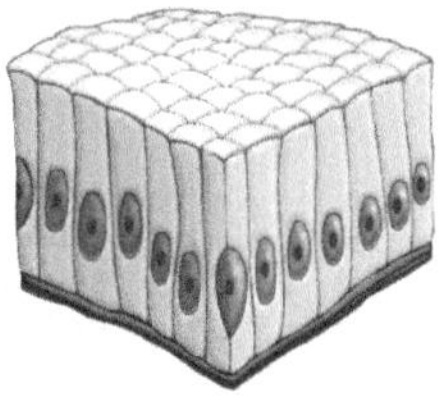

Function: Absorption; secretion of mucus, enzymes, and other substances; ciliated type propels mucus (or reproductive cells) by ciliary action.

Location: Nonciliated type lines most of the digestive tract (stomach to anal canal), gallbladder, and excretory ducts of some glands; ciliated variety lines small bronchi, uterine tubes, and some regions of the uterus.

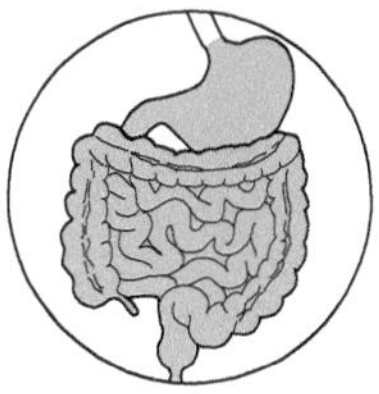

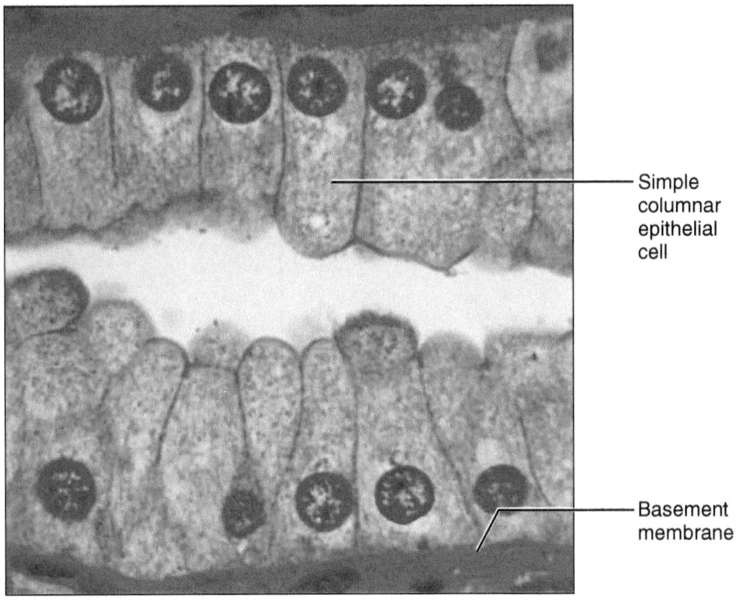
Simple columnar epithelial cell
Basement membrane

Photomicrograph: Simple columnar epithelium of the stomach mucosa (1300×).

Cabisco/ Visuals Unlimited

(d) Pseudostratified columnar epithelium

Description: Single layer of cells of differing heights, some not reaching the free surface; nuclei seen at different levels; may contain goblet cells and bear cilia.

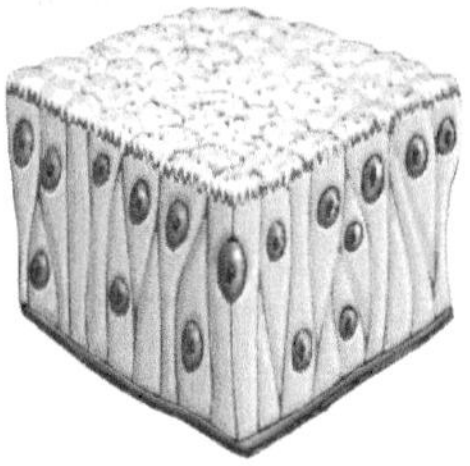

Function: Secretion, particularly of mucus; propulsion of mucus by ciliary action.

Location: Nonciliated type in male's sperm-carrying ducts and ducts of large glands; ciliated variety lines the trachea, most of the upper respiratory tract.

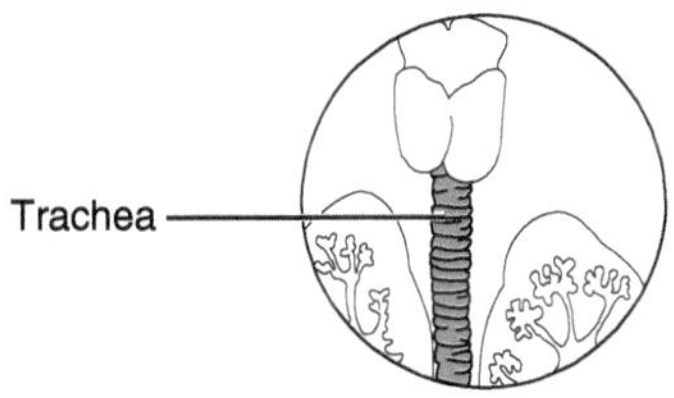
Trachea

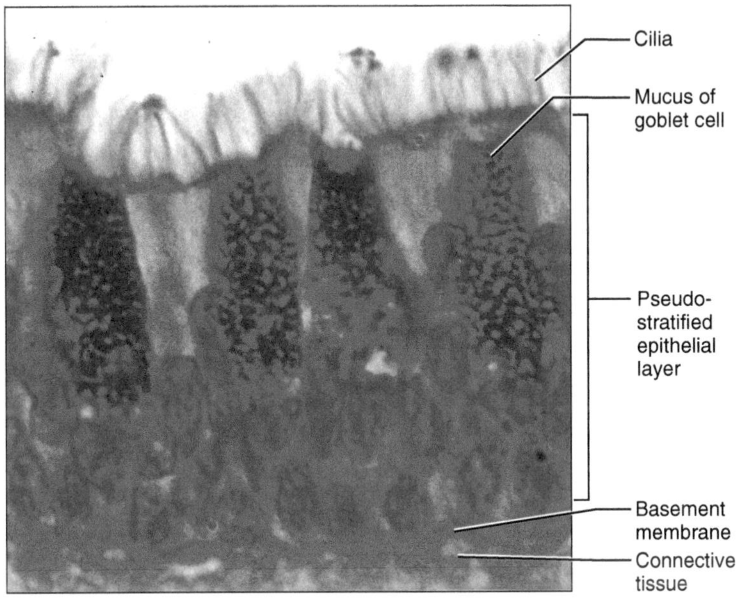
Cilia
Mucus of goblet cell
Pseudo-stratified epithelial layer
Basement membrane
Connective tissue

Photomicrograph: Pseudostratified ciliated columnar epithelium lining the human trachea (400×).

R. Calentine/ Visuals Unlimited

FIGURE 3 *(continued)* Simple epithelia **(c** and **d).**

(e) Stratified squamous epithelium

Description: Thick membrane composed of several cell layers; basal cells are cuboidal or columnar and metabolically active; surface cells are flattened (squamous); in the keratinized type, the surface cells are full of keratin and dead; basal cells are active in mitosis and produce the cells of the more superficial layers.

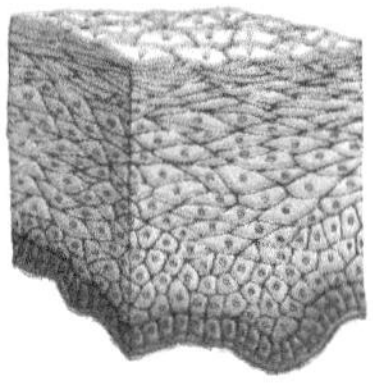

Function: Protects underlying tissues in areas subjected to abrasion.

Location: Nonkeratinized type forms the moist linings of the esophagus, mouth, and vagina; keratinized variety forms the epidermis of the skin, a dry membrane.

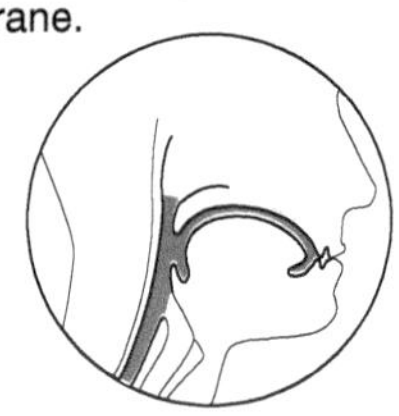

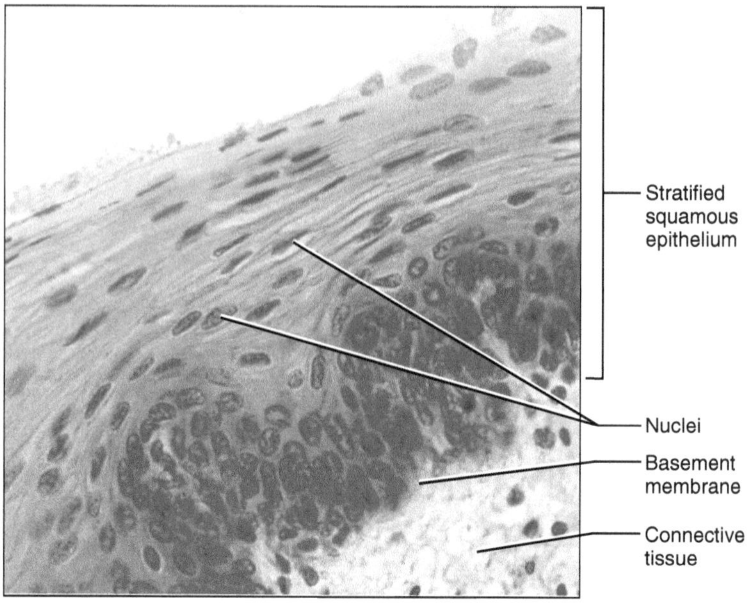

Photomicrograph: Stratified squamous epithelium lining the esophagus (425×).

Nina Zanetti, Pearson Benjamin Cummings

(f) Stratified cuboidal epithelium

Description: Generally two layers of cubelike cells.

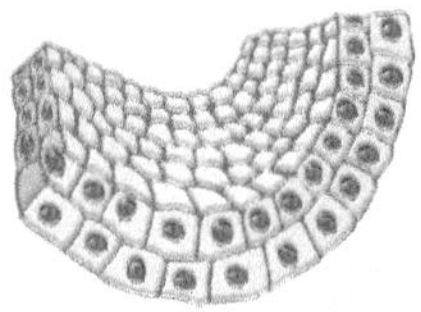

Function: Protection

Location: Largest ducts of sweat glands, mammary glands, and salivary glands.

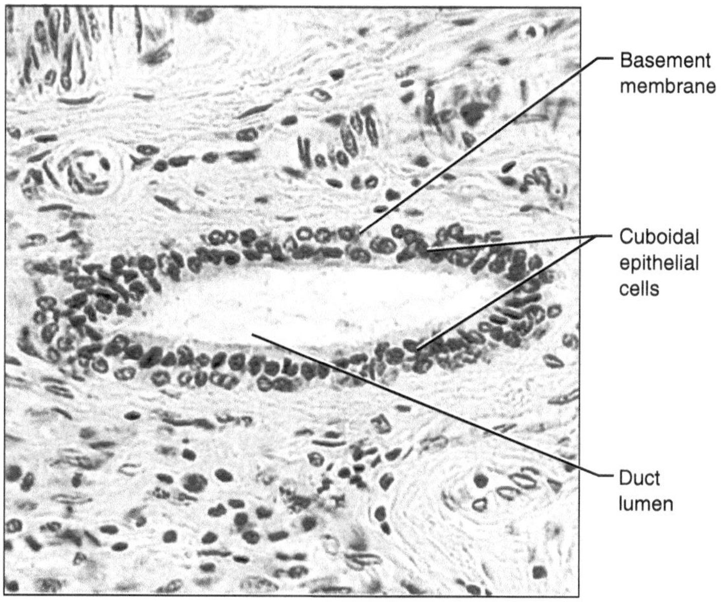

Photomicrograph: Stratified cuboidal epithelium forming a salivary gland duct.

Allen Bell, University of New England; Pearson Benjamin Cummings

FIGURE 3 *(continued)* **Epithelial tissues.** Stratified epithelia (**e** and **f**).

(g) Stratified columnar epithelium

Description: Several cell layers; basal cells usually cuboidal; superficial cells elongated and columnar.

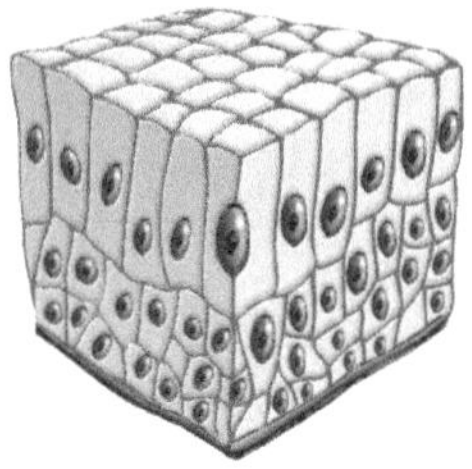

Function: Protection; secretion.

Location: Rare in the body; small amounts in male urethra and in large ducts of some glands.

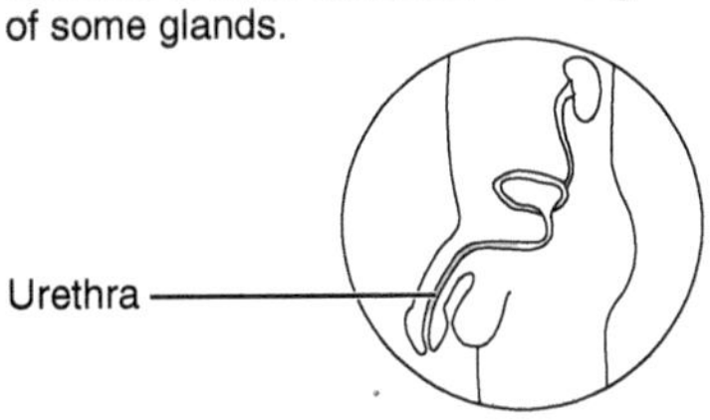

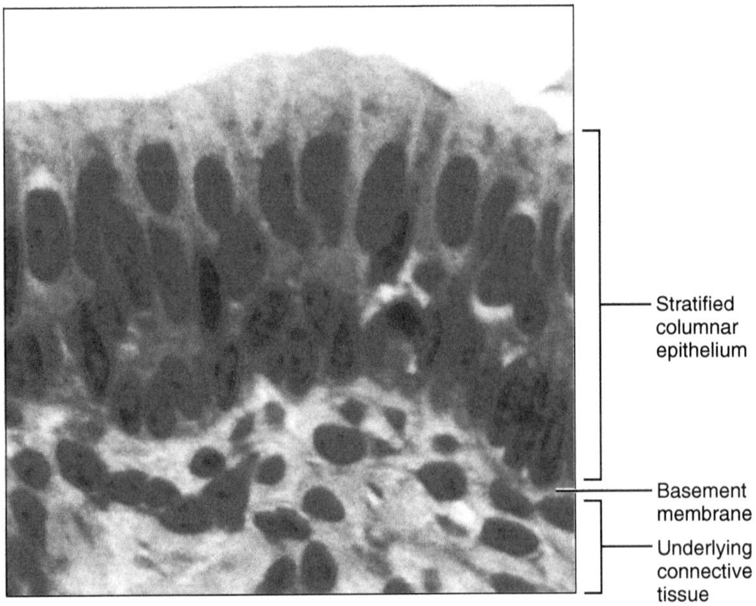

Photomicrograph: Stratified columnar epithelium lining of the male urethra (900×).

Richard Kessel/Visuals Unlimited

(h) Transitional epithelium

Description: Resembles both stratified squamous and stratified cuboidal; basal cells cuboidal or columnar; surface cells dome shaped or squamouslike, depending on degree of organ stretch.

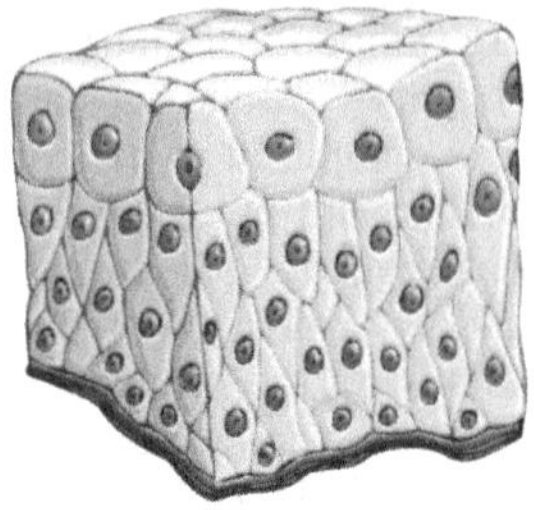

Function: Stretches readily and permits distension of urinary organ by contained urine.

Location: Lines the ureters, bladder, and part of the urethra.

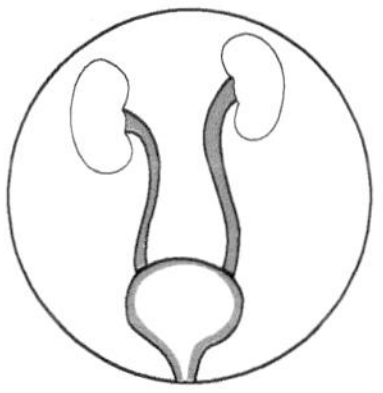

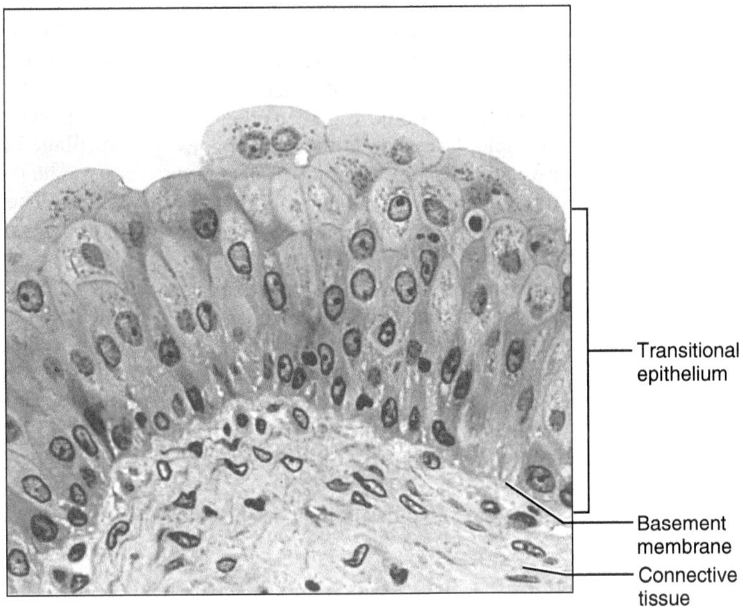

Photomicrograph: Transitional epithelium lining the bladder, relaxed state (500×); note the bulbous, or rounded, appearance of the cells at the surface; these cells flatten and become elongated when the bladder is filled with urine.

Allen Bell, University of New England; Pearson Benjamin Cummings

FIGURE 3 *(continued)* Stratified epithelia **(g** and **h).**

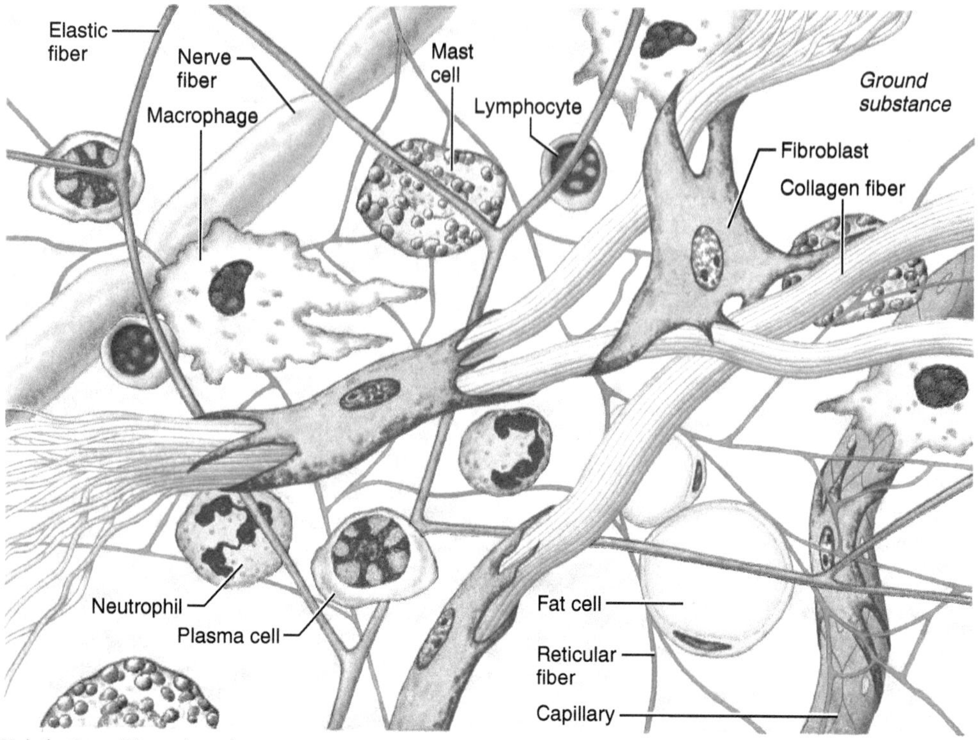

Kristin Otwell/Imagineering

FIGURE 4 **Areolar connective tissue: A prototype (model) connective tissue.** This tissue underlies epithelia and surrounds capillaries. Note the various cell types and the three classes of fibers (collagen, reticular, elastic) embedded in the ground substance.

Connective Tissue

Connective tissue is found in all parts of the body as discrete structures or as part of various body organs. It is the most abundant and widely distributed of the tissue types.

Connective tissues perform a variety of functions, but they primarily protect, support, and bind together other tissues of the body. For example, bones are composed of connective tissue **(bone,** or **osseous tissue),** and they protect and support other body tissues and organs. The ligaments and tendons **(dense connective tissue)** bind the bones together or bind skeletal muscles to bones.

Areolar connective tissue (Figure 4) is a soft packaging material that cushions and protects body organs. **Adipose** (fat) tissue provides insulation for the body tissues and a source of stored food. Blood-forming **(hematopoietic)** tissue replenishes the body's supply of red blood cells. Connective tissue also serves a vital function in the repair of all body tissues since many wounds are repaired by connective tissue in the form of scar tissue.

The characteristics of connective tissue include the following:

- With a few exceptions (cartilages, which are avascular, and tendons and ligaments, which are poorly vascularized), connective tissues have a rich supply of blood vessels.
- Connective tissues are composed of many types of cells.
- There is a great deal of noncellular, nonliving material (matrix) between the cells of connective tissue.

The nonliving material between the cells—the **extracellular matrix**—deserves a bit more explanation because it distinguishes connective tissue from all other tissues. It is produced by the cells and then extruded. The matrix is primarily responsible for the strength associated with connective tissue, but there is variation. At one extreme, adipose tissue is composed mostly of cells. At the opposite extreme, bone and cartilage have few cells and large amounts of matrix.

The matrix has two components—ground substance and fibers. The **ground substance** is composed chiefly of interstitial fluid, cell adhesion proteins, and proteoglycans. Depending on its specific composition, the ground substance may be liquid, semisolid, gel-like, or very hard. When the matrix is firm, as in cartilage and bone, the connective tissue cells reside in cavities in the matrix called *lacunae.* The fibers, which provide support, include **collagen** (white) **fibers, elastic** (yellow) **fibers,** and **reticular** (fine collagen) **fibers.** Of these, the collagen fibers are most abundant.

Generally speaking, the ground substance functions as a molecular sieve, or medium, through which nutrients and other dissolved substances can diffuse between the blood capillaries and the cells. The fibers in the matrix hinder diffusion somewhat and make the ground substance less pliable. The properties of the connective tissue cells and the makeup and arrangement of their matrix elements vary tremendously, accounting for the amazing diversity of this tissue type. Nonetheless, the connective tissues have a common structural plan seen best in *areolar connective tissue* (Figure 4), a soft packing tissue that occurs throughout the body. Since all

(a) Embryonic connective tissue: Mesenchyme

Description: Embryonic connective tissue; gel-like ground substance containing fibers; star-shaped mesenchymal cells.

Function: Gives rise to all other connective tissue types.

Location: Primarily in embryo.

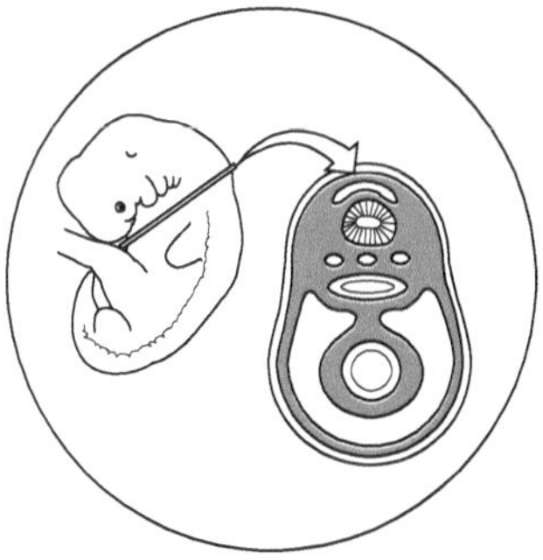

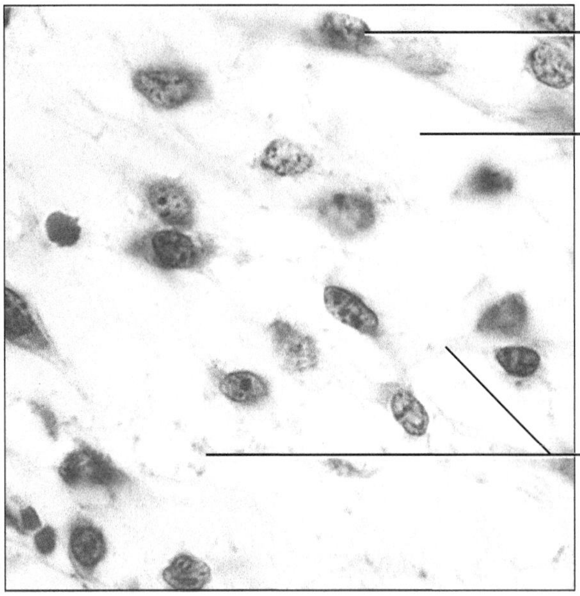

Photomicrograph: Mesenchymal tissue, an embryonic connective tissue (400×); the clear-appearing background is the fluid ground substance of the matrix; notice the fine, sparse fibers.

Ed Reschke

Imagineering

FIGURE 5 **Connective tissues.** Embryonic connective tissue **(a).**

other connective tissues are variations of areolar, it is considered the model or prototype of the connective tissues. Notice in Figure 4 that areolar tissue has all three varieties of fibers, but they are sparsely arranged in its transparent gel-like ground substance. The cell type that secretes its matrix is the *fibroblast,* but a wide variety of other cells including phagocytic cells like macrophages and certain white blood cells and mast cells that act in the inflammatory response are present as well. The more durable connective tissues, such as bone, cartilage, and the dense fibrous varieties, characteristically have a firm ground substance and many more fibers.

There are four main types of adult connective tissue, all of which typically have large amounts of matrix. These are **connective tissue proper** (which includes areolar, adipose, reticular, and dense [fibrous] connective tissues), **cartilage, bone,** and **blood.** All of these derive from an embryonic tissue called *mesenchyme.* Figure 5 lists the general characteristics, location, and function of some of the connective tissues found in the body.

ACTIVITY 2

Examining Connective Tissue Under the Microscope

Obtain prepared slides of mesenchyme; of adipose, areolar, reticular, dense regular and irregular connective tissue; of hyaline and elastic cartilage and fibrocartilage; of osseous connective tissue (bone); and of blood. Compare your observations with the views illustrated in Figure 5.

Distinguish between the living cells and the matrix and pay particular attention to the denseness and arrangement of the matrix. For example, notice how the matrix of the dense fibrous connective tissues, making up tendons and the dermis of the skin, is packed with collagen fibers, and that in the *regular* variety (tendon), the fibers are all running in the same direction, whereas in the dermis (a dense *irregular* connective tissue) they appear to be running in many directions.

While examining the areolar connective tissue, notice how much empty space there appears to be (*areol* = small empty space), and distinguish between the collagen fibers and the coiled elastic fibers. Identify the starlike fibroblasts. Also, try to locate a **mast cell,** which has large, darkly staining granules in its cytoplasm (*mast* = stuffed full of granules). This cell type releases histamine that makes capillaries

Text continues

(b) Connective tissue proper: loose connective tissue, areolar

Description: Gel-like matrix with all three fiber types; cells: fibroblasts, macrophages, mast cells, and some white blood cells.

Function: Wraps and cushions organs; its macrophages phagocytize bacteria; plays important role in inflammation; holds and conveys tissue fluid.

Location: Widely distributed under epithelia of body, e.g., forms lamina propria of mucous membranes; packages organs; surrounds capillaries.

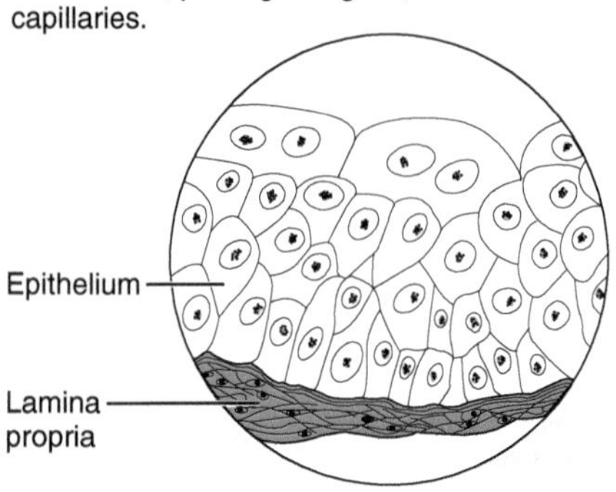
Epithelium
Lamina propria

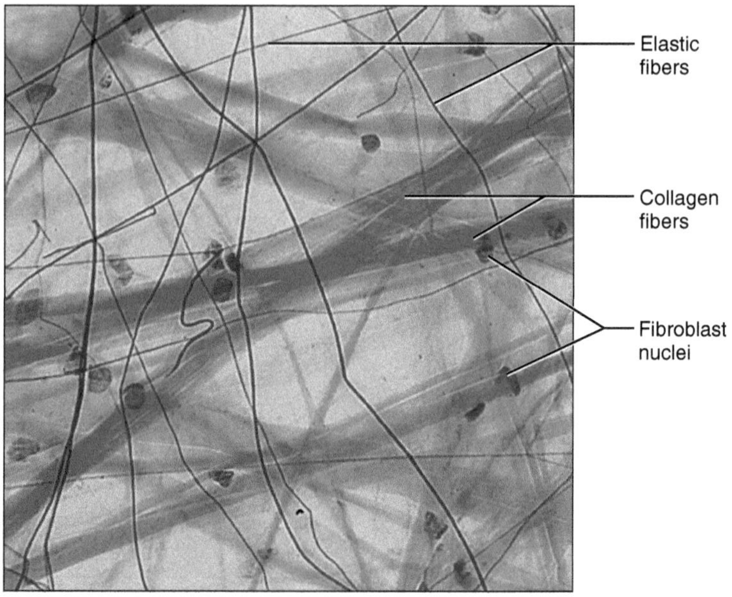
Elastic fibers
Collagen fibers
Fibroblast nuclei

Photomicrograph: Areolar connective tissue, a soft packaging tissue of the body (400×).

(c) Connective tissue proper: loose connective tissue, adipose

Description: Matrix as in areolar, but very sparse; closely packed adipocytes, or fat cells, have nucleus pushed to the side by large fat droplet.

Function: Provides reserve fuel; insulates against heat loss; supports and protects organs.

Location: Under skin; around kidneys and eyeballs; within abdomen; in breasts.

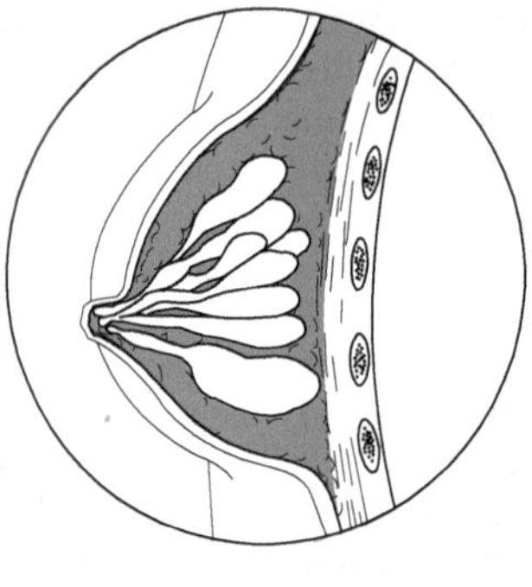

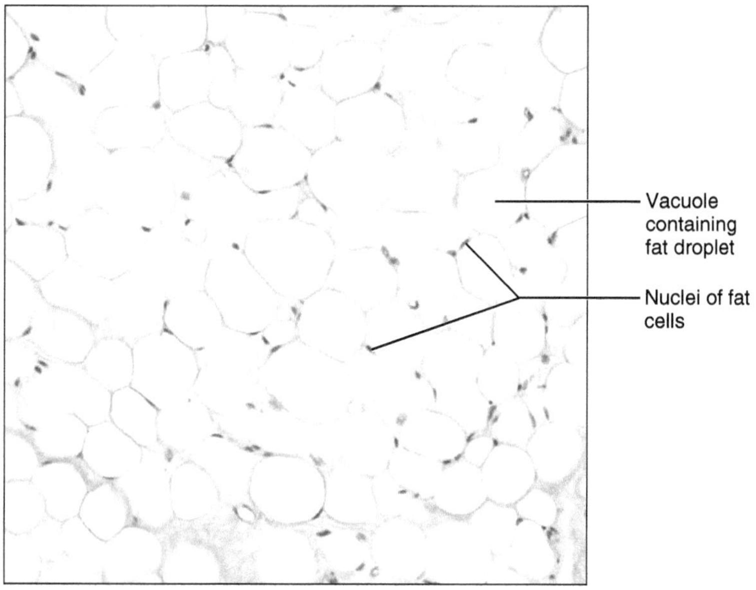
Vacuole containing fat droplet
Nuclei of fat cells

Photomicrograph: Adipose tissue from the subcutaneous layer under the skin (450×).

FIGURE 5 *(continued)* **Connective tissues.** Connective tissue proper **(b** and **c).**

(d) Connective tissue proper: loose connective tissue, reticular

Description: Network of reticular fibers in a typical loose ground substance; reticular cells lie on the network.

Function: Fibers form a soft internal skeleton (stroma) that supports other cell types including white blood cells, mast cells, and macrophages.

Location: Lymphoid organs (lymph nodes, bone marrow, and spleen).

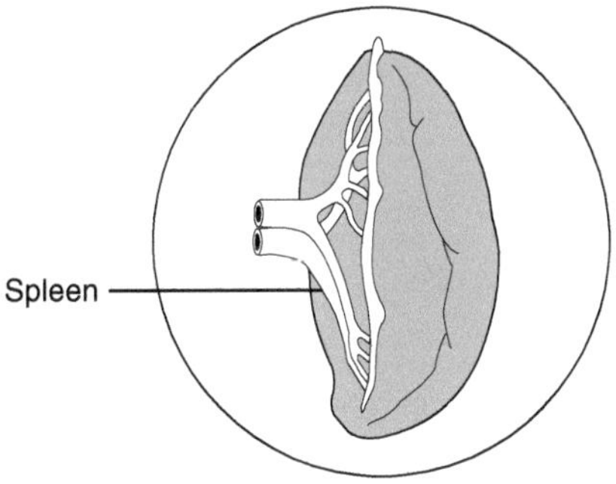
Spleen

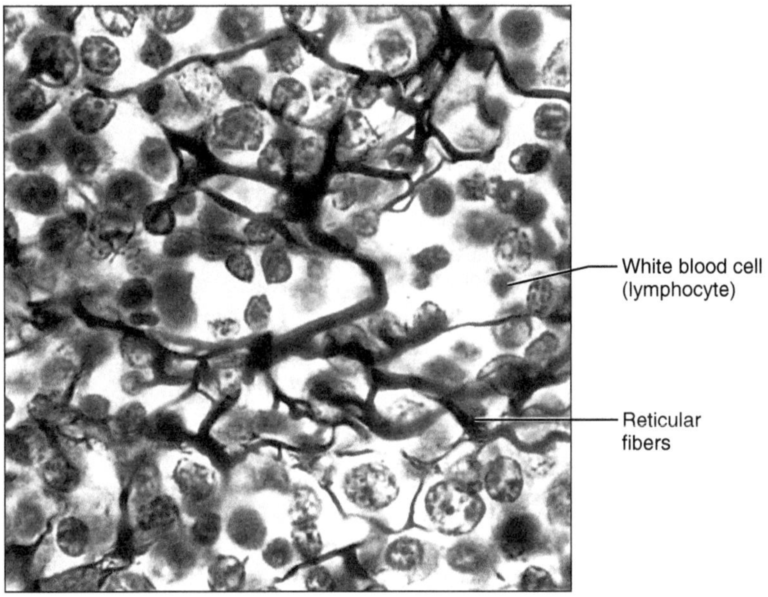
White blood cell (lymphocyte)
Reticular fibers

Photomicrograph: Dark-staining network of reticular connective tissue fibers forming the internal skeleton of the spleen (350×).

(e) Connective tissue proper: dense connective tissue, dense regular

Description: Primarily parallel collagen fibers; a few elastin fibers; major cell type is the fibroblast.

Function: Attaches muscles to bones or to muscles; attaches bones to bones; withstands great tensile stress when pulling force is applied in one direction.

Location: Tendons, most ligaments, aponeuroses.

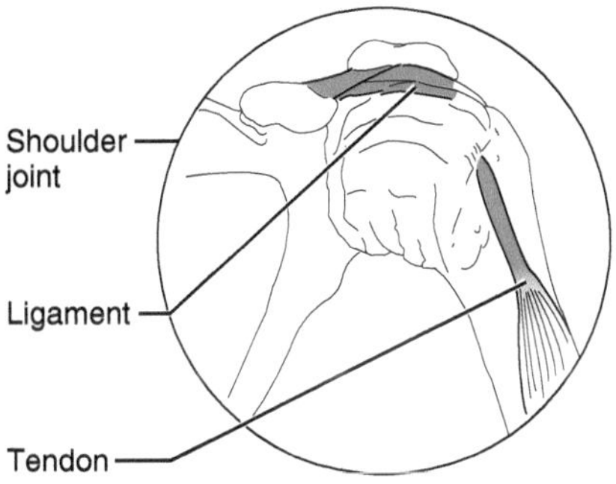
Shoulder joint
Ligament
Tendon

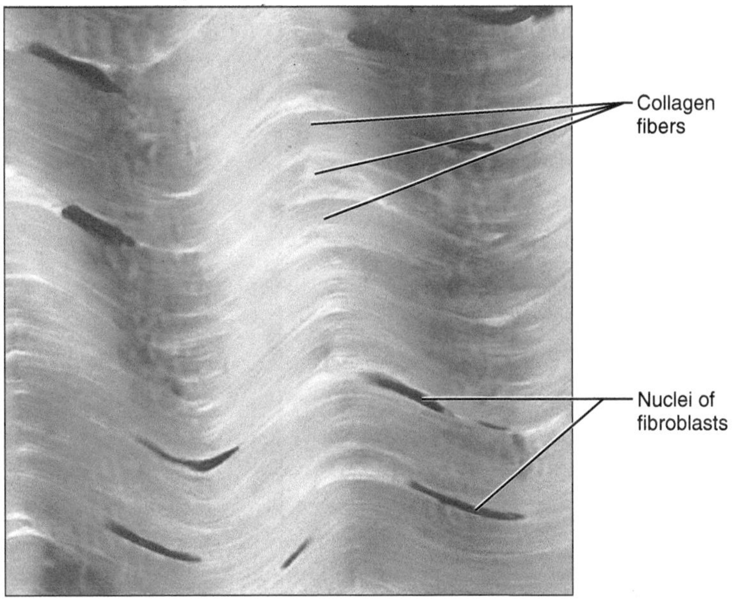
Collagen fibers
Nuclei of fibroblasts

Photomicrograph: Dense regular connective tissue from a tendon (1000×).

FIGURE 5 *(continued)* Connective tissue proper **(d** and **e).**

(f) Connective tissue proper: dense connective tissue, dense irregular

Description: Primarily irregularly arranged collagen fibers; some elastic fibers; major cell type is the fibroblast.

Function: Able to withstand tension exerted in many directions; provides structural strength.

Location: Dermis of the skin; submucosa of digestive tract; fibrous capsules of organs and of joints.

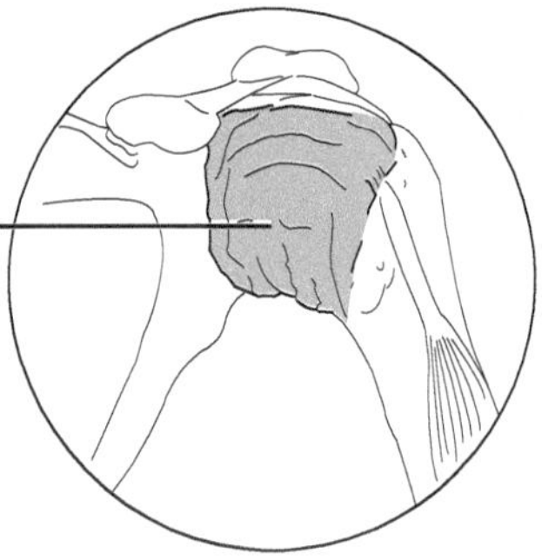
Fibrous joint capsule

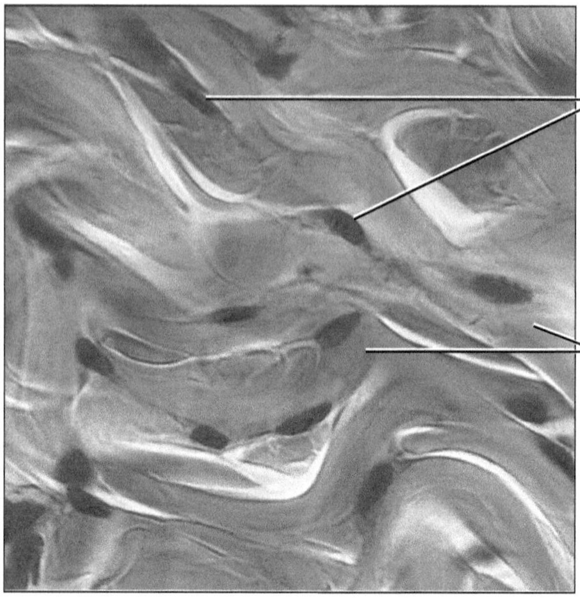
Nuclei of fibroblasts
Collagen fibers

Photomicrograph: Dense irregular connective tissue from the dermis of the skin (400×).

Ed Reschke

(g) Cartilage: hyaline

Description: Amorphous but firm matrix; collagen fibers form an imperceptible network; chondroblasts produce the matrix and when mature (chondrocytes) lie in lacunae.

Function: Supports and reinforces; has resilient cushioning properties; resists compressive stress.

Location: Forms most of the embryonic skeleton; covers the ends of long bones in joint cavities; forms costal cartilages of the ribs; cartilages of the nose, trachea, and larynx.

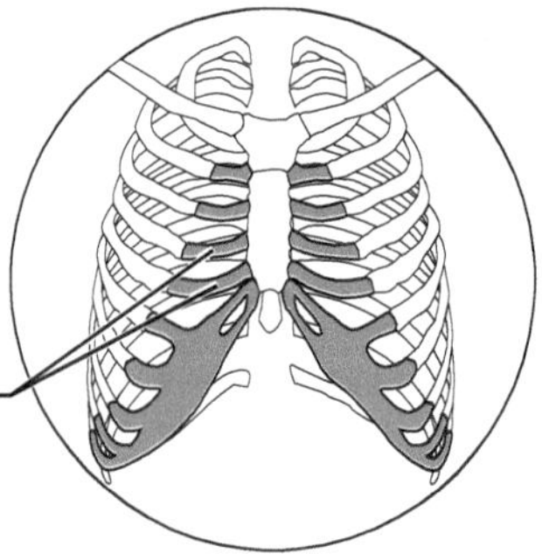
Costal cartilages

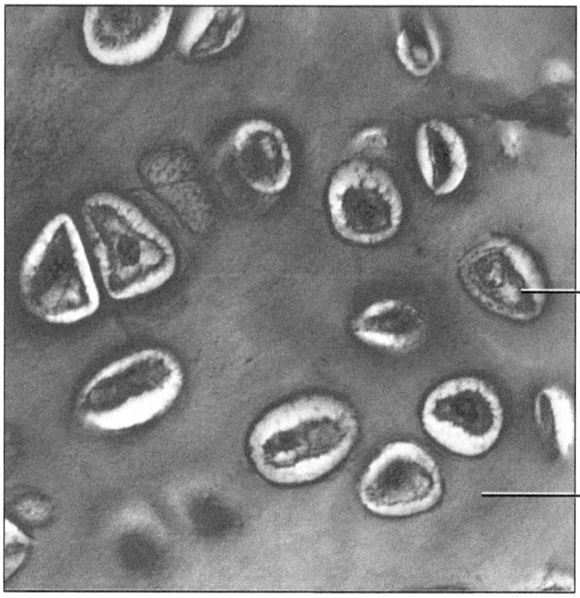
Chondrocyte in lacuna
Matrix

Photomicrograph: Hyaline cartilage from the trachea (300×).

Ed Reschke

FIGURE 5 *(continued)* **Connective tissues.** Connective tissue proper **(f)** and Cartilage **(g).**

(h) Cartilage: elastic

Description: Similar to hyaline cartilage, but more elastic fibers in matrix.

Function: Maintains the shape of a structure while allowing great flexibility.

Location: Supports the external ear (pinna); epiglottis.

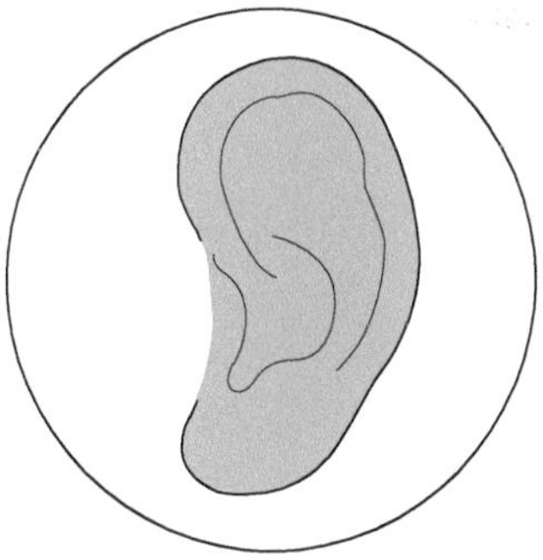

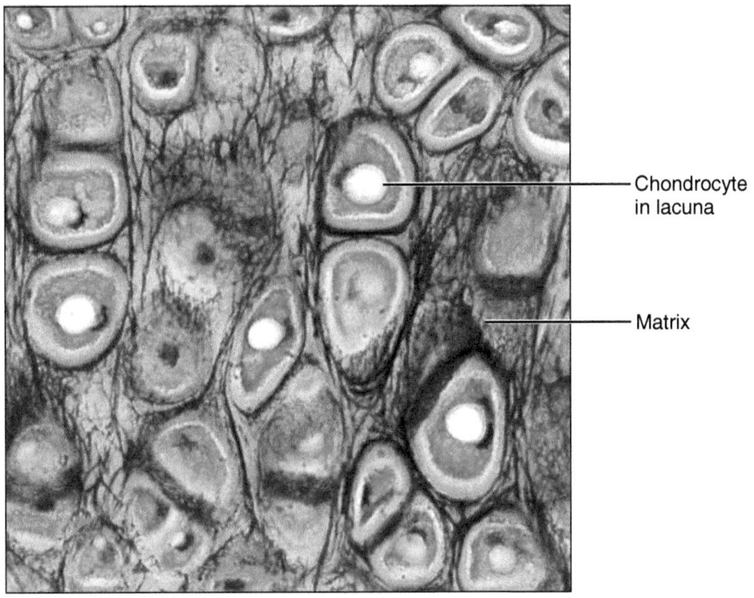

Photomicrograph: Elastic cartilage from the human ear pinna; forms the flexible skeleton of the ear (640×).

(i) Cartilage: fibrocartilage

Description: Matrix similar to but less firm than that in hyaline cartilage; thick collagen fibers predominate.

Function: Tensile strength with the ability to absorb compressive shock.

Location: Intervertebral discs; pubic symphysis; discs of knee joint.

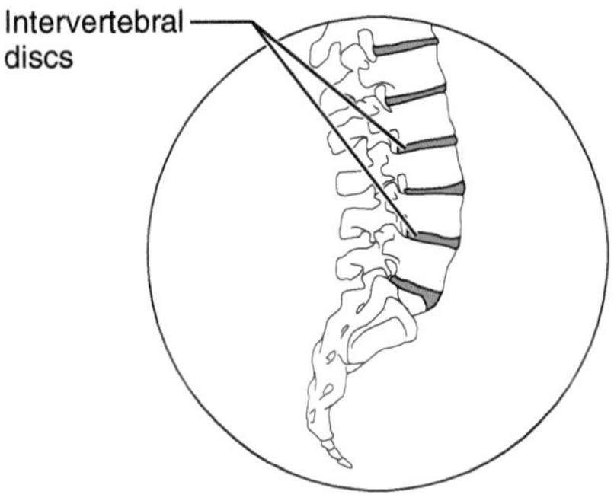

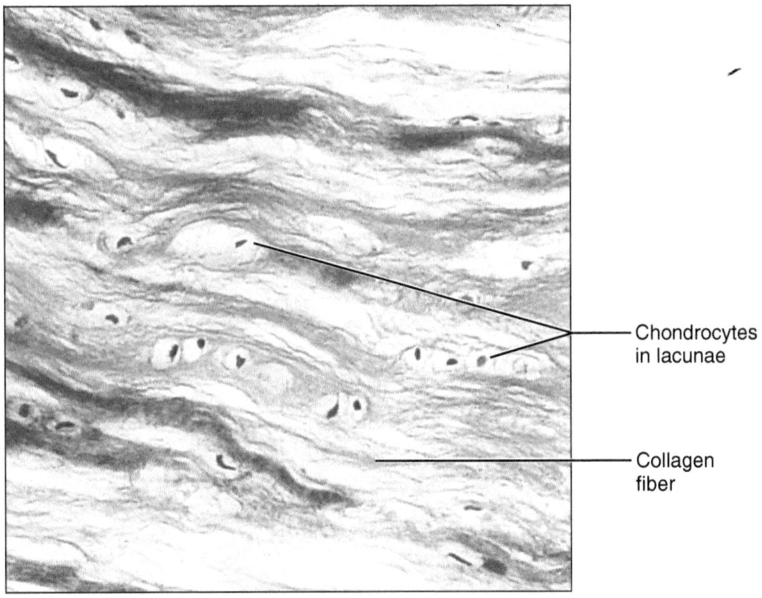

Photomicrograph: Fibrocartilage of an intervertebral disc (200×). Special staining produced the blue color seen.

FIGURE 5 *(continued)* Cartilage (**h** and **i**).

(j) Others: bone (osseous tissue)

Description: Hard, calcified matrix containing many collagen fibers; osteocytes lie in lacunae. Very well vascularized.

Function: Bone supports and protects (by enclosing); provides levers for the muscles to act on; stores calcium and other minerals and fat; marrow inside bones is the site for blood cell formation (hematopoiesis).

Location: Bones

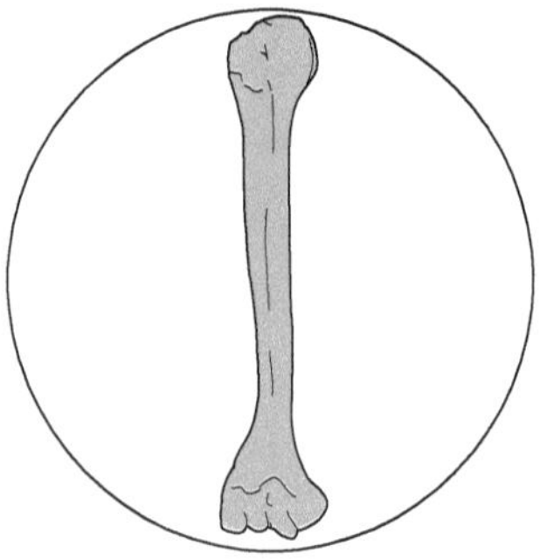

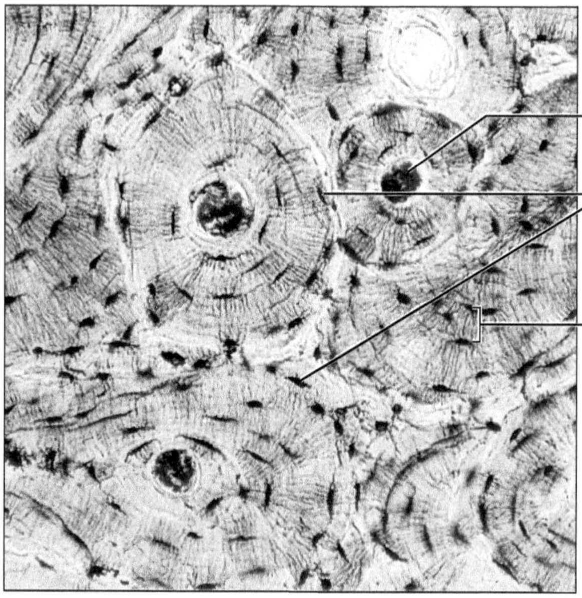
Central canal
Lacunae
Lamella

Photomicrograph: Cross-sectional view of bone (70×).

Allen Bell, University of New England; Pearson Benjamin Cummings

(k) Others: blood

Description: Red and white blood cells in a fluid matrix (plasma).

Function: Transport of respiratory gases, nutrients, wastes, and other substances.

Location: Contained within blood vessels.

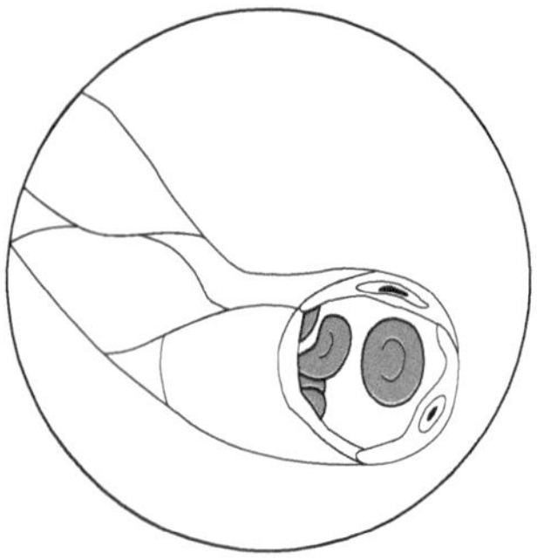

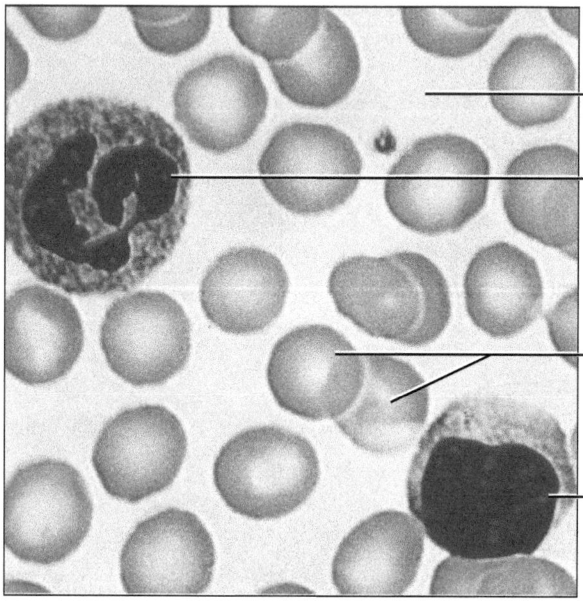
Plasma
Neutrophil
Red blood cells
Lymphocyte

Photomicrograph: Smear of human blood (1500×); two white blood cells (neutrophil in upper left and lymphocyte in lower right) are seen surrounded by red blood cells.

Ed Reschke

FIGURE 5 *(continued)* **Connective tissues.** Bone **(j)** and blood **(k).**

Nervous tissue

Description: Neurons are branching cells; cell processes that may be quite long extend from the nucleus-containing cell body; also contributing to nervous tissue are nonirritable supporting cells (not illustrated).

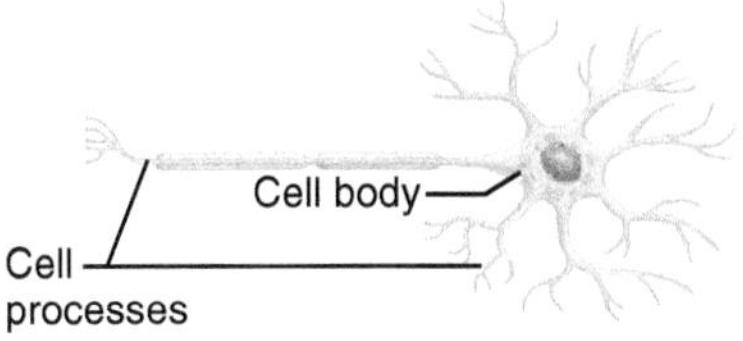
Cell body
Cell processes

Function: Transmit electrical signals from sensory receptors and to effectors (muscles and glands) which control their activity.

Location: Brain, spinal cord, and nerves.

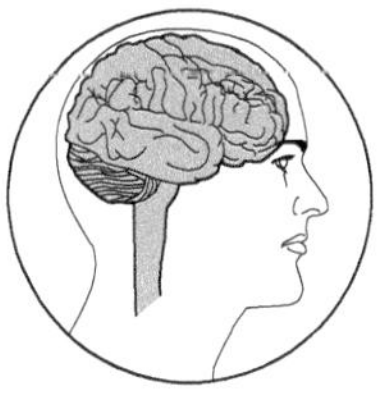

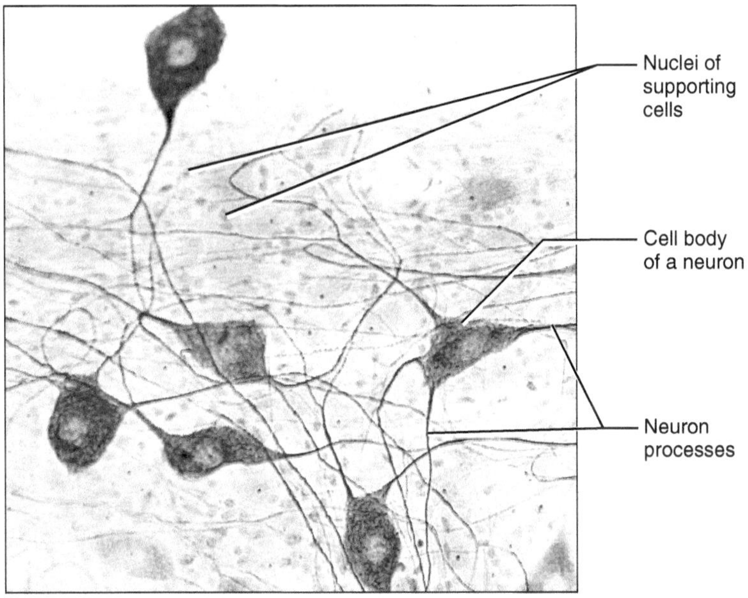
Nuclei of supporting cells
Cell body of a neuron
Neuron processes

Photomicrograph: Neurons (100×)

Biphoto Associates/Photo Researchers

Imagineering

FIGURE 6 **Nervous tissue.**

more permeable during inflammatory reactions and allergies and thus is partially responsible for that "runny nose" of some allergics.

In adipose tissue, locate a "signet ring" cell, a fat cell in which the nucleus can be seen pushed to one side by the large, fat-filled vacuole that appears to be a large empty space. Also notice how little matrix there is in adipose (fat) tissue. Distinguish between the living cells and the matrix in the dense fibrous, bone, and hyaline cartilage preparations.

Scan the blood slide at low and then high power to examine the general shape of the red blood cells. Then, switch to the oil immersion lens for a closer look at the various types of white blood cells. How does blood differ from all other connective tissues?

____

____

Nervous Tissue

Nervous tissue is composed of two major cell populations. The **neuroglia** are special supporting cells that protect, support, and insulate the more delicate neurons. The **neurons** are highly specialized to receive stimuli (irritability) and to conduct waves of excitation, or impulses, to all parts of the body (conductivity). They are the cells that are most often associated with nervous system functioning.

The structure of neurons is markedly different from that of all other body cells. They all have a nucleus-containing cell body, and their cytoplasm is drawn out into long extensions (cell processes)—sometimes as long as 1 m (about 3 feet), which allows a single neuron to conduct an impulse over relatively long distances.

ACTIVITY 3

Examining Nervous Tissue Under the Microscope

Obtain a prepared slide of a spinal cord smear. Locate a neuron and compare it to Figure 6. Keep the light dim—this will help you see the cellular extensions of the neurons. See also Plates 5 and 6 in the Histology Atlas.

(a) Skeletal muscle

Description: Long, cylindrical, multinucleate cells; obvious striations.

Function: Voluntary movement; locomotion; manipulation of the environment; facial expression; voluntary control.

Location: In skeletal muscles attached to bones or occasionally to skin.

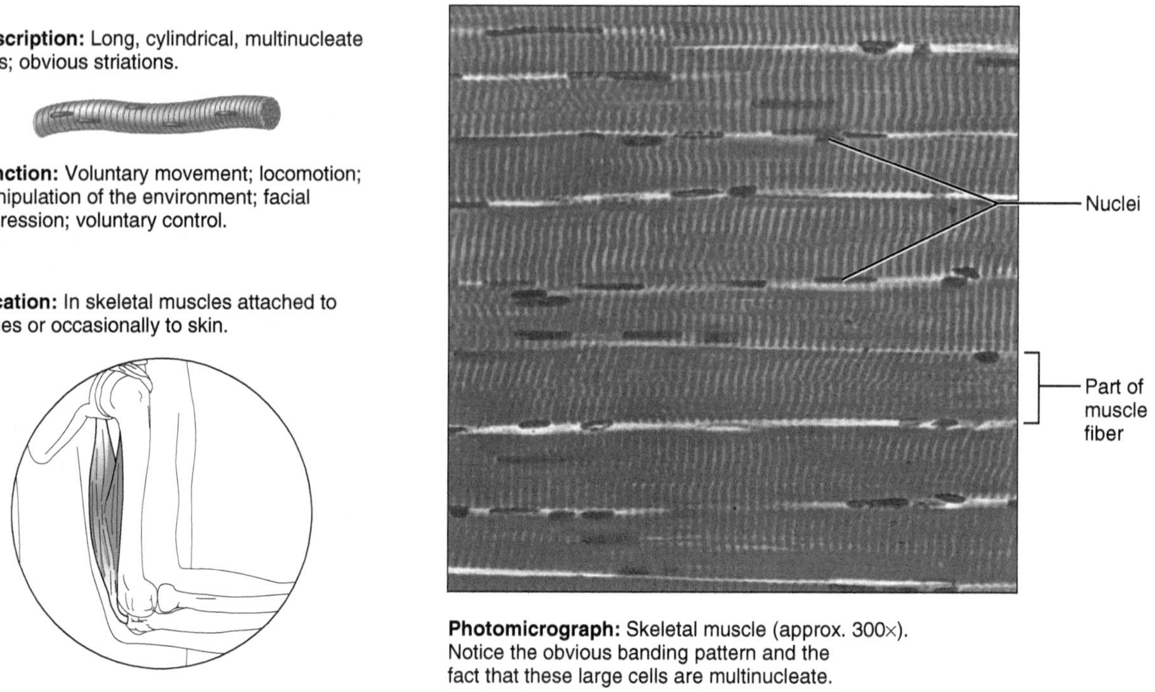
Nuclei
Part of muscle fiber
Eric Graves/Photo Researchers

Photomicrograph: Skeletal muscle (approx. 300×). Notice the obvious banding pattern and the fact that these large cells are multinucleate.

Imagineering

FIGURE 7 **Muscle tissues.** Skeletal muscle **(a).**

Muscle Tissue

Muscle tissue (Figure 7) is highly specialized to contract and produces most types of body movement. As you might expect, muscle cells tend to be elongated, providing a long axis for contraction. The three basic types of muscle tissue are described briefly here. Cardiac and skeletal muscles are treated more completely in later exercises.

Skeletal muscle, the "meat," or flesh, of the body, is attached to the skeleton. It is under voluntary control (consciously controlled), and its contraction moves the limbs and other external body parts. The cells of skeletal muscles are long, cylindrical, and multinucleate (several nuclei per cell), with the nuclei pushed to the periphery of the cells; they have obvious *striations* (stripes).

Cardiac muscle is found only in the heart. As it contracts, the heart acts as a pump, propelling the blood into the blood vessels. Cardiac muscle, like skeletal muscle, has striations, but cardiac cells are branching uninucleate cells that interdigitate (fit together) at junctions called **intercalated discs.** These structural modifications allow the cardiac muscle to act as a unit. Cardiac muscle is under involuntary control, which means that we cannot voluntarily or consciously control the operation of the heart.

Smooth muscle, or *visceral muscle,* is found mainly in the walls of hollow organs (digestive and urinary tract organs, uterus, blood vessels). Typically it has two layers that run at right angles to each other; consequently its contraction can constrict or dilate the lumen (cavity) of an organ and propel substances along predetermined pathways. Smooth muscle cells are quite different in appearance from those of skeletal or cardiac muscle. No striations are visible, and the uninucleate smooth muscle cells are spindle-shaped.

ACTIVITY 4

Examining Muscle Tissue Under the Microscope

Obtain and examine prepared slides of skeletal, cardiac, and smooth muscle. Notice their similarities and dissimilarities in your observations and in the illustrations in Figure 7. Teased smooth muscle shows individual cell shape clearly

(b) Cardiac muscle

Description: Branching, striated, generally uninucleate cells that interdigitate at specialized junctions (intercalated discs).

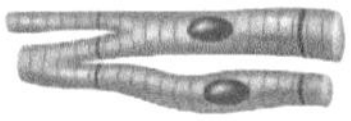

Function: As it contracts, it propels blood into the circulation; involuntary control.

Location: The walls of the heart.

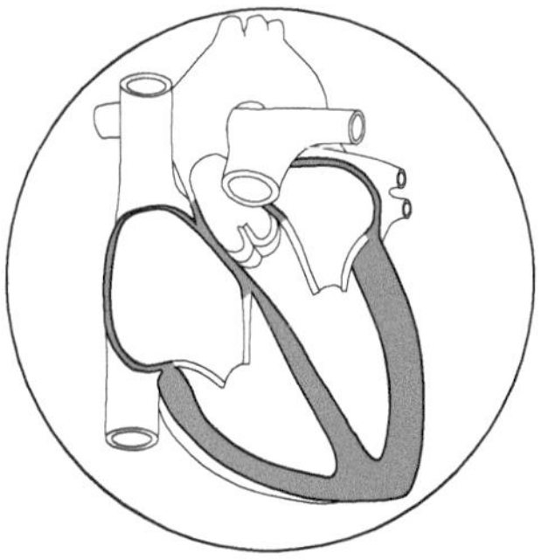

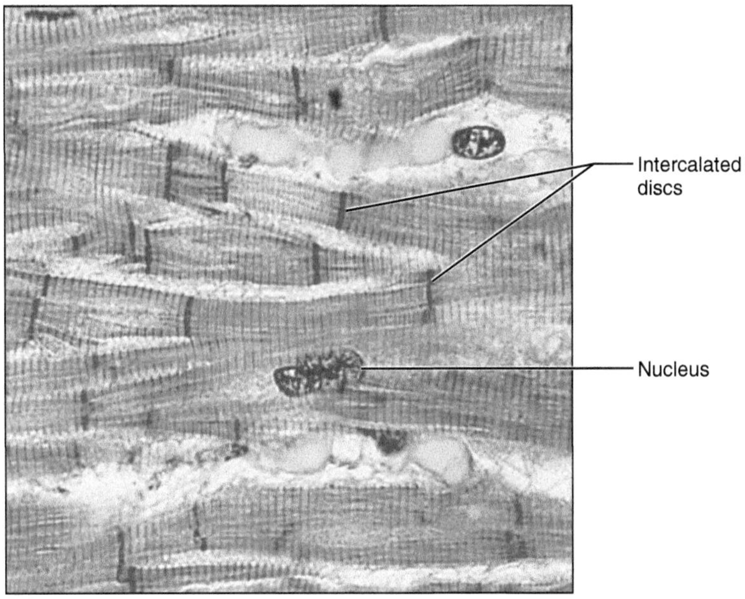

Photomicrograph: Cardiac muscle (800×); notice the striations, branching of cells, and the intercalated discs.

Ed Reschke

(c) Smooth muscle

Description: Spindle-shaped cells with central nuclei; no striations; cells arranged closely to form sheets.

Function: Propels substances or objects (foodstuffs, urine, a baby) along internal passageways; involuntary control.

Location: Mostly in the walls of hollow organs.

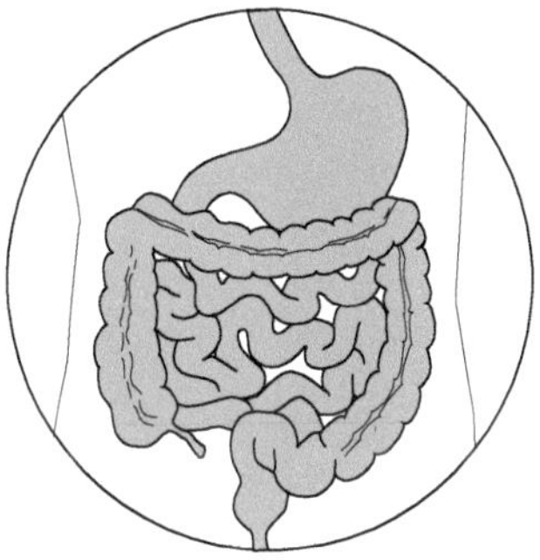

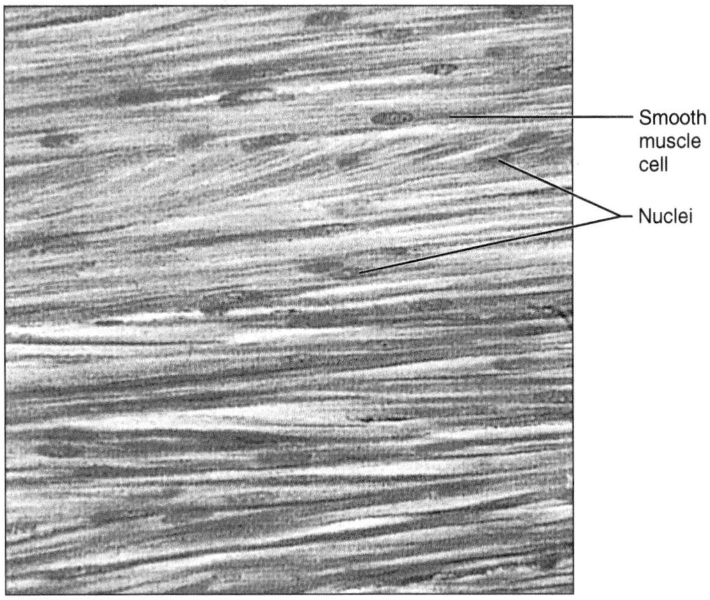

Photomicrograph: Sheet of smooth muscle (approx. 600×).

Allen Bell, University of New England; Pearson Benjamin Cummings

FIGURE 7 *(continued)* Cardiac muscle **(b)** and smooth muscle **(c)**.

REVIEW SHEET

NAME ______________________

LAB TIME/DATE ______________________

Classification of Tissues

Tissue Structure and Function—General Review

1. Define *tissue.* ______________________

2. Use the key choices to identify the major tissue types described below.

Key: a. connective tissue b. epithelium c. muscle d. nervous tissue

b 1. lines body cavities and covers the body's external surface

c 2. pumps blood, flushes urine out of the body, allows one to swing a bat

d 3. transmits electrochemical impulses

a 4. anchors, packages, and supports body organs

b 5. cells may absorb, secrete, and filter

______ 6. most involved in regulating and controlling body functions

c 7. major function is to contract

______ 8. synthesizes hormones

c 9. the most durable tissue type

a 10. abundant nonliving extracellular matrix

a 11. most widespread tissue in the body

d 12. forms nerves and the brain

Epithelial Tissue

3. Describe five general characteristics of epithelial tissue. Polarity, cellularity & specialized contacts, supported by connective tissue, avascularity, & regeneration

4. On what basis are epithelial tissues classified? arrangement / relative # of layers & cell shape

5. List five major functions of epithelium in the body, and give examples of each. ______

Function 1: ______ Example: ______

Function 2: ______ Example: ______

Function 3: ______ Example: ______

Function 4: ______ Example: ______

Function 5: ______ Example: ______

6. How does the function of stratified epithelia differ from the function of simple epithelia? ______

______

______

7. Where is ciliated epithelium found? ______

______

What role does it play? ______

______

8. Transitional epithelium is actually stratified squamous epithelium with special characteristics.

How does it differ structurally from other stratified squamous epithelia? ______

______

How does the structural difference support its function? ______

______

______

9. How do the endocrine and exocrine glands differ in structure and function? ______

______

______

______

10. Respond to the following with the key choices.

Key: a. pseudostratified ciliated columnar
b. simple columnar
c. simple cuboidal
d. simple squamous
e. stratified squamous
f. transitional

___e___ 1. lining of the esophagus

___b___ 2. lining of the stomach

d 3. alveolar sacs of lungs

c 4. tubules of the kidney

_______ 5. epidermis of the skin

_______ 6. lining of bladder; peculiar cells that have the ability to slide over each other

_______ 7. forms the thin serous membranes; a single layer of flattened cells

Connective Tissue

11. What are three general characteristics of connective tissues? _______

12. What functions are performed by connective tissue? _______

13. How are the functions of connective tissue reflected in its structure? _______

14. Using the key, choose the best response to identify the connective tissues described below.

Key:
a. adipose connective tissue
b. areolar connective tissue
c. dense fibrous connective tissue
d. elastic cartilage
e. fibrocartilage
f. hematopoietic tissue
g. hyaline cartilage
h. osseous tissue

c 1. attaches bones to bones and muscles to bones

a 2. acts as a storage depot for fat

_______ 3. the dermis of the skin

e 4. makes up the intervertebral discs

e 5. forms the hip bone

_______ 6. composes basement membranes; a soft packaging tissue with a jellylike matrix

g 7. forms the larynx, the costal cartilages of the ribs, and the embryonic skeleton

d 8. provides a flexible framework for the external ear

_______ 9. firm, structurally amorphous matrix heavily invaded with fibers; appears glassy and smooth

_______ 10. matrix hard owing to calcium salts; provides levers for muscles to act on

a 11. insulates against heat loss

15. Why do adipose cells remind people of a ring with a single jewel? _______

Nervous Tissue

16. What two physiological characteristics are highly developed in neurons (nerve cells)? ____________________

____

17. In what ways are neurons similar to other cells? ____________________

____

How are they different? ____________________

18. Describe how the unique structure of a neuron relates to its function in the body.

____

____

Muscle Tissue

19. The three types of muscle tissue exhibit similarities as well as differences. Check the appropriate space in the chart to indicate which muscle types exhibit each characteristic.

Characteristic	Skeletal	Cardiac	Smooth
Voluntarily controlled			
Involuntarily controlled			
Striated			
Has a single nucleus in each cell			
Has several nuclei per cell			
Found attached to bones			
Allows you to direct your eyeballs			
Found in the walls of the stomach, uterus, and arteries			
Contains spindle-shaped cells			
Contains branching cylindrical cells			
Contains long, nonbranching cylindrical cells			
Has intercalated discs			
Concerned with locomotion of the body as a whole			
Changes the internal volume of an organ as it contracts			
Tissue of the heart			

For Review

20. Label the tissue types illustrated here and on the next pages, and identify all structures provided with leaders.

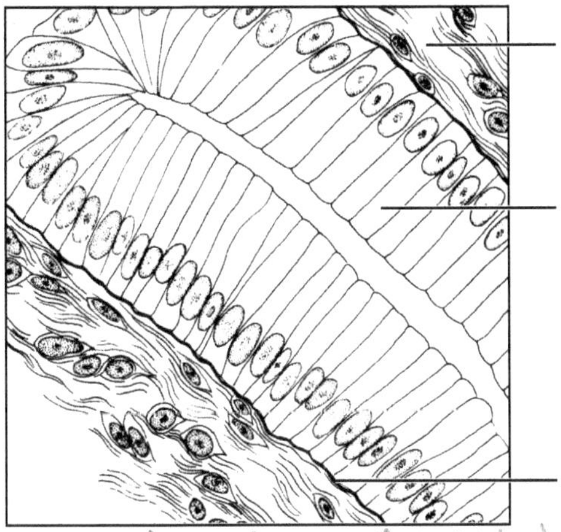

(a) Simple columnar epithelium

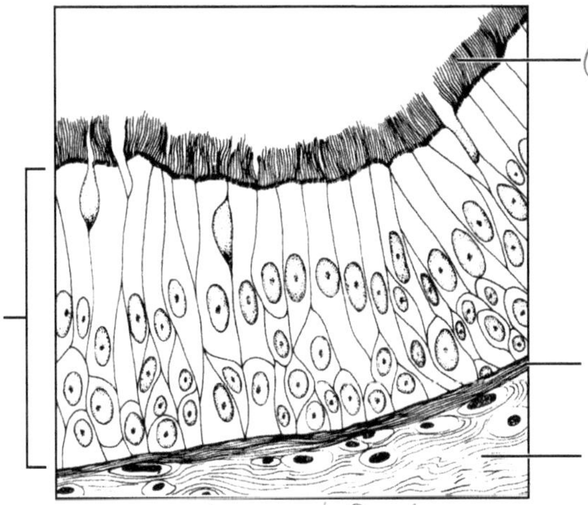

(b) pseudostratified columnar epithelium

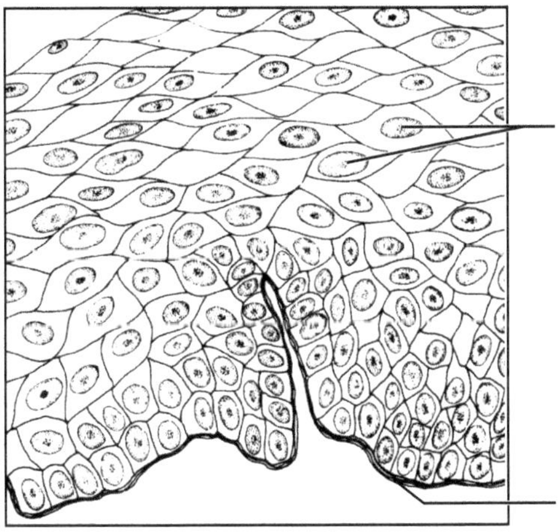

(c) ______________________

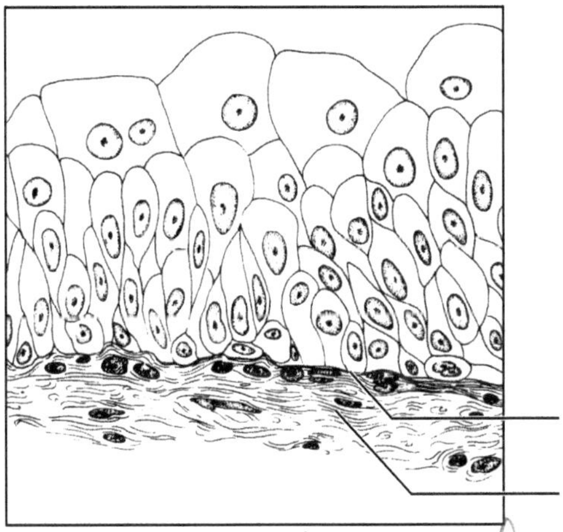

(d) transitional epithelium

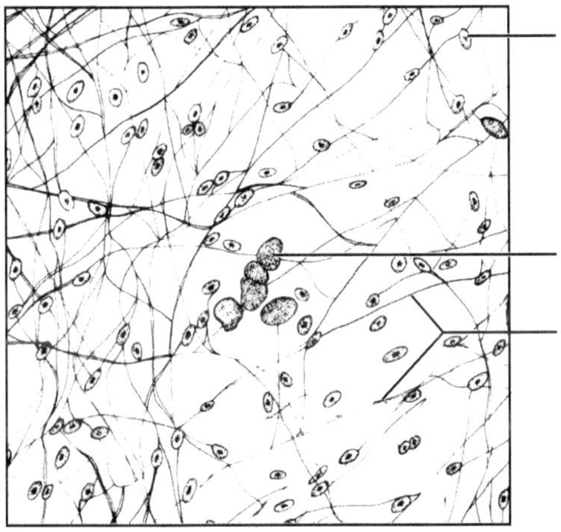

(e) areolar tissue

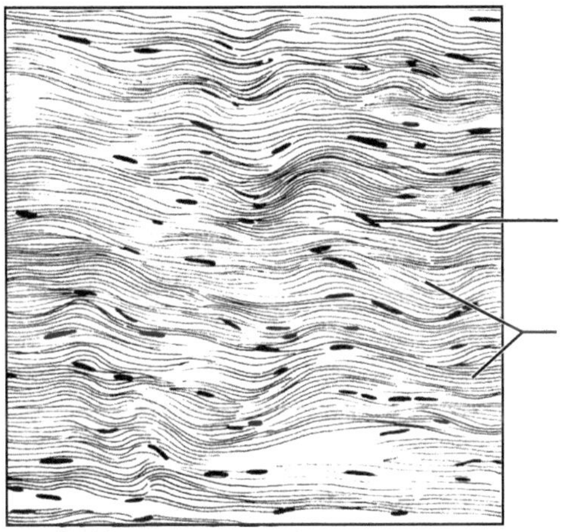

(f) connective tissue

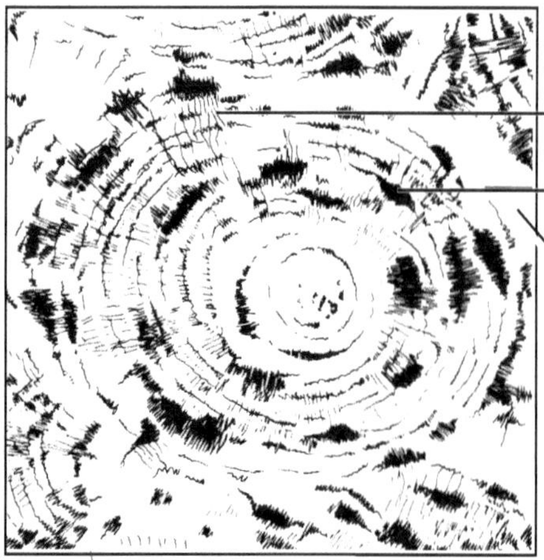
canalliculi
lacunae

(g) bone

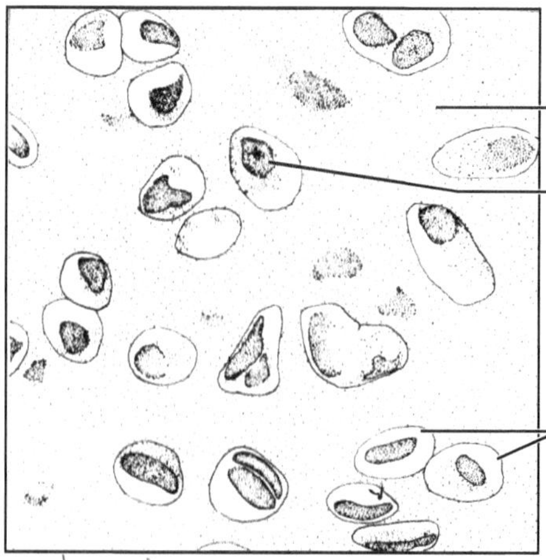

(h) hyaline cartilage

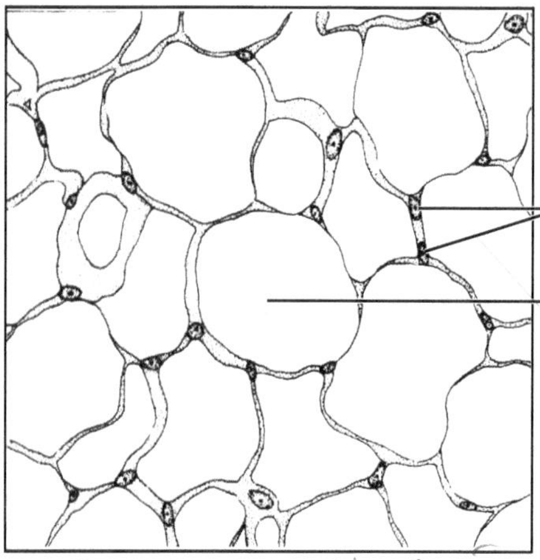
nuclei
air sac

(i) squamous epithelium

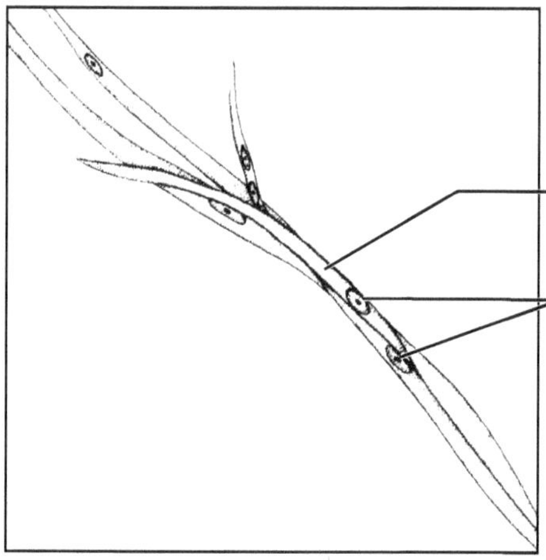
collagen fiber
fibroblast nuclei

(j) connective tissue proper

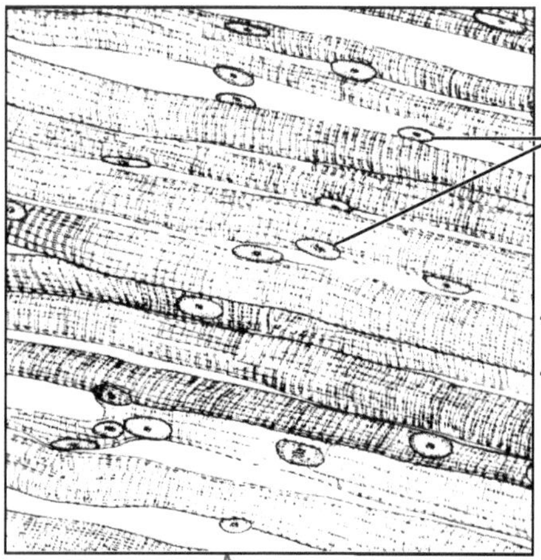
nucleus
fiber

(k) skeletal muscle

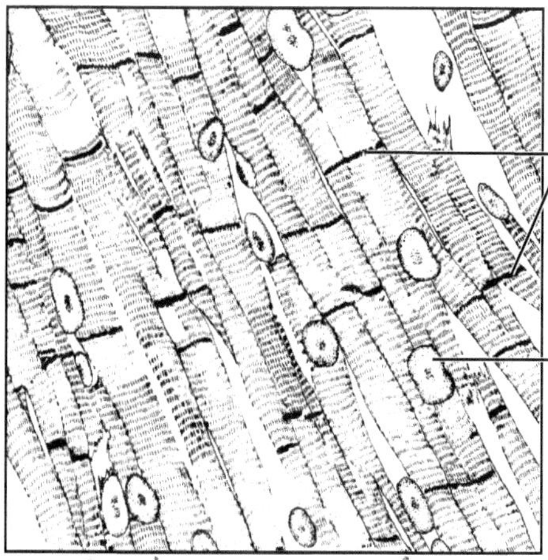
intercalated disc
nucleus

(l) cardiac muscle

General Sensation

MATERIALS

- ☐ Compound microscope
- ☐ Immersion oil
- ☐ Prepared slides (longitudinal sections) of Pacinian corpuscles, Meissner's corpuscles, Golgi tendon organs, and muscle spindles
- ☐ Calipers or esthesiometer
- ☐ Small metric ruler
- ☐ Fine-point, felt-tipped markers (black, red, and blue)
- ☐ Mall probes (obtainable from Carolina Biological Supply), or pointed metal rods of approximately 1-in. diameter and 2- to 3-in. length, with insulated blunt end
- ☐ Von Frey's hairs (or 1-in. lengths of horsehair glued to a matchstick) or sharp pencil
- ☐ Large beaker of ice water; chipped ice
- ☐ Hot water bath set at 45°C; laboratory thermometer
- ☐ Towel
- ☐ Four coins (nickels or quarters)
- ☐ Three large finger bowls or 1000-ml beakers

OBJECTIVES

1. To recognize various types of general sensory receptors as studied in the laboratory, and to describe the function and location of each type.
2. To define *exteroceptor, interoceptor,* and *proprioceptor.*
3. To explain the tactile two-point discrimination test, and to state its anatomical basis.
4. To define *tactile localization,* and to describe how this ability varies in different areas of the body.
5. To demonstrate and relate differences in relative density and distribution of tactile and thermoreceptors in the skin.
6. To define *adaptation* and *negative afterimage.*
7. To define *referred pain* and *projection.*

People are irritable creatures. Hold a sizzling steak before them and their mouths water. Flash your high beams in their eyes on the highway and they cuss. Tickle them and they giggle. These "irritants" (the steak, the light, and the tickle) and many others are stimuli that continually assault us.

The body's **sensory receptors** react to stimuli or changes within the body and in the external environment. The tiny sensory receptors of the **general senses** react to touch, pressure, pain, heat, cold, stretch, vibration, and changes in position and are distributed throughout the body. In contrast to these widely distributed *general sensory receptors,* the receptors of the special senses are large, complex *sense organs* or small, localized groups of receptors. The **special senses** include sight, hearing, equilibrium, smell, and taste.

Sensory receptors may be classified according to the source of their stimulus. **Exteroceptors** react to stimuli in the external environment, and typically they are found close to the body surface. Exteroceptors include the simple cutaneous receptors in the skin and the highly specialized receptor structures of the special senses (the vision apparatus of the eye, and the hearing and equilibrium receptors of the ear, for example). **Interoceptors** or **visceroceptors** respond to stimuli arising within the body. Interoceptors are found in the internal visceral organs and include stretch receptors (in walls of hollow organs), chemoreceptors, and others. **Proprioceptors,** like interoceptors, respond to internal stimuli but are restricted to skeletal muscles, tendons, joints, ligaments, and connective tissue coverings of bones and muscles. They provide information on the position and degree of stretch of those structures.

The receptors of the special sense organs are complex and deserve considerable study. Thus the special senses (vision, hearing, equilibrium, taste, and smell) are covered separately. Only the anatomically simpler **general sensory receptors**—cutaneous receptors and proprioceptors—will be studied in this exercise.

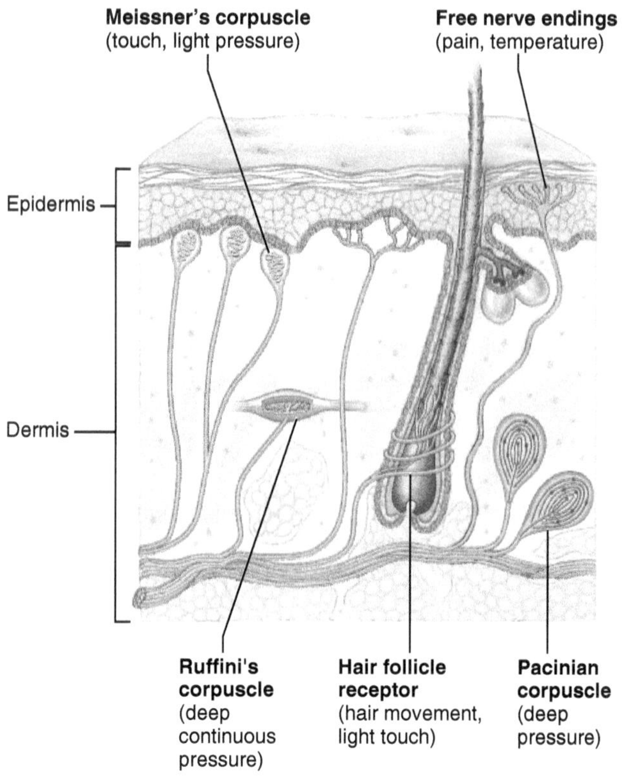
Meissner's corpuscle
(touch, light pressure)
Free nerve endings
(pain, temperature)
Epidermis
Dermis
Ruffini's corpuscle
(deep continuous pressure)
Hair follicle receptor
(hair movement, light touch)
Pacinian corpuscle
(deep pressure)

Imagineering

FIGURE 1 **Cutaneous receptors.** Free nerve endings, hair follicle receptor, Meissner's corpuscle, Pacinian corpuscle, and Ruffini's corpuscle. Merkel discs are not illustrated. (See also Plates 11, 12, and 13 in the Histology Atlas.)

Structure of General Sensory Receptors

You cannot become aware of changes in the environment unless your sensory neurons and their receptors are operating properly. Sensory receptors are modified dendritic endings (or specialized cells associated with the dendrites) that are sensitive to specific environmental stimuli. They react to such stimuli by initiating a nerve impulse. Several histologically distinct types of general sensory receptors have been identified in the skin. Their structures are depicted in Figure 1.

Many references link each type of receptor to specific stimuli, but there is still considerable controversy about the precise qualitative function of each receptor. Responses of all these receptors probably overlap considerably. Certainly, intense stimulation of any of them is always interpreted as pain.

The least specialized of the cutaneous receptors are the **free,** or **naked, nerve endings** of sensory neurons (Figure 1 and Plate 12 of the Histology Atlas), which respond chiefly to pain and temperature. The pain receptors are widespread in the skin and make up a sizable portion of the visceral interoceptors. Certain free nerve endings associate with specific epidermal cells to form **Merkel discs,** or entwine in hair follicles to form **hair follicle receptors.** Both Merkel discs and hair follicle receptors function as light touch receptors.

The other cutaneous receptors are a bit more complex, and the nerve endings are *encapsulated* by connective tissue cells. **Meissner's corpuscles,** commonly referred to as *tactile receptors* because they respond to light touch, are located in the dermal papillae of hairless (glabrous) skin only. **Ruffini's corpuscles** appear to respond to deep pressure and stretch stimuli. **Pacinian corpuscles** are anatomically more distinctive and lie deepest in the dermis. Pacinian corpuscles respond only when deep pressure is first applied. They are best suited to monitor high-frequency vibrations.

ACTIVITY 1

Studying the Structure of Selected Sensory Receptors

1. Obtain a compound microscope and histologic slides of Pacinian and Meissner's corpuscles. Locate, under low power, a Meissner's corpuscle in the dermal layer of the skin. As mentioned above, these are usually found in the dermal papillae. Then switch to the oil immersion lens for a detailed study. Notice that the naked nerve fibers within the capsule are aligned parallel to the skin surface. Compare your observations to Figure 1.

2. Next observe a Pacinian corpuscle located much deeper in the dermis. Try to identify the slender naked nerve ending in the center of the receptor and the heavy capsule of connective tissue surrounding it (which looks rather like an onion cut lengthwise). Also, notice how much larger the Pacinian corpuscles are than the Meissner's corpuscles. Compare your observations to the views shown in Figure 1.

3. Obtain slides of muscle spindles and Golgi tendon organs, the two major types of proprioceptors (Figure 2). In the slide of **muscle spindles,** note that minute extensions of the nerve endings of the sensory neurons coil around specialized slender skeletal muscle cells called **intrafusal cells,** or **fibers.** The **Golgi tendon organs** are composed of nerve endings that ramify through the tendon tissue close to the attachment between muscle and tendon. Stretching of muscles or tendons excites these receptors, which then transmit impulses that ultimately reach the cerebellum for interpretation. Compare your observations to Figure 2.

Receptor Physiology

Sensory receptors act as **transducers,** changing environmental stimuli into afferent nerve impulses. Since the action potential generated in all nerve fibers is essentially identical, the stimulus is identified entirely by the area of the brain's sensory cortex that is stimulated (which, of course, differs for the various afferent nerves).

Four qualities of cutaneous sensations have traditionally been recognized: tactile (touch), heat, cold, and pain. Mapping these sensations on the skin has revealed that the sensory receptors for these qualities are not distributed uniformly. Instead, they have discrete locations and are characterized by clustering at certain points—**punctate distribution.**

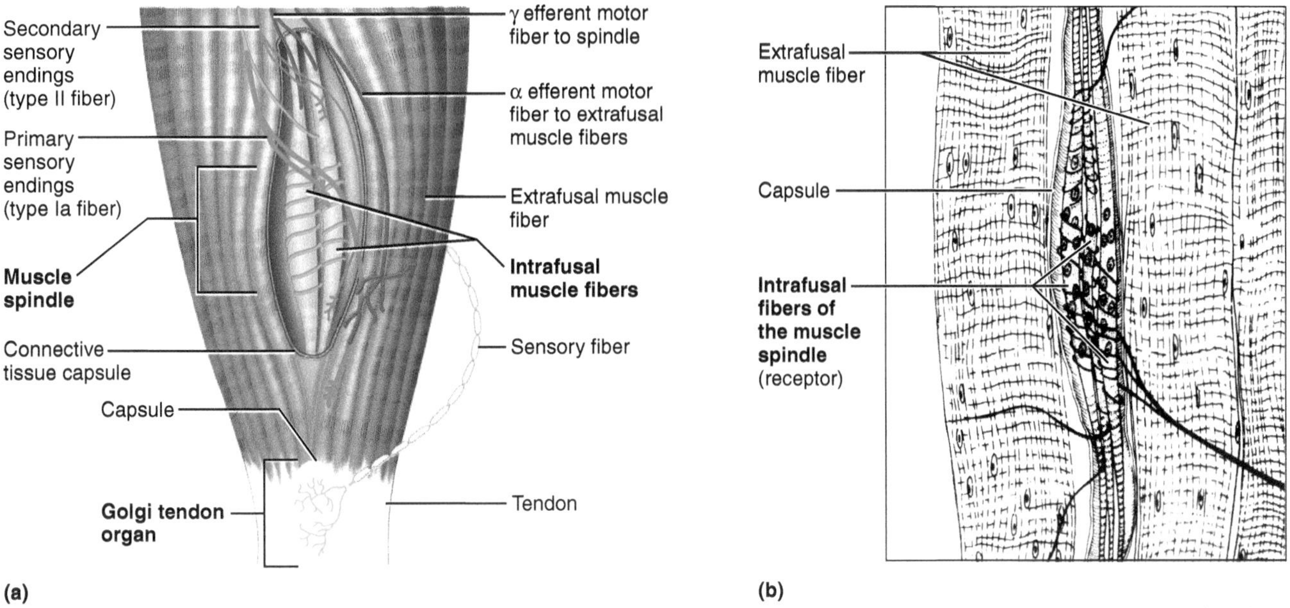

Imagineering

FIGURE 2 **Proprioceptors.** (**a**) Diagrammatic view of a muscle spindle and Golgi tendon organ. (**b**) Drawing of a photomicrograph of a muscle spindle.

The simple pain receptors, extremely important in protecting the body, are the most numerous. Touch receptors cluster where greater sensitivity is desirable, as on the hands and face. It may be surprising to learn that rather large areas of the skin are quite insensitive to touch because of a relative lack of touch receptors.

There are several simple experiments you can conduct to investigate the location and physiology of cutaneous receptors. In each of the following activities, work in pairs with one person as the subject and the other as the experimenter. After you have completed an experiment, switch roles and go through the procedures again so that all class members obtain individual results. Keep an accurate account of each test that you perform.

Two-Point Discrimination Test

As noted, the density of the touch receptors varies significantly in different areas of the body. In general, areas that have the greatest density of tactile receptors have a heightened ability to "feel." These areas correspond to areas that receive the greatest motor innervation; thus they are also typically areas of fine motor control.

On the basis of this information, which areas of the body do you *predict* will have the greatest density of touch receptors?

____

ACTIVITY 2

Determining the Two-Point Threshold

1. Using calipers or an esthesiometer and a metric ruler, test the ability of the subject to differentiate two distinct sensations when the skin is touched simultaneously at two points. Beginning with the face, start with the caliper arms completely together. Gradually increase the distance between the arms, testing the subject's skin after each adjustment. Continue with this testing procedure until the subject reports that *two points* of contact can be felt. This measurement, the smallest distance at which two points of contact can be felt, is the **two-point threshold.**

Determining Two-Point Threshold

Body area tested	Two-point threshold (millimeters)
Face	
Back of hand	
Palm of hand	
Fingertips	
Lips	
Back of neck	
Ventral forearm	

2. Repeat this procedure on the back and palm of the hand, fingertips, lips, back of the neck, and ventral forearm. Record your results in the chart Determining Two-Point Threshold on the previous page.

3. Which area has the smallest two-point threshold?

____

Tactile Localization

Tactile localization is the ability to determine which portion of the skin has been touched. The tactile receptor field of the body periphery has a corresponding "touch" field in the brain's somatosensory association area. Some body areas are well represented with touch receptors, allowing tactile stimuli to be localized with great accuracy, but touch-receptor density in other body areas allows only crude discrimination.

ACTIVITY 3

Testing Tactile Localization

1. The subject's eyes should be closed during the testing. The experimenter touches the palm of the subject's hand with a pointed black felt-tipped marker. The subject should then try to touch the exact point with his or her own marker, which should be of a different color. Measure the error of localization in millimeters.

2. Repeat the test in the same spot twice more, recording the error of localization for each test. Average the results of the three determinations, and record it in the chart Testing Tactile Location.

Testing Tactile Localization

Body area tested	Average error of localization (millimeters)
Palm of hand	
Fingertip	
Ventral forearm	
Back of hand	
Back of neck	

Does the ability to localize the stimulus improve the second time? ____________ The third time? ____________

Explain. ____

____

____

3. Repeat the above procedure on a fingertip, the ventral forearm, the back of a hand, and the back of the neck. Record the averaged results in the chart above.

4. Which area has the smallest error of localization?

____

Density and Location of Touch and Temperature Receptors

ACTIVITY 4

Plotting the Relative Density and Location of Touch and Temperature Receptors

1. Obtain two Mall probes (or temperature rods), metric ruler, Von Frey's hair (or a sharp pencil), a towel, and black, red, and blue felt-tipped markers and bring them to your laboratory bench.

2. Place one Mall probe (or temperature rod) in a beaker of ice water and the other in a water bath controlled at 45°C. With a felt marker, draw a square (2 cm on each side) on the ventral surface of the subject's forearm. The square should not contain dots made previously. During the following tests, the subject's eyes are to remain closed. The subject should tell the examiner when a stimulus is detected.

3. Working in a systematic manner from one side of the marked square to the other, gently touch the Von Frey's hair or a sharp pencil tip to different points within the square. The *hairs* should be applied with a pressure that just causes them to bend; use the same pressure for each contact. Do not apply deep pressure. The goal is to stimulate only the more superficially located Meissner's corpuscles (as opposed to the Pacinian corpuscles located in the subcutaneous tissue). Mark with a *black dot* all points at which the touch is perceived.

4. Go to the area where the ice bath and 45°C water bath are set up. Remove the Mall probe (or temperature rod) from the ice water and, using a towel, quickly wipe it dry. Repeat the procedure outlined above, noting all points of cold perception with a *blue dot*.* Perception should be for temperature, not simply touch.

5. Remove the second Mall probe from the 45°C water bath and repeat the procedure once again, marking all points of heat perception with a *red dot*.*

6. After each student has acted as the subject, draw a "map" of your own and your partner's receptor areas in the squares provided here. Use the same color codes as on the skin.

* The Mall probes will have to be returned to the water baths approximately every 2 minutes to maintain the desired testing temperatures.

Student 1: ____________ Student 2: ____________

2 cm 2 cm

How does the density of the heat receptors correspond to that of the touch receptors?

____

To that of the cold receptors? ______________________

On the basis of your observations, which of these three types of receptors appears to be most abundant (at least in the area tested)?

____

Adaptation of Sensory Receptors

The number of impulses transmitted by sensory receptors often changes both with the intensity of the stimulus and with the length of time the stimulus is applied. In many cases, when a stimulus is applied for a prolonged period, the rate of receptor discharge slows and conscious awareness of the stimulus declines or is lost until some type of stimulus change occurs. This phenomenon is referred to as **adaptation.** The touch receptors adapt particularly rapidly, which is highly desirable. Who, for instance, would want to be continually aware of the pressure of clothing on their skin? The simple experiments to be conducted next allow you to investigate the phenomenon of adaptation.

ACTIVITY 5

Demonstrating Adaptation of Touch Receptors

1. The subject's eyes should be closed. Obtain four coins. Place one coin on the anterior surface of the subject's forearm, and determine how long the sensation persists for the subject. Duration of the sensation:

____________ sec

2. Repeat the test, placing the coin at a different forearm location. How long does the sensation persist at the second location?

____________ sec

3. After awareness of the sensation has been lost at the second site, stack three more coins atop the first one.

Does the pressure sensation return? ______________

If so, for how long is the subject aware of the pressure in this instance?

____________ sec

Are the same receptors being stimulated when the four coins, rather than the one coin, are used? __________

Explain. ______________________________

____

4. To further illustrate the adaptation of touch receptors—in this case, the hair follicle receptors—gently and slowly bend one hair shaft with a pen or pencil until it springs back (away from the pencil) to its original position. Is the tactile sensation greater when the hair is being slowly bent or when it springs back?

____

Why is the adaptation of the touch receptors in the hair follicles particularly important to a woman who wears her hair in a ponytail? If the answer is not immediately apparent, consider the opposite phenomenon: what would happen, in terms of sensory input from her hair follicles, if these receptors did not exhibit adaptation?

____

____

ACTIVITY 6

Demonstrating Adaptation of Temperature Receptors

Adaptation of the temperature receptors can be tested using some very unsophisticated methods.

1. Obtain three large finger bowls or 1000-ml beakers and fill the first with 45°C water. Have the subject immerse her or his left hand in the water and report the sensation. Keep the left hand immersed for 1 minute and then also immerse the right hand in the same bowl.

What is the sensation of the left hand when it is first immersed?

____

What is the sensation of the left hand after 1 minute as compared to the sensation in the right hand just immersed?

____

Had adaptation occurred in the left hand? ____________

2. Rinse both hands in tap water, dry them, and wait 5 minutes before conducting the next test. Just before beginning the test, refill the finger bowl with fresh 45°C water, fill a second with ice water, and fill a third with water at room temperature.

3. Place the *left* hand in the ice water and the *right* hand in the 45°C water. What is the sensation in each hand after 2 minutes as compared to the sensation perceived when the hands were first immersed?

____

____

Which hand seemed to adapt more quickly?

____

4. After reporting these observations, the subject should then place both hands simultaneously into the finger bowl containing the water at room temperature. Record the sensation in the left hand: ______________________________

The right hand: ______________________________

The sensations that the subject experiences when both hands were put into room-temperature water are called **negative afterimages.** They are explained by the fact that sensations of heat and cold depend on the rapidity of heat loss or gain by the skin and differences in the temperature gradient.

Referred Pain

Experiments on pain receptor localization and adaptation are commonly conducted in the laboratory. However, there are certain problems with such experiments. Pain receptors are densely distributed in the skin, and they adapt very little, if at all. (This lack of adaptability is due to the protective function of the receptors. The sensation of pain often indicates tissue damage or trauma to body structures.) Thus no attempt will be made in this exercise to localize the pain receptors or to prove their nonadaptability, since both would cause needless discomfort to those of you acting as subjects and would not add any additional insight.

However, the phenomenon of referred pain is easily demonstrated in the laboratory, and such experiments provide information that may be useful in explaining common examples of this phenomenon. **Referred pain** is a sensory experience in which pain is perceived as arising in one area of the body when in fact another, often quite remote area is receiving the painful stimulus. Thus the pain is said to be "referred" to a different area. The phenomenon of **projection,** the process by which the brain refers sensations to their *usual* point of stimulation, provides the most simple explanation of such experiences. Many of us have experienced referred pain as a radiating pain in the forehead after quickly swallowing an ice-cold drink. Referred pain is important in many types of clinical diagnosis because damage to many visceral organs results in this phenomenon. For example, inadequate oxygenation of the heart muscle often results in pain being referred to the chest wall and left shoulder *(angina pectoris)*, and the reflux of gastric juice into the esophagus causes a sensation of intense discomfort in the thorax referred to as *heartburn.*

ACTIVITY 7

Demonstrating the Phenomenon of Referred Pain

Immerse the subject's elbow in a finger bowl containing ice water. In the chart below, record the quality (such as discomfort, tingling, or pain) and the quality progression of the sensations he or she reports for the intervals indicated. The elbow should be removed from ice water after the 2-minute reading. The last recording is to occur 3 minutes after removal of the subject's elbow from the ice water.

Also record the location of the perceived sensations. The ulnar nerve, which serves the medial third of the hand, is involved in the phenomenon of referred pain experienced during this test. How does the localization of this referred pain correspond to the areas served by the ulnar nerve?

Demonstrating Referred Pain

Time of observation	Quality of sensation	Localization of sensation
On immersion		
After 1 min		
After 2 min		
3 min after removal		

REVIEW SHEET

NAME ______________________

LAB TIME/DATE ______________________

General Sensation

Structure of General Sensory Receptors

1. Differentiate between interoceptors and exteroceptors relative to location and stimulus source.

interoceptor: ______________________

exteroceptor: ______________________

2. A number of activities and sensations are listed in the chart below. For each, check whether the receptors would be exteroceptors or interoceptors; and then name the specific receptor types. (Because visceral receptors were not described in detail in this exercise, you need only indicate that the receptor is a visceral receptor if it falls into that category.)

Activity or sensation	Exteroceptor	Interoceptor	Specific receptor type
Backing into a sun-heated iron railing			
Someone steps on your foot			
Reading a book			
Leaning on your elbows			
Doing sit-ups			
The "too full" sensation			
Seasickness			

Receptor Physiology

3. Explain how the sensory receptors act as transducers. ______________________

____

4. Define *stimulus*. ______________________

5. What was demonstrated by the two-point discrimination test? ______________________

____

How well did your results correspond to your predictions? ______________________

____

What is the relationship between the accuracy of the subject's tactile localization and the results of the two-point discrimnation test? ______________________

6. Define *punctate distribution.* ______________________________

____

7. Several questions regarding general sensation are posed below. Answer each by placing your response in the appropriately numbered blanks to the right.

1. Which cutaneous receptors are the most numerous?

2–3. Which two body areas tested were most sensitive to touch?

4–5. Which two body areas tested were least sensitive to touch?

6. Which appear to be more numerous—receptors that respond to cold or to heat?

7–9. Where would referred pain appear if the following organs were receiving painful stimuli—(7) gallbladder, (8) kidneys, and (9) appendix? (Use your textbook if necessary.)

10. Where was referred pain felt when the elbow was immersed in ice water during the laboratory experiment?

11. What region of the cerebrum interprets the kind and intensity of stimuli that cause cutaneous sensations?

1. ______________________________
2. ______________________________
3. ______________________________
4. ______________________________
5. ______________________________
6. ______________________________
7. ______________________________
8. ______________________________
9. ______________________________
10. ______________________________
11. ______________________________

8. Define *adaptation of sensory receptors.* ______________________________

____

9. Why is it advantageous to have pain receptors that are sensitive to all vigorous stimuli, whether heat, cold, or pressure?

____

Why is the nonadaptability of pain receptors important? ______________________________

____

10. Imagine yourself without any cutaneous sense organs. Why might this be very dangerous? ______________________________

____

____

11. Define *referred pain.* ______________________________

____

What is the probable explanation for referred pain? (Consult your textbook or an appropriate reference if necessary.)

____

____

Special Senses: Vision

MATERIALS

- ☐ Chart of eye anatomy
- ☐ Dissectible eye model
- ☐ Prepared slide of longitudinal section of an eye showing retinal layers
- ☐ Compound microscope
- ☐ Preserved cow or sheep eye
- ☐ Dissecting instruments and tray
- ☐ Disposable gloves
- ☐ Metric ruler; meter stick
- ☐ Common (straight) pins
- ☐ Snellen eye chart (floor marked with chalk to indicate 20-ft. distance from posted Snellen chart)
- ☐ Ishihara's color plates
- ☐ Two pencils
- ☐ Test tubes
- ☐ Laboratory lamp or penlight
- ☐ Ophthalmoscope (if available)

AIA This exercise uses the A.D.A.M.® Interactive Anatomy program.

OBJECTIVES

1. To describe the structure and function of the accessory visual structures.
2. To identify the structural components of the eye when provided with a model, an appropriate diagram, or a preserved sheep or cow eye, and to list the function(s) of each.
3. To describe the cellular makeup of the retina.
4. To discuss the mechanism of image formation on the retina.
5. To trace the visual pathway to the visual cortex, and to indicate the effects of damage to various parts of this pathway.
6. To define the following terms:

refraction	hyperopia
accommodation	astigmatism
convergence	conjunctivitis
emmetropia	cataract
myopia	glaucoma

7. To discuss the importance of the pupillary and convergence reflexes.
8. To explain the difference between rods and cones with respect to visual perception and retinal localization.
9. To state the importance of an ophthalmoscopic examination.

Anatomy of the Eye

External Anatomy and Accessory Structures

The adult human eye is a sphere measuring about 2.5 cm (1 inch) in diameter. Only about one-sixth of the eye's anterior surface is observable (Figure 1); the remainder is enclosed and protected by a cushion of fat and the walls of the bony orbit.

The **lacrimal apparatus** consists of the lacrimal gland, lacrimal canaliculi, lacrimal sac, and the nasolacrimal duct. The **lacrimal glands** are situated superior to the lateral aspect of each eye. They continually liberate a dilute salt solution (tears) that flows onto the anterior surface of the eyeball through several small ducts. The tears flush across the eyeball and through the **lacrimal puncta,** the tiny openings of the **lacrimal canaliculi** medially, then into the **lacrimal sac,** and finally into the **nasolacrimal duct,** which empties into the nasal cavity. The lacrimal secretion also contains **lysozyme,** an antibacterial enzyme. Because it constantly flushes the eyeball, the lacrimal fluid cleanses and protects the eye surface as it moistens and lubricates it. As we age, our eyes tend to become dry due to decreased lacrimation, and thus are more vulnerable to bacterial invasion and irritation.

The anterior surface of each eye is protected by the **eyelids,** or **palpebrae.** (See Figure 1.) The medial and lateral junctions of the upper and lower eyelids are referred to as the **medial** and **lateral commissures** *(canthi),* respectively. The **lacrimal caruncle,** a fleshy elevation at the medial commissure, produces a whitish oily secretion. A mucous membrane, the **conjunctiva,** lines the internal surface of the eyelids (as the *palpebral conjunctiva*) and continues over the anterior surface of the eyeball to its junction with the corneal epithelium (as the *bulbar conjunctiva*). The conjunctiva secretes mucus, which aids in lubricating the eyeball. Inflammation of the conjunctiva, often accompanied by redness of the eye, is called **conjunctivitis.**

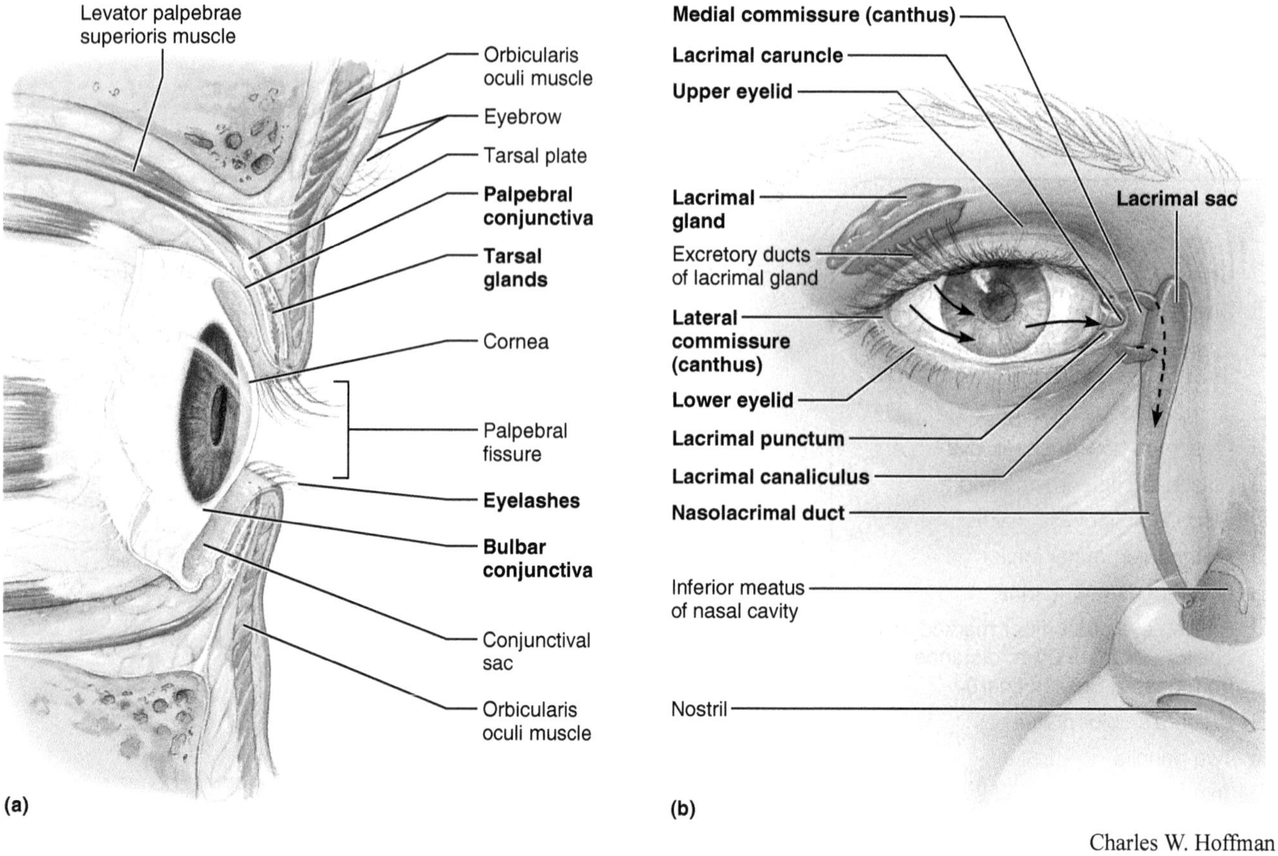
Levator palpebrae superioris muscle
Orbicularis oculi muscle
Eyebrow
Tarsal plate
Palpebral conjunctiva
Tarsal glands
Cornea
Palpebral fissure
Eyelashes
Bulbar conjunctiva
Conjunctival sac
Orbicularis oculi muscle
(a)
Medial commissure (canthus)
Lacrimal caruncle
Upper eyelid
Lacrimal gland
Lacrimal sac
Excretory ducts of lacrimal gland
Lateral commissure (canthus)
Lower eyelid
Lacrimal punctum
Lacrimal canaliculus
Nasolacrimal duct
Inferior meatus of nasal cavity
Nostril
(b)
Charles W. Hoffman

FIGURE 1 External anatomy of the eye and accessory structures. (**a**) Sagittal section. (**b**) Anterior view.

Projecting from the border of each eyelid is a row of short hairs, the **eyelashes.** The **ciliary glands,** modified sweat glands, lie between the eyelash hair follicles and help lubricate the eyeball. Small sebaceous glands associated with the hair follicles and the larger **tarsal** *(meibomian)* **glands,** located posterior to the eyelashes, secrete an oily substance. An inflammation of one of the ciliary glands or a small oil gland is called a **sty.**

Six **extrinsic eye muscles** attached to the exterior surface of each eyeball control eye movement and make it possible for the eye to follow a moving object. The names and positioning of these extrinsic muscles are noted in Figure 2. Their actions are given in the chart accompanying that figure.

ACTIVITY 1

Identifying Accessory Eye Structures

Using Figure 1 or a chart of eye anatomy, observe the eyes of another student, and identify as many of the accessory structures as possible. Ask the student to look to the left. What extrinsic eye muscles are responsible for this action?

Right eye: ______________________________

Left eye: ______________________________

Internal Anatomy of the Eye

Anatomically, the wall of the eye is constructed of three layers (Figure 3). The outermost **fibrous layer** is a protective layer composed of dense avascular connective tissue. It has two obviously different regions: The opaque white **sclera** forms the bulk of the fibrous layer and is observable anteriorly as the "white of the eye." Its anteriormost portion is modified structurally to form the transparent **cornea,** through which light enters the eye.

The middle layer, called the **uvea,** is the **vascular layer.** Its posteriormost part, the **choroid,** is a blood-rich nutritive region containing a dark pigment that prevents light scattering within the eye. Anteriorly, the choroid is modified to form the **ciliary body,** which is chiefly composed of *ciliary muscles,* important in controlling lens shape, and *ciliary processes.* The ciliary processes secrete aqueous humor. The most anterior part of the uvea is the pigmented **iris.** The iris is incomplete, resulting in a rounded opening, the **pupil,** through which light passes.

The iris is composed of circularly and radially arranged smooth muscle fibers and acts as a reflexively activated diaphragm to regulate the amount of light entering the eye. In close vision and bright light, the circular muscles of the iris contract, and the pupil constricts. In distant vision and in dim light, the radial fibers contract, enlarging (dilating) the pupil and allowing more light to enter the eye.

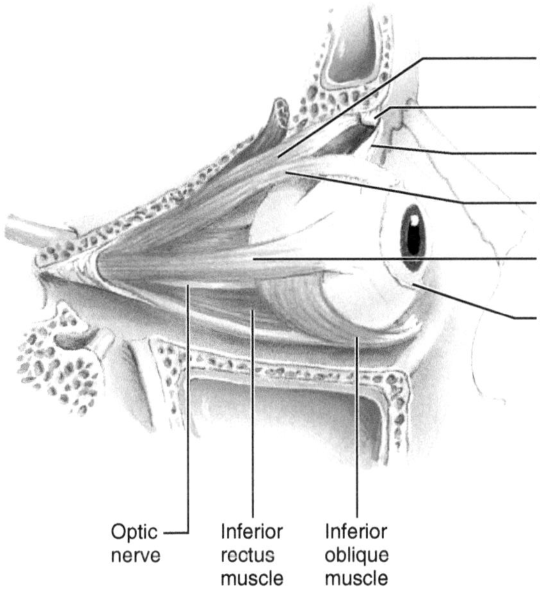

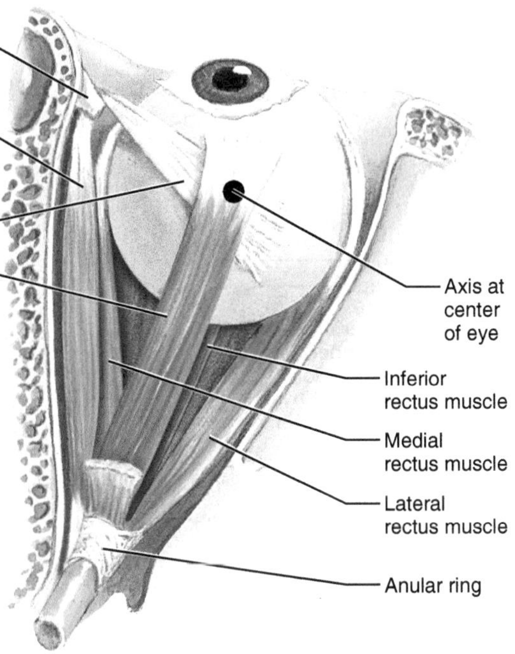

Name	Action	Controlling cranial nerve
Lateral rectus	Moves eye laterally	VI (abducens)
Medial rectus	Moves eye medially	III (oculomotor)
Superior rectus	Elevates eye and turns it medially	III (oculomotor)
Inferior rectus	Depresses eye and turns it medially	III (oculomotor)
Inferior oblique	Elevates eye and turns it laterally	III (oculomotor)
Superior oblique	Depresses eye and turns it laterally	IV (trochlear)

(c)

Imagineering

FIGURE 2 **Extrinsic muscles of the eye.** (**a**) Lateral view of the right eye. (**b**) Superior view of the right eye. (**c**) Summary of actions of the extrinsic eye muscles and cranial nerves that control them.

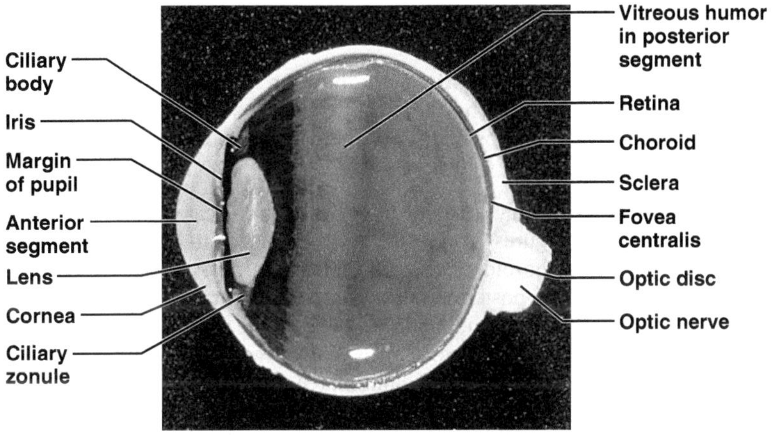

From *A Stereoscopic Atlas of Human Anatomy* by David L. Bassett

FIGURE 3 **Sagittal section of the internal anatomy of the eye.** (**a**) Photograph.

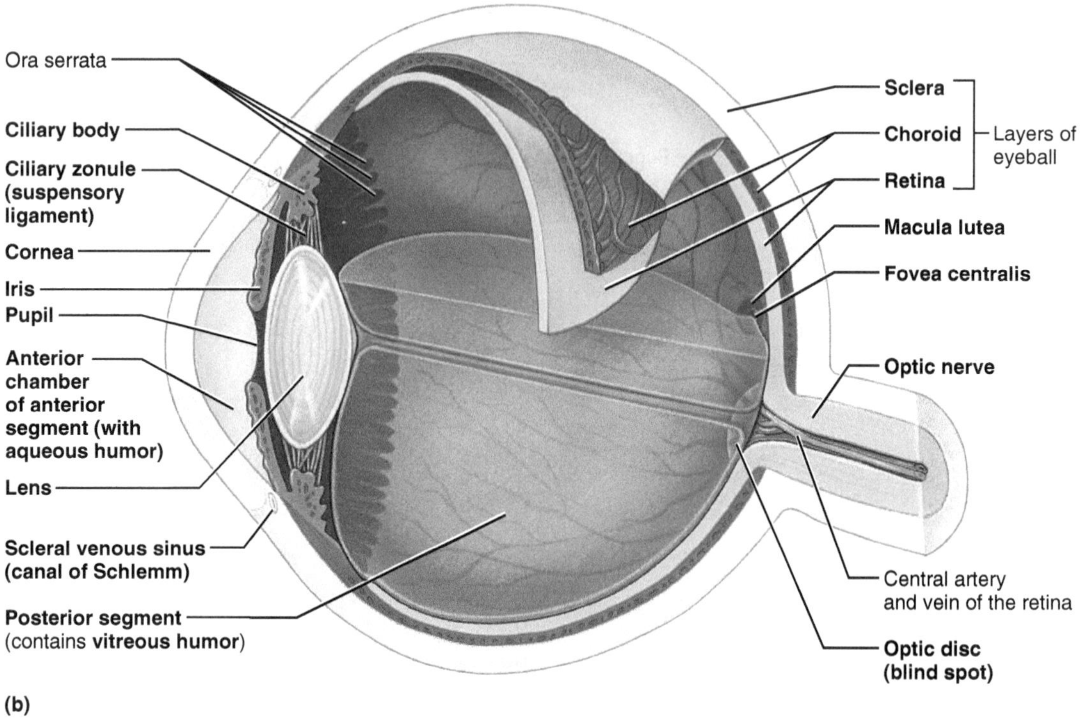
Ora serrata
Ciliary body
Ciliary zonule (suspensory ligament)
Cornea
Iris
Pupil
Anterior chamber of anterior segment (with aqueous humor)
Lens
Scleral venous sinus (canal of Schlemm)
Posterior segment (contains vitreous humor)
Sclera
Choroid
Retina
Layers of eyeball
Macula lutea
Fovea centralis
Optic nerve
Central artery and vein of the retina
Optic disc (blind spot)
(b)

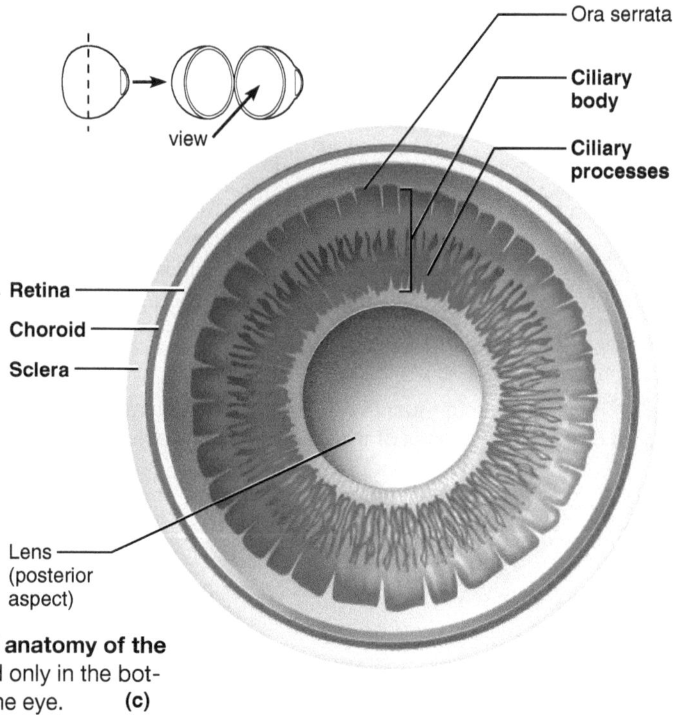
Ora serrata
Ciliary body
Ciliary processes
view
Retina
Choroid
Sclera
Lens (posterior aspect)
(c)

FIGURE 3 *(continued)* **Sagittal section of the internal anatomy of the eye.** (**b**) Diagrammatic view. The vitreous humor is illustrated only in the bottom half of the eyeball. (**c**) Posterior view of anterior half of the eye.

The innermost **sensory layer** of the eye is the delicate, two-layered **retina** (Figures 3 and 4). The outer **pigmented epithelium** abuts the choroid and extends anteriorly to cover the ciliary body and the posterior side of the iris. The transparent inner **neural layer** extends anteriorly only to the ciliary body. It contains the photoreceptors, **rods** and **cones,** which begin the chain of electrical events that ultimately result in the transduction of light energy into nerve impulses that are transmitted to the optic cortex of the brain. Vision is the result. The photoreceptor cells are distributed over the entire neural retina, except where the optic nerve leaves the eyeball. This site is called the **optic disc,** or *blind spot.* Lateral to each blind spot, and directly posterior to the lens, is an area called the **macula lutea** ("yellow spot"), an area of high cone density. In its center is the **fovea centralis,** a minute pit about 0.4 mm in diameter, which contains mostly cones and is the area of greatest visual acuity. Focusing for discriminative vision occurs in the fovea centralis.

Light entering the eye is focused on the retina by the **lens,** a flexible crystalline structure held vertically in the eye's interior by the **suspensory ligament,** more specifically called the **ciliary zonule,** attached to the ciliary body. Activity of the ciliary muscle, which accounts for the bulk of ciliary body tissue, changes lens thickness to allow light to be properly focused on the retina.

In the elderly the lens becomes increasingly hard and opaque. **Cataracts,** which often result from this process, cause vision to become hazy or entirely obstructed. ●

The lens divides the eye into two segments: the **anterior segment** anterior to the lens, which contains a clear watery fluid called the **aqueous humor,** and the **posterior segment** behind the lens, filled with a gel-like substance, the **vitreous humor,** or **vitreous body.** The anterior segment is further divided into **anterior** and **posterior chambers,** located before and after the iris, respectively. The aqueous humor is continually formed by the capillaries of the **ciliary processes** of the ciliary body. It helps to maintain the intraocular pressure of the eye and provides nutrients for the avascular lens and cornea. The aqueous humor is reabsorbed into the **scleral venous sinus (canal of Schlemm).** The vitreous humor provides the major internal reinforcement of the posterior part of the eyeball, and helps to keep the retina pressed firmly against the wall of the eyeball. It is formed *only* before birth.

Anything that interferes with drainage of the aqueous fluid increases intraocular pressure. When intraocular pressure reaches dangerously high levels, the retina and optic nerve are compressed, resulting in pain and possible blindness, a condition called **glaucoma.** ●

ACTIVITY 2

Identifying Internal Structures of the Eye

Obtain a dissectible eye model and identify its internal structures described above. As you work, also refer to Figure 3.

Microscopic Anatomy of the Retina

As described above, the retina consists of two main types of cells: a pigmented *epithelium,* which abuts the choroid, and an inner cell layer composed of *neurons,* which is in contact with the vitreous humor (see Figure 4). The inner, nervous layer is composed of three major neuronal populations. These are, from outer to inner aspect, the **photoreceptors** (rods and cones), the **bipolar cells,** and the **ganglion cells.**

The **rods** are the specialized receptors for dim light. Visual interpretation of their activity is in gray tones. The **cones** are color receptors that permit high levels of visual acuity, but they function only under conditions of high light intensity; thus, for example, no color vision is possible in moonlight. Mostly cones are found in the fovea centralis, and their number decreases as the retinal periphery is approached. By contrast, rods are most numerous in the periphery, and their density decreases as the macula is approached.

Light must pass through the ganglion cell layer and the bipolar neuron layer to reach and excite the rods and cones. As a result of a light stimulus, the photoreceptors undergo changes in their membrane potential that influence the bipolar neurons. These in turn stimulate the ganglion cells, whose axons leave the retina in the tight bundle of fibers known as the **optic nerve** (Figure 3). The retinal layer is thickest where the optic nerve attaches to the eyeball because an increasing number of ganglion cell axons converge at this point. It thins as it approaches the ciliary body. In addition to these three major cell types, the retina also contains horizontal cells and amacrine cells, which play a role in visual processing.

ACTIVITY 3

Studying the Microscopic Anatomy of the Retina

Use a compound microscope to examine a histologic slide of a longitudinal section of the eye. Identify the retinal layers by comparing your view to Figure 4.

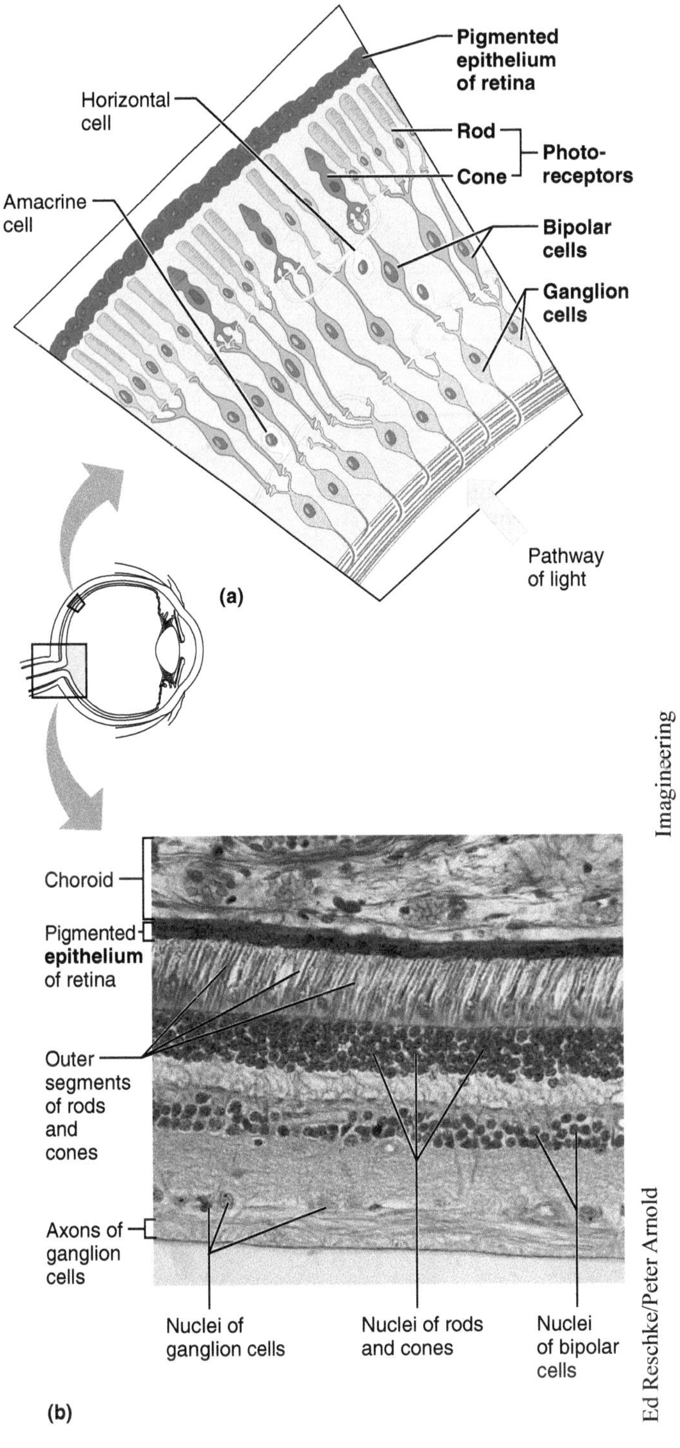

FIGURE 4 Microscopic anatomy of the cellular layers of the retina. (a) Diagrammatic view. (b) Photomicrograph of the retina (180×).

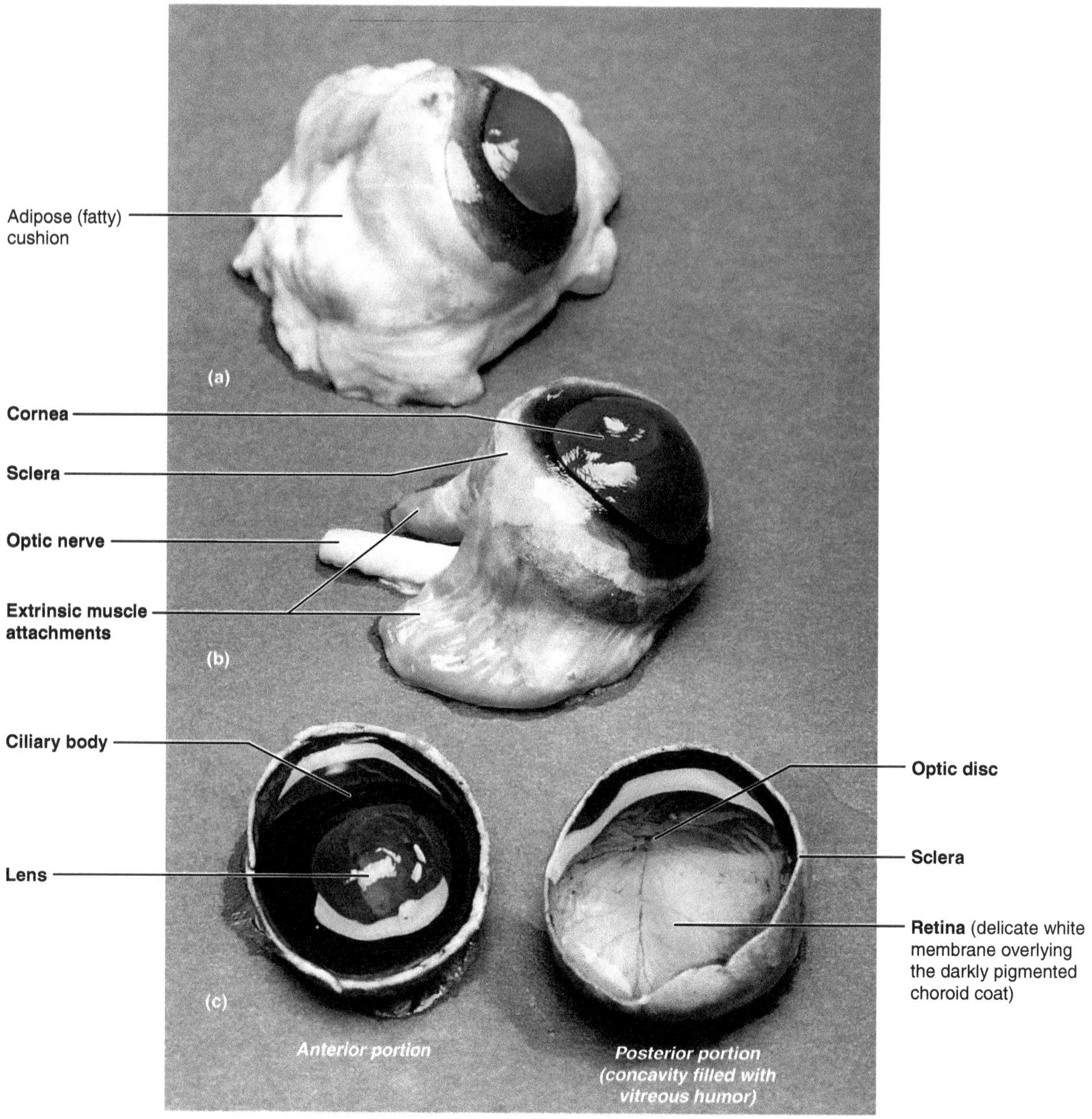
Adipose (fatty) cushion
(a)
Cornea
Sclera
Optic nerve
Extrinsic muscle attachments
(b)
Ciliary body
Lens
Optic disc
Sclera
Retina (delicate white membrane overlying the darkly pigmented choroid coat)
(c)
Anterior portion
Posterior portion (concavity filled with vitreous humor)

Elena Dorfman, Pearson Benjamin Cummings

FIGURE 5 Anatomy of the cow eye. (**a**) Cow eye (entire) removed from orbit (notice the large amount of fat cushioning the eyeball). (**b**) Cow eye (entire) with fat removed to show the extrinsic muscle attachments and optic nerve. (**c**) Cow eye cut along the frontal plane to reveal internal structures.

DISSECTION: The Cow (Sheep) Eye

1. Obtain a preserved cow or sheep eye, dissecting instruments, and a dissecting tray. Don disposable gloves.

2. Examine the external surface of the eye, noting the thick cushion of adipose tissue. Identify the optic nerve (cranial nerve II) as it leaves the eyeball, the remnants of the extrinsic eye muscles, the conjunctiva, the sclera, and the cornea. The normally transparent cornea is opalescent or opaque if the eye has been preserved. Refer to Figure 5 as you work.

3. Trim away most of the fat and connective tissue, but leave the optic nerve intact. Holding the eye with the cornea facing downward, carefully make an incision with a sharp scalpel into the sclera about 6 mm (¼ inch) above the cornea. (The sclera of the preserved eyeball is *very* tough, so you will have to apply substantial pressure to penetrate it.) Using scissors, complete the incision around the circumference of the eyeball paralleling the corneal edge.

4. Carefully lift the anterior part of the eyeball away from the posterior portion. Conditions being proper, the vitreous body should remain with the posterior part of the eyeball.

5. Examine the anterior part of the eye, and identify the following structures:

Ciliary body: Black pigmented body that appears to be a halo encircling the lens.

Lens: Biconvex structure that is opaque in preserved specimens.

Carefully remove the lens and identify the adjacent structures:

Iris: Anterior continuation of the ciliary body penetrated by the pupil.

Cornea: More convex anteriormost portion of the sclera; normally transparent but cloudy in preserved specimens.

6. Examine the posterior portion of the eyeball. Carefully remove the vitreous humor, and identify the following structures:

Retina: The neural layer of the retina appears as a delicate tan, probably crumpled membrane that separates easily from the pigmented choroid.

Note its point of attachment. What is this point called?

____

Pigmented choroid coat: Appears iridescent in the cow or sheep eye owing to a special reflecting surface called the **tapetum lucidum.** This specialized surface reflects the light within the eye and is found in the eyes of animals that live under conditions of low-intensity light. It is not found in humans.

Visual Pathways to the Brain

The axons of the ganglion cells of the retina converge at the posterior aspect of the eyeball and exit from the eye as the optic nerve. At the **optic chiasma,** the fibers from the medial side of each eye cross over to the opposite side (Figure 6). The fiber tracts thus formed are called the **optic tracts.** Each optic tract contains fibers from the lateral side of the eye on the same side and from the medial side of the opposite eye.

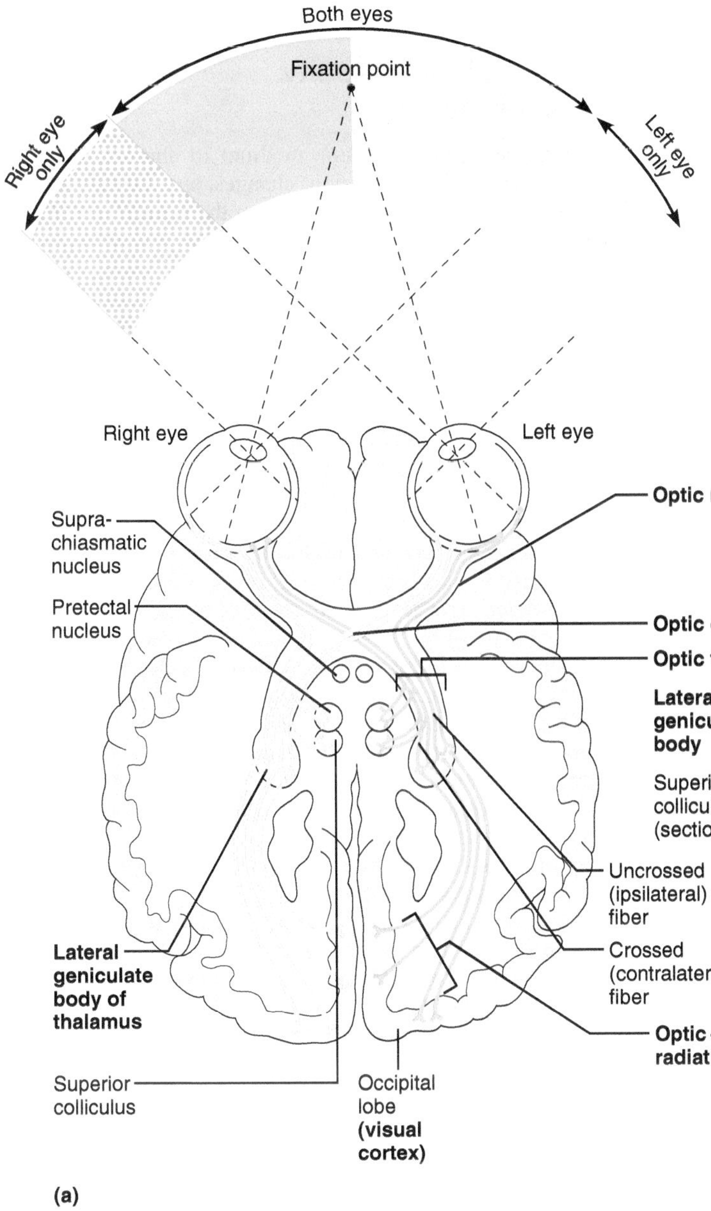

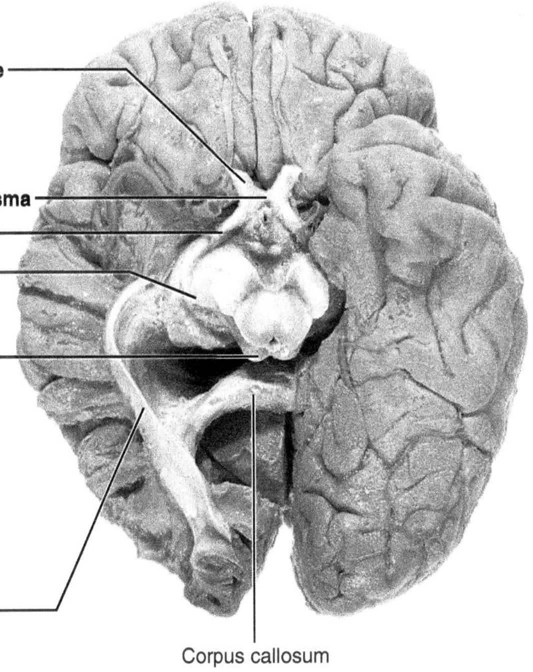

FIGURE 6 **Inferior views of the visual pathway to the brain.** (**a**) Diagram. (Note that fibers from the lateral portion of each retinal field do not cross at the optic chiasma.) (**b**) Photograph.

The optic tract fibers synapse with neurons in the **lateral geniculate body** of the thalamus, whose axons form the **optic radiation,** terminating in the **visual cortex** in the occipital lobe of the brain. Here they synapse with the cortical cells, and visual interpretation occurs.

ACTIVITY 4

Predicting the Effects of Visual Pathway Lesions

After examining Figure 6, determine what effects lesions in the following areas would have on vision:

In the right optic nerve: ____________________

____

Through the optic chiasma: ____________________

____

In the left optic tract: ____________________

____

In the right cerebral cortex (visual area): ____________________

____

Visual Tests and Experiments

The Blind Spot

ACTIVITY 5

Demonstrating the Blind Spot

1. Hold Figure 7 about 46 cm (18 inches) from your eyes. Close your left eye, and focus your right eye on the X, which should be positioned so that it is directly in line with your right eye. Move the figure slowly toward your face, keeping your right eye focused on the X. When the dot focuses on the blind spot, which lacks photoreceptors, it will disappear.

2. Have your laboratory partner record in metric units the distance at which this occurs. The dot will reappear as the figure is moved closer. Distance at which the dot disappears:

Right eye ____________________

Repeat the test for the left eye, this time closing the right eye and focusing the left eye on the dot. Record the distance at which the X disappears:

Left eye ____________________

Shirley Bortoli

FIGURE 7 **Blind spot test figure.**

Refraction, Visual Acuity, and Astigmatism

When light rays pass from one medium to another, their velocity, or speed of transmission, changes, and the rays are bent, or **refracted.** Thus the light rays in the visual field are refracted as they encounter the cornea, lens, and vitreous humor of the eye.

The refractive index (bending power) of the cornea and vitreous humor are constant. But the lens's refractive index can be varied by changing the lens's shape—that is, by making it more or less convex so that the light is properly converged and focused on the retina. The greater the lens convexity, or bulge, the more the light will be bent and the stronger the lens. Conversely, the less the lens convexity (the flatter it is), the less it bends the light.

In general, light from a distant source (over 6 m, or 20 feet) approaches the eye as parallel rays, and no change in lens convexity is necessary for it to focus properly on the retina. However, light from a close source tends to diverge, and the convexity of the lens must increase to make close vision possible. To achieve this, the ciliary muscle contracts, decreasing the tension on the suspensory ligament attached to the lens and allowing the elastic lens to "round up." Thus, a lens capable of bringing a *close* object into sharp focus is stronger (more convex) than a lens focusing on a more distant object. The ability of the eye to focus differentially for objects of near vision (less than 6 m, or 20 feet) is called **accommodation.** It should be noted that the image formed on the retina as a result of the refractory activity of the lens (Figure 8) is a **real image** (reversed from left to right, inverted, and smaller than the object).

The normal, or **emmetropic, eye** is able to accommodate properly (Figure 9a). However, visual problems may result (1) from lenses that are too strong or too "lazy" (overconverging and underconverging, respectively), (2) from structural problems such as an eyeball that is too long or too short to provide for proper focusing by the lens, or (3) from a cornea or lens with improper curvatures.

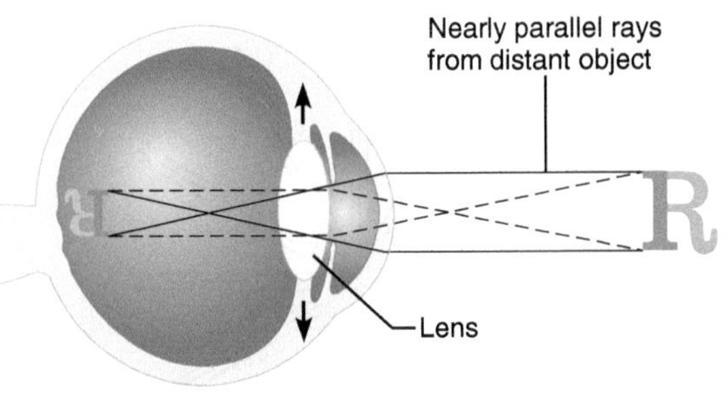

Imagineering.

FIGURE 8 Refraction and real images. The refraction of light in the eye produces a real image (reversed, inverted, and reduced) on the retina.

Individuals in whom the image normally focuses in front of the retina are said to have **myopia,** or nearsightedness (Figure 9b); they can see close objects without difficulty, but distant objects are blurred or seen indistinctly. Correction requires a concave lens, which causes the light reaching the eye to diverge.

If the image focuses behind the retina, the individual is said to have **hyperopia,** or farsightedness. Such persons have no problems with distant vision but need glasses with convex lenses to augment the converging power of the lens for close vision (Figure 9c).

Irregularities in the curvatures of the lens and/or the cornea lead to a blurred vision problem called **astigmatism.** Cylindrically ground lenses, which compensate for inequalities in the curvatures of the refracting surfaces, are prescribed to correct the condition. ●

Near-Point Accommodation The elasticity of the lens decreases dramatically with age, resulting in difficulty in focusing for near or close vision. This condition is called **presbyopia**—literally, old vision. Lens elasticity can be tested by measuring the **near point of accommodation.** The near point of vision is about 10 cm from the eye in young adults. It is closer in children and farther in old age.

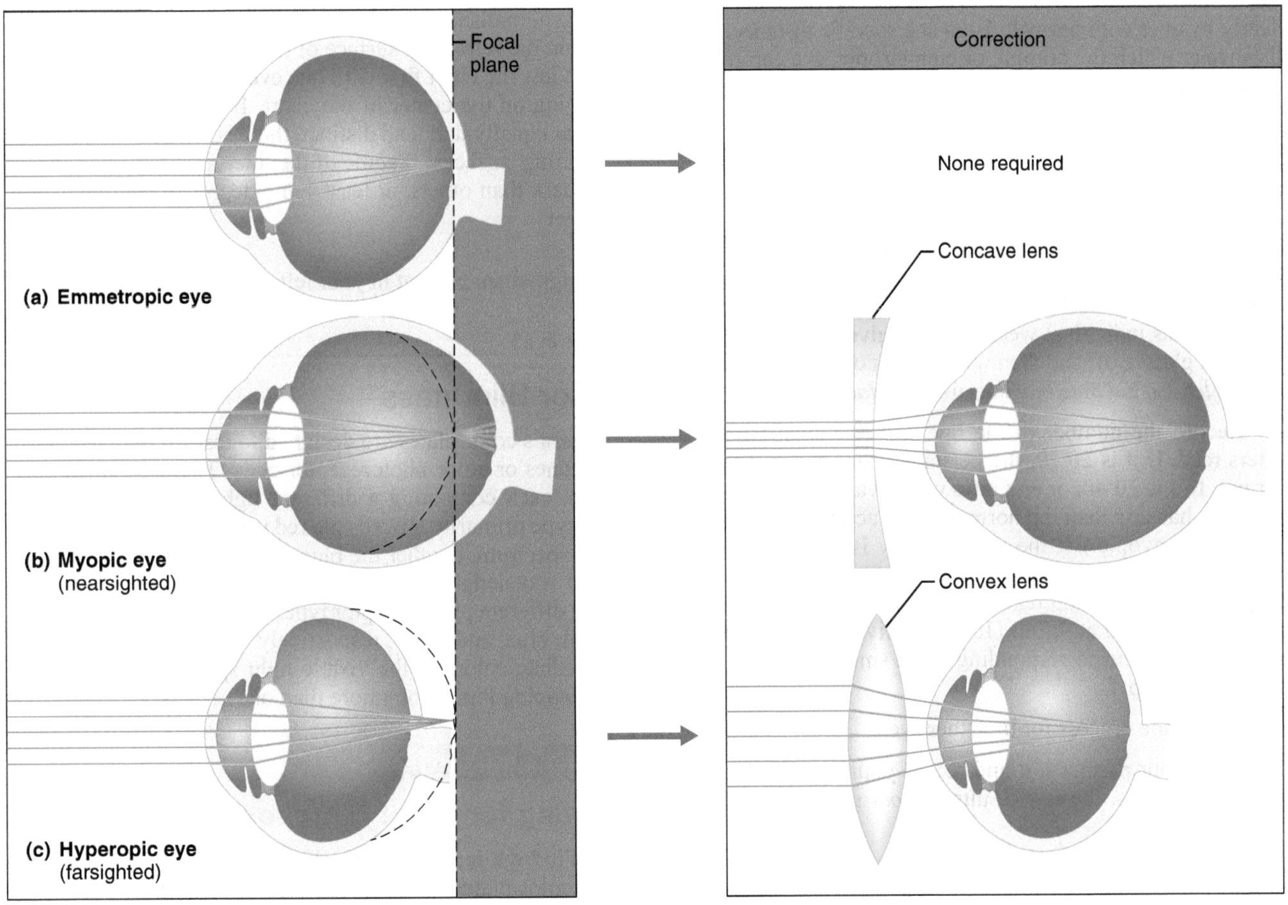

Imagineering

FIGURE 9 Problems of refraction. (**a**) In the emmetropic (normal) eye, light from both near and far objects is focused properly on the retina. (**b**) In a myopic eye, light from distant objects is brought to a focal point before reaching the retina. It then diverges. (**c**) In the hyperopic eye, light from a near object is brought to a focal point behind (past) the retina. (Refractory effect of cornea is ignored.)

ACTIVITY 6

Determining Near Point of Accommodation

To determine your near point of accommodation, hold a common straight pin at arm's length in front of one eye. (If desired, the text in the lab manual can be used rather than a pin.) Slowly move the pin toward that eye until the pin image becomes distorted. Have your lab partner use a metric ruler to measure the distance from your eye to the pin at this point, and record the distance below. Repeat the procedure for the other eye.

Near point for right eye: ______________________________

Near point for left eye: ______________________________

Visual Acuity **Visual acuity,** or sharpness of vision, is generally tested with a Snellen eye chart, which consists of letters of various sizes printed on a white card. This test is based on the fact that letters of a certain size can be seen clearly by eyes with normal vision at a specific distance. The distance at which the normal, or emmetropic, eye can read a line of letters is printed at the end of that line.

ACTIVITY 7

Testing Visual Acuity

1. Have your partner stand 6 m (20 feet) from the posted Snellen eye chart and cover one eye with a card or hand. As your partner reads each consecutive line aloud, check for accuracy. If this individual wears glasses, give the test twice—first with glasses off and then with glasses on. *Do not remove contact lenses, but note that they were in place during the test.*

2. Record the number of the line with the smallest-sized letters read. If it is 20/20, the person's vision for that eye is normal. If it is 20/40, or any ratio with a value less than one, he or she has less than the normal visual acuity. (Such an individual is myopic.) If the visual acuity is 20/15, vision is better than normal, because this person can stand at 6 m (20 feet) from the chart and read letters that are only discernible by the normal eye at 4.5 m (15 feet). Give your partner the number of the line corresponding to the smallest letters read, to record in step 4.

3. Repeat the process for the other eye.

4. Have your partner test and record your visual acuity. If you wear glasses, the test results *without* glasses should be recorded first.

Visual acuity, right eye without glasses: ____________________

Visual acuity, right eye with glasses: ____________________

Visual acuity, left eye without glasses: ____________________

Visual acuity, left eye with glasses: ____________________

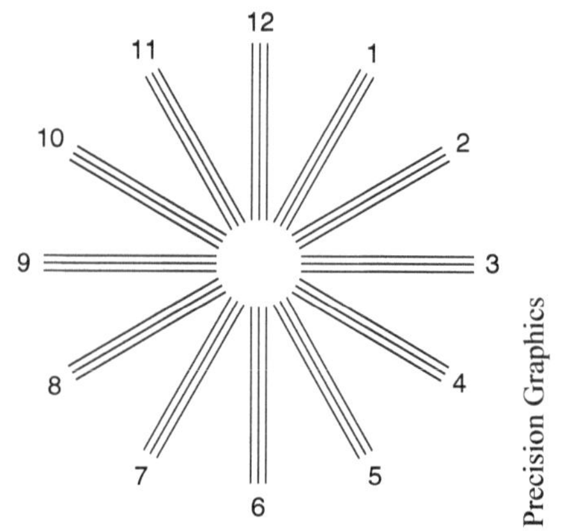

FIGURE 10 **Astigmatism testing chart.**

ACTIVITY 8

Testing for Astigmatism

The astigmatism chart (Figure 10) is designed to test for defects in the refracting surface of the lens and/or cornea.

View the chart first with one eye and then with the other, focusing on the center of the chart. If all the radiating lines appear equally dark and distinct, there is no distortion of your refracting surfaces. If some of the lines are blurred or appear less dark than others, at least some degree of astigmatism is present.

Is astigmatism present in your left eye? ____________________

Right eye? ______________________________

Color Blindness

Ishihara's color plates are designed to test for deficiencies in the cones or color photoreceptor cells. There are three cone types, each containing a different light-absorbing pigment. One type primarily absorbs the red wavelengths of the visible light spectrum, another the blue wavelengths, and a third the green wavelengths. Nerve impulses reaching the brain from these different photoreceptor types are then interpreted (seen) as red, blue, and green, respectively. Interpretation of the intermediate colors of the visible light spectrum is a result of overlapping input from more than one cone type.

ACTIVITY 9

Testing for Color Blindness

1. Find the interpretation table that accompanies the Ishihara color plates, and prepare a sheet to record data for the test. Note which plates are patterns rather than numbers.

2. View the color plates in bright light or sunlight while holding them about 0.8 m (30 inches) away and at right angles to your line of vision. Report to your laboratory partner what you see in each plate. Take no more than 3 seconds for each decision.

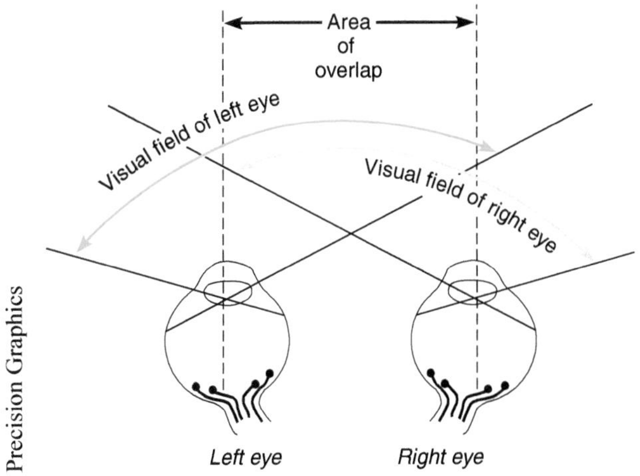

FIGURE 11 Overlapping of the visual fields.

3. Your partner should record your responses and then check their accuracy with the correct answers provided in the color plate book. Is there any indication that you have some degree of color blindness? ______________ If so, what type?

____

____

Repeat the procedure to test your partner's color vision.

Binocular Vision

Humans, cats, predatory birds, and most primates are endowed with **binocular** (two-eyed) **vision.** Although both eyes look in approximately the same direction, they see slightly different views. Their visual fields, each about 170 degrees, overlap to a considerable extent; thus there is two-eyed vision at the overlap area (Figure 11).

In contrast, the eyes of many animals (rabbits, pigeons, and others) are more on the sides of their head. Such animals see in two different directions and thus have a panoramic field of view and **panoramic vision.** A mnemonic device to keep these straight is "Eyes in the front—likes to hunt. Eyes on the side—likes to hide."

Although both types of vision have their good points, binocular vision provides three-dimensional vision and an accurate means of locating objects in space. The slight differences between the views seen by the two eyes are fused by the higher centers of the visual cortex to give us *depth perception.* Because of the manner in which the visual cortex resolves these two different views into a single image, it is sometimes referred to as the "cyclopean eye of the binocular animal."

ACTIVITY 10

Testing for Binocular Vision

1. To demonstrate that a slightly different view is seen by each eye, perform the following simple experiment.

Close your left eye. Hold a pencil at arm's length directly in front of your right eye. Position another pencil directly beneath it and then move the lower pencil about half the distance toward you. As you move the lower pencil, make sure it remains in the *same plane* as the stationary pencil, so that the two pencils continually form a straight line. Then, without moving the pencils, close your right eye and open your left eye. Notice that with only the right eye open, the moving pencil stays in the same plane as the fixed pencil, but that when viewed with the left eye, the moving pencil is displaced laterally away from the plane of the fixed pencil.

2. To demonstrate the importance of two-eyed binocular vision for depth perception, perform this second simple experiment.

Have your laboratory partner hold a test tube erect about arm's length in front of you. With both eyes open, quickly insert a pencil into the test tube. Remove the pencil, bring it back close to your body, close one eye, and quickly and without hesitation insert the pencil into the test tube. (*Do not feel for the test tube with the pencil!*) Repeat with the other eye closed.

Was it as easy to dunk the pencil with one eye closed as with both eyes open?

____

Eye Reflexes

Both intrinsic (internal) and extrinsic (external) muscles are necessary for proper eye functioning. The *intrinsic muscles,* controlled by the autonomic nervous system, are those of the ciliary body (which alters the lens curvature in focusing) and the radial and circular muscles of the iris (which control pupillary size and thus regulate the amount of light entering the eye). The *extrinsic muscles* are the rectus and oblique muscles, which are attached to the eyeball exterior (see Figure 2). These muscles control eye movement and make it possible to keep moving objects focused on the fovea centralis. They are also responsible for **convergence,** or medial eye movements, which is essential for near vision. When convergence occurs, both eyes are directed toward the near object viewed. The extrinsic eye muscles are controlled by the somatic nervous system.

ACTIVITY 11

Demonstrating Reflex Activity of Intrinsic and Extrinsic Eye Muscles

Involuntary activity of both the intrinsic and extrinsic muscle types is brought about by reflex actions that can be observed in the following experiments.

Photopupillary Reflex

Sudden illumination of the retina by a bright light causes the pupil to constrict reflexively in direct proportion to the light intensity. This protective response prevents damage to the delicate photoreceptor cells.

Obtain a laboratory lamp or penlight. Have your laboratory partner sit with eyes closed and hands over his or her eyes. Turn on the light and position it so that it shines on the subject's right hand. After 1 minute, ask your partner to uncover and open the right eye. Quickly observe the pupil of that eye. What happens to the pupil?

____

Shut off the light and ask your partner to uncover and open the opposite eye. What are your observations of the pupil?

____

____

Accommodation Pupillary Reflex

Have your partner gaze for approximately 1 minute at a distant object in the lab—*not* toward the windows or another light source. Observe your partner's pupils. Then hold some printed material 15 to 25 cm (6 to 10 inches) from his or her face, and direct him or her to focus on it.

How does pupil size change as your partner focuses on the printed material?

____

Explain the value of this reflex. ______________________

____

____

____

Convergence Reflex

Repeat the previous experiment, this time using a pen or pencil as the close object to be focused on. Note the position of your partner's eyeballs while he or she gazes at the distant object, and then at the close object. Do they change position as the object of focus is changed?

______________ In what way? ______________________

____

____

____

Explain the importance of the convergence reflex.

____

____

____

Ophthalmoscopic Examination of the Eye (Optional)

The ophthalmoscope is an instrument used to examine the *fundus,* or eyeball interior, to determine visually the condition of the retina, optic disc, and internal blood vessels. Certain pathologic conditions such as diabetes mellitus, arteriosclerosis, and degenerative changes of the optic nerve and retina can be detected by such an examination. The ophthalmoscope consists of a set of lenses mounted on a rotating disc (the **lens selection disc**), a light source regulated by a **rheostat control,** and a mirror that reflects the light so that the eye interior can be illuminated (Figure 12a).

The lens selection disc is positioned in a small slit in the mirror, and the examiner views the eye interior through this slit, appropriately called the **viewing window.** The focal length of each lens is indicated in diopters preceded by a plus (+) sign if the lens is convex and by a negative (−) sign if the lens is concave. When the zero (0) is seen in the **diopter window,** there is no lens positioned in the slit. The depth of focus for viewing the eye interior is changed by changing the lens.

The light is turned on by depressing the red **rheostat lock button** and then rotating the rheostat control in the clockwise direction. The **aperture selection dial** on the front of the instrument allows the nature of the light beam to be altered. Generally, green light allows for clearest viewing of the blood vessels in the eye interior and is most comfortable for the subject.

Once you have examined the ophthalmoscope and have become familiar with it, you are ready to conduct an eye examination.

ACTIVITY 12

Conducting an Ophthalmoscopic Examination

1. Conduct the examination in a dimly lit or darkened room with the subject comfortably seated and gazing straight ahead. To examine the right eye, sit face-to-face with the subject, hold the instrument in your right hand, and use your right eye to view the eye interior (Figure 12b). You may want to steady yourself by resting your left hand on the subject's shoulder. To view the left eye, use your left eye, hold the instrument in your left hand, and steady yourself with your right hand.

2. Begin the examination with the 0 (no lens) in position. Grasp the instrument so that the lens disc may be rotated with the index finger. Holding the ophthalmoscope about 15 cm (6 inches) from the subject's eye, direct the light into the pupil at a slight angle—through the pupil edge rather than directly through its center. You will see a red circular area that is the illuminated eye interior.

3. Move in as close as possible to the subject's cornea (to within 5 cm, or 2 inches) as you continue to observe the area. Steady your instrument-holding hand on the subject's cheek if necessary. If both your eye and that of the subject are normal, the fundus can be viewed clearly without further adjustment of the ophthalmoscope. If the fundus cannot be focused, slowly rotate the lens disc counterclockwise until the fundus

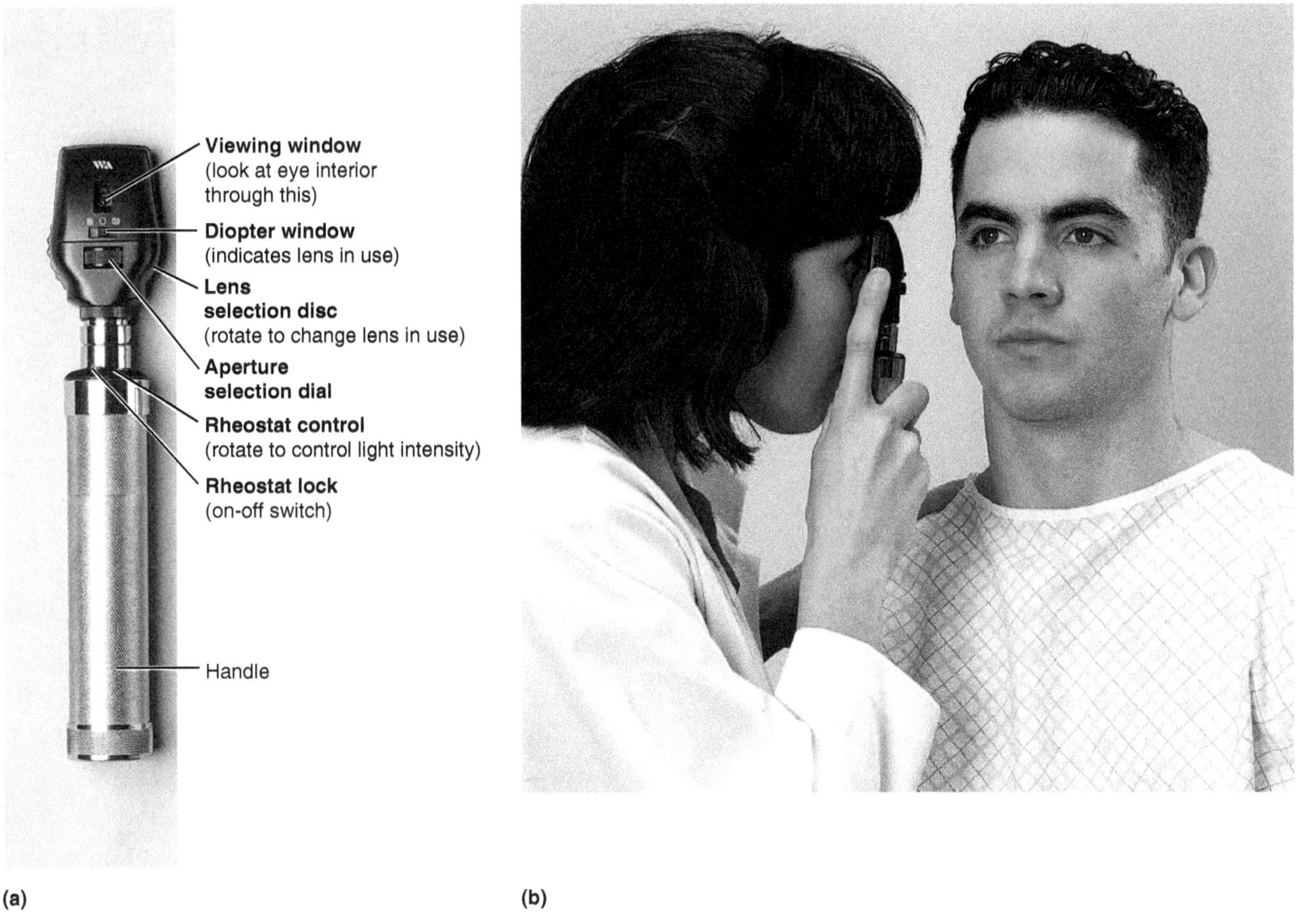
Viewing window
(look at eye interior
through this)
Diopter window
(indicates lens in use)
Lens
selection disc
(rotate to change lens in use)
Aperture
selection dial
Rheostat control
(rotate to control light intensity)
Rheostat lock
(on-off switch)
Handle
(a)
(b)

Richard Tauber, Pearson Benjamin Cummings

Richard Tauber, Pearson Benjamin Cummings

FIGURE 12 **Structure and use of an ophthalmoscope.** (**a**) Structure of an ophthalmoscope. (**b**) Proper position for beginning to examine the right eye with an ophthalmoscope.

can be clearly seen. When the ophthalmoscope is correctly set, the fundus of the right eye should appear as shown in Figure 13. (**Note:** If a positive [convex] lens is required and your eyes are normal, the subject has hyperopia. If a negative [concave] lens is necessary to view the fundus and your eyes are normal, the subject is myopic.)

When the examination is proceeding correctly, the subject can often see images of retinal vessels in his own eye that appear rather like cracked glass. If you are unable to achieve a sharp focus or to see the optic disc, move medially or laterally and begin again.

4. Examine the optic disc for color, elevation, and sharpness of outline, and observe the blood vessels radiating from near its center. Locate the macula, lateral to the optic disc. It is a darker area in which blood vessels are absent, and the fovea appears to be a slightly lighter area in its center. The macula is most easily seen when the subject looks directly into the light of the ophthalmoscope.

! Do not examine the macula for longer than 1 second at a time.

5. When you have finished examining your partner's retina, shut off the ophthalmoscope. Change places with your partner (become the subject) and repeat steps 1–4.

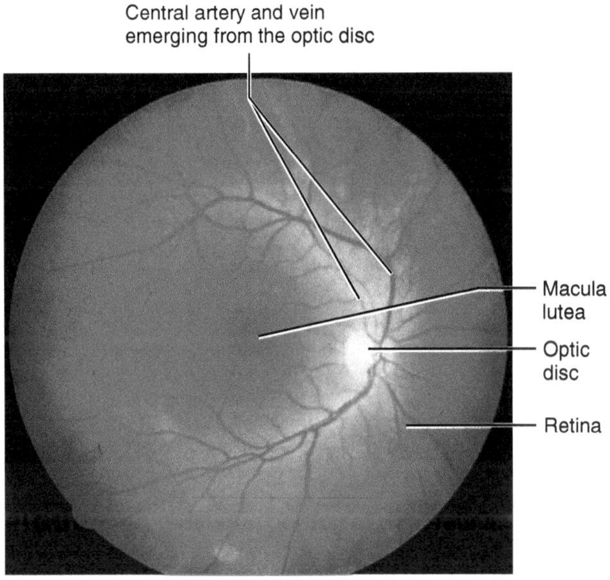
Central artery and vein
emerging from the optic disc
Macula
lutea
Optic
disc
Retina

A. L. Blum/Visuals Unlimited

FIGURE 13 **Posterior portion of right retina.**

NAME ______________________________

LAB TIME/DATE ______________________

REVIEW SHEET

Special Senses: Vision

Anatomy of the Eye

1. Name five accessory eye structures that contribute to the formation of tears and/or aid in lubrication of the eyeball, and then name the major secretory product of each. Indicate which has antibacterial properties by circling the correct secretory product.

Accessory structures	Product

2. The eyeball is wrapped in adipose tissue within the orbit. What is the function of the adipose tissue?

____

3. Why does one often have to blow one's nose after crying? ______________________________

____

4. Identify the extrinsic eye muscle predominantly responsible for each action described below.

______________________ 1. turns the eye laterally

______________________ 2. turns the eye medially

______________________ 3. turns the eye up and laterally

______________________ 4. turns the eye inferiorly

______________________ 5. turns the eye superiorly

______________________ 6. turns the eye down and laterally

5. What is a sty? ______________________________

____

Conjunctivitis? ______________________________

6. Correctly identify each lettered structure in the diagram by writing the letter next to its name in the numbered list.

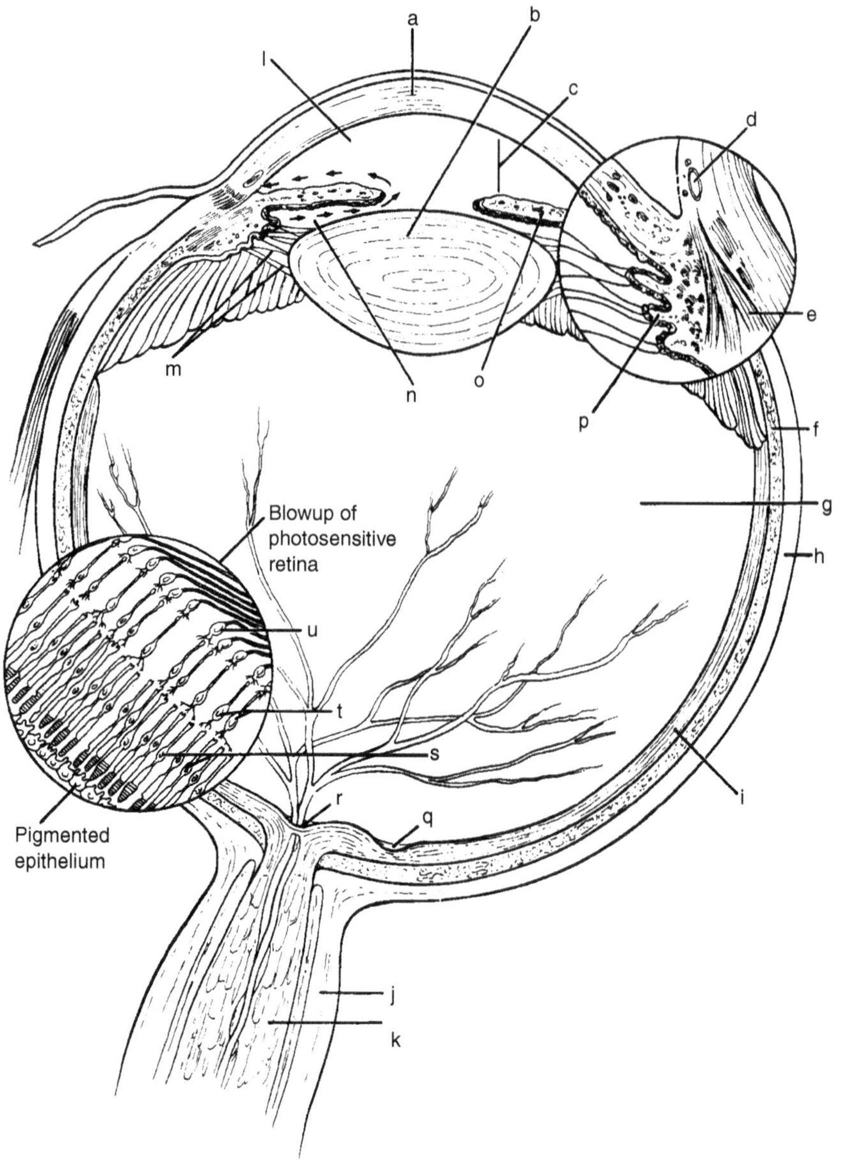

_______ 1. anterior chamber

_______ 2. anterior segment

_______ 3. bipolar neurons

_______ 4. choroid

_______ 5. ciliary body and processes

_______ 6. ciliary muscle

_______ 7. cornea

_______ 8. dura mater

_______ 9. fovea centralis

_______ 10. ganglion cells

_______ 11. iris

_______ 12. lens

_______ 13. optic disc

_______ 14. optic nerve

_______ 15. photoreceptors

_______ 16. posterior chamber

_______ 17. retina

_______ 18. sclera

_______ 19. scleral venous sinus

_______ 20. suspensory ligaments (ciliary zonule)

_______ 21. posterior segment

Notice the arrows drawn close to the left side of the iris in the diagram above. What do they indicate?

____

7. The iris is composed primarily of two smooth muscle layers, one arranged radially and the other circularly.

Which of these dilates the pupil? ____

8. You would expect the pupil to be dilated in which of the following circumstances? Circle the correct response(s).

a. in bright light b. in dim light c. focusing for near vision d. observing distant objects

9. The intrinsic eye muscles are controlled by (circle the correct response):

autonomic nervous system somatic nervous system

10. Match the key responses with the descriptive statements that follow.

Key:
a. aqueous humor
b. choroid
c. ciliary body
d. ciliary processes of the ciliary body
e. cornea
f. fovea centralis
g. iris
h. lens
i. optic disc
j. retina
k. sclera
l. scleral venous sinus
m. vitreous humor

_______________ 1. fluid filling the anterior segment of the eye

_______________ 2. the "white" of the eye

_______________ 3. part of the retina that lacks photoreceptors

_______________ 4. modification of the choroid that controls the shape of the crystalline lens and contains the ciliary muscle

_______________ 5. drains the aqueous humor from the eye

_______________ 6. layer containing the rods and cones

_______________ 7. substance occupying the posterior segment of the eyeball

_______________ 8. forms the bulk of the heavily pigmented vascular layer

_______, _______ 9. smooth muscle structures (2)

_______________ 10. area of critical focusing and discriminatory vision

_______________ 11. form (by filtration) the aqueous humor

_______, _______ 12. light-bending media of the eye (4)

_______, _______

_______________ 13. anterior continuation of the sclera—your "window on the world"

_______________ 14. composed of tough, white, opaque, fibrous connective tissue

Microscopic Anatomy of the Retina

11. The two major layers of the retina are the epithelial and neural layers. In the neural layer, the neuron populations are arranged as follows from the pigmented epithelial layer to the vitreous humor. (Circle the proper response.)

bipolar cells, ganglion cells, photoreceptors

photoreceptors, ganglion cells, bipolar cells

ganglion cells, bipolar cells, photoreceptors

photoreceptors, bipolar cells, ganglion cells

12. The axons of the _______________ cells form the optic nerve, which exits from the eyeball.

13. Complete the following statements by writing either *rods* or *cones* on each blank.

The dim light receptors are the _______________. Only _______________ are found in the fovea centralis, whereas mostly _______________ are found in the periphery of the retina. _______________ are the photoreceptors that operate best in bright light and allow for color vision.

Dissection of the Cow (Sheep) Eye

14. What modification of the choroid that is not present in humans is found in the cow eye? ______________________

What is its function? ______________________

____

15. What does the retina look like? ______________________

At what point is it attached to the posterior aspect of the eyeball? ______________________

Visual Pathways to the Brain

16. The visual pathway to the occipital lobe of the brain consists most simply of a chain of five cells. Beginning with the photoreceptor cell of the retina, name them and note their location in the pathway.

1. ______________________
2. ______________________
3. ______________________
4. ______________________
5. ______________________

17. Visual field tests are done to reveal destruction along the visual pathway from the retina to the optic region of the brain. Note where the lesion is likely to be in the following cases.

Normal vision in left eye visual field; absence of vision in right eye visual field: ______________________

Normal vision in both eyes for right half of the visual field; absence of vision in both eyes for left half of the visual field:

____

18. How is the right optic *tract* anatomically different from the right optic *nerve*? ______________________

____

____

Visual Tests and Experiments

19. Match the terms in column B with the descriptions in column A.

	Column A	Column B
________	1. light bending	a. accommodation
________	2. ability to focus for close (less than 20 feet) vision	b. astigmatism
________	3. normal vision	c. convergence
________	4. inability to focus well on close objects (farsightedness)	d. emmetropia
________	5. nearsightedness	e. hyperopia
________	6. blurred vision due to unequal curvatures of the lens or cornea	f. myopia
________	7. medial movement of the eyes during focusing on close objects	g. refraction

20. Complete the following statements:

In farsightedness, the light is focused __1__ the retina. The lens required to treat myopia is a __2__ lens. The "near point" increases with age because the __3__ of the lens decreases as we get older. A convex lens, like that of the eye, produces an image that is upside down and reversed from left to right. Such an image is called a __4__ image.

1. ______________________________

2. ______________________________

3. ______________________________

4. ______________________________

21. Use terms from the key to complete the statements concerning near and distance vision.

Key: a. contracted b. decreased c. increased d. relaxed e. taut

During distance vision, the ciliary muscle is _______, the suspensory ligament is _______, the convexity of the lens is _______, and light refraction is _______. During close vision, the ciliary muscle is _______, the suspensory ligament is _______, lens convexity is _______, and light refraction is _______.

22. Explain why vision is lost when light hits the blind spot. ______________________________

23. Using your Snellen eye test results, answer the following questions.

Is your visual acuity normal, less than normal, or better than normal? ______________________________

Explain your answer. ______________________________

____

Explain why each eye is tested separately when using the Snellen eye chart. ______________________________

____

Explain 20/40 vision. ______________________________

____

Explain 20/10 vision. ______________________________

____

24. Define *astigmatism.* ______________________________

____

How can it be corrected? ______________________________

25. Define *presbyopia.* ______________________________

____

What causes it? ______________________________

26. To which wavelengths of light do the three cone types of the retina respond maximally?

______________________, ______________________, and ______________________

27. How can you explain the fact that we see a great range of colors even though only three cone types exist?

____

____

28. Explain the difference between binocular and panoramic vision. ______________________

____

____

What is the advantage of binocular vision? ______________________

What factor(s) are responsible for binocular vision? ______________________

____

29. In the experiment on the convergence reflex, what happened to the position of the eyeballs as the object was moved closer to the subject's eyes? ______________________

What extrinsic eye muscles control the movement of the eyes during this reflex? ______________________

What is the value of this reflex? ______________________

____

30. In the experiment on the photopupillary reflex, what happened to the pupil of the eye exposed to light?

______________________ What happened to the pupil of the nonilluminated eye?______________________

Explanation? ______________________

____

31. Why is the ophthalmoscopic examination an important diagnostic tool? ______________________

____

32. Many college students struggling through mountainous reading assignments are told that they need glasses for "eyestrain." Why is it more of a strain on the extrinsic and intrinsic eye muscles to look at close objects than at far objects?

____

____

Special Senses: Hearing and Equilibrium

MATERIALS

- ☐ Three-dimensional dissectible ear model and/or chart of ear anatomy
- ☐ Otoscope (if available)
- ☐ Disposable otoscope tips (if available) and autoclave bag
- ☐ Alcohol swabs
- ☐ Compound microscope
- ☐ Prepared slides of the cochlea of the ear
- ☐ Absorbent cotton
- ☐ Pocket watch or clock that ticks
- ☐ Metric ruler
- ☐ Tuning forks (range of frequencies)
- ☐ Rubber mallet
- ☐ Audiometer
- ☐ Red and blue pencils
- ☐ Demonstration: Microscope focused on a slide of a crista ampullaris receptor of a semicircular canal
- ☐ Blackboard and chalk

OBJECTIVES

1. To identify, by appropriately labeling a diagram, the anatomical structures of the external, middle, and internal ear, and to explain their functions.
2. To describe the anatomy of the organ of hearing (spiral organ of Corti in the cochlea), and to explain its function in sound reception.
3. To describe the anatomy of the equilibrium organs of the internal ear (cristae ampullares and maculae), and to explain their relative function in maintaining equilibrium.
4. To explain how one is able to localize the source of sounds.
5. To define or explain *sensorineural deafness, conduction deafness,* and *nystagmus.*
6. To state the purpose of the Weber, Rinne, balance, Barany, and Romberg tests.
7. To describe the effects of acceleration on the semicircular canals.
8. To explain the role of vision in maintaining equilibrium.

The ear is a complex structure containing sensory receptors for hearing and equilibrium. The ear is divided into three major areas: the *external ear,* the *middle ear,* and the *internal ear* (Figure 1). The external and middle ear structures serve the needs of the sense of hearing *only,* whereas internal ear structures function both in equilibrium and hearing reception.

Anatomy of the Ear

Gross Anatomy

ACTIVITY 1

Identifying Structures of the Ear

Obtain a dissectible ear model or chart of ear anatomy and identify the structures described below. Refer to Figure 1 as you work.

The **external,** or **outer, ear** is composed primarily of the auricle and the external acoustic meatus. The **auricle,** or **pinna,*** is the skin-covered cartilaginous structure encircling the auditory canal opening. In many animals, it collects and directs sound waves into the external auditory canal. In humans this function of the pinna is largely lost. The portion of the pinna lying inferior to the external auditory canal is the **lobule.**

The **external acoustic meatus,** or **external auditory canal,*** is a short, narrow (about 2.5 cm long by 0.6 cm wide) chamber carved into the temporal bone. In its skin-lined walls are wax-secreting glands called **ceruminous glands.** Sound waves that enter the external auditory meatus eventually encounter the **tympanic membrane,** or **eardrum,** which vibrates at exactly the same frequency

*Although the preferred anatomical terms for *pinna* and *external auditory canal* are *auricle* and *external acoustic meatus,* "pinna" and "external auditory canal" are heard often in clinical situations and will continue to be used here.

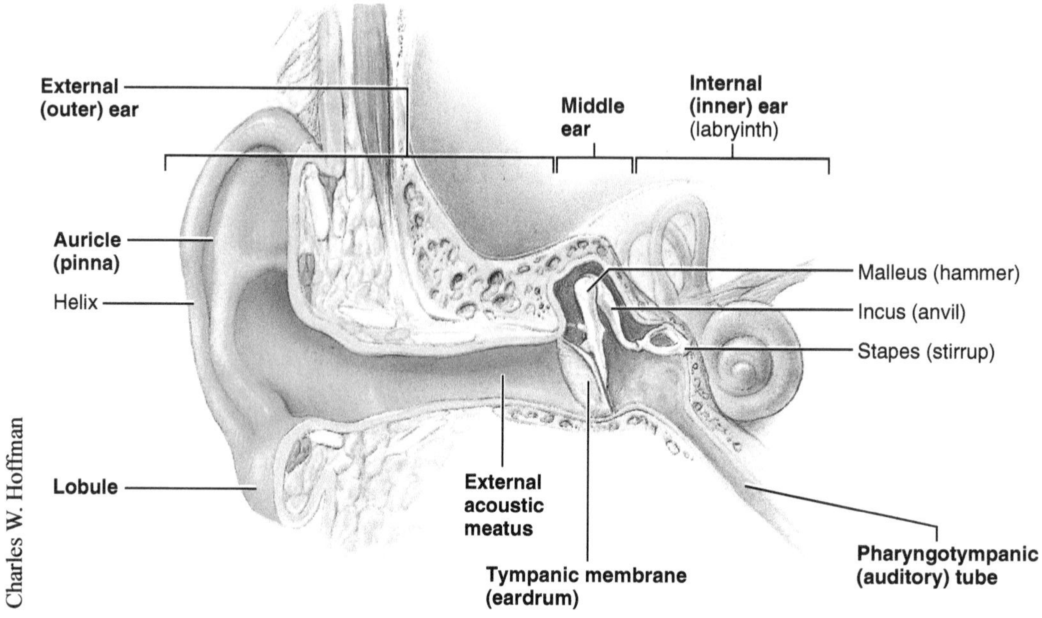

FIGURE 1 **Anatomy of the ear.**

as the sound wave(s) hitting it. The membranous eardrum separates the external from the middle ear.

The **middle ear** is essentially a small chamber—the **tympanic cavity**—found within the temporal bone. The cavity is spanned by three small bones, collectively called the **ossicles (malleus, incus,** and **stapes**), which articulate to form a lever system that amplifies and transmits the vibratory motion of the eardrum to the fluids of the inner ear via the **oval window.** The ossicles are often referred to by their common names, that is, hammer, anvil, and stirrup, respectively.

Connecting the middle ear chamber with the nasopharynx is the **pharyngotympanic,** or **auditory, tube** (formerly known as the eustachian tube). Normally this tube is flattened and closed, but swallowing or yawning can cause it to open temporarily to equalize the pressure of the middle ear cavity with external air pressure. This is an important function. The eardrum does not vibrate properly unless the pressure on both of its surfaces is the same.

Because the mucosal membranes of the middle ear cavity and nasopharynx are continuous through the pharyngotympanic tube, **otitis media,** or inflammation of the middle ear, is a fairly common condition, especially among youngsters prone to sore throats. In cases where large amounts of fluid or pus accumulate in the middle ear cavity, an emergency myringotomy (lancing of the eardrum) may be necessary to relieve the pressure. Frequently, tiny ventilating tubes are put in during the procedure. ●

The **internal,** or **inner, ear** consists of a system of bony and rather tortuous chambers called the **osseous,** or **bony, labyrinth,** which is filled with an aqueous fluid called **perilymph** (Figure 2). Suspended in the perilymph is the **membranous labyrinth,** a system that mostly follows the contours of the osseous labyrinth. The membranous labyrinth is filled with a more viscous fluid called **endolymph.** The three subdivisions of the bony labyrinth are the cochlea, the vestibule, and the semicircular canals, with the vestibule situated between the cochlea and semicircular canals. The **vestibule** and the **semicircular canals** are involved with equilibrium.

The snail-like **cochlea** (see Figures 2 and 3) contains the sensory receptors for hearing. The cochlear membranous labyrinth, the **cochlear duct,** is a soft wormlike tube about 3.8 cm long. It winds through the full two and three-quarter turns of the cochlea and separates the perilymph-containing cochlear cavity into upper and lower chambers, the **scala vestibuli** and **scala tympani** (the vestibular and tympanic ducts), respectively. The scala vestibuli terminates at the oval window, which "seats" the foot plate of the stirrup located laterally in the tympanic cavity. The scala tympani is bounded by a membranous area called the **round window.** The cochlear duct, itself filled with endolymph, supports the **spiral organ (of Corti),** which contains the receptors for hearing—the sensory hair cells and nerve endings of the **cochlear nerve,** a division of the vestibulocochlear nerve (VIII).

ACTIVITY 2

Examining the Ear with an Otoscope (Optional)

1. Obtain an otoscope and two alcohol swabs. Inspect your partner's external ear canal and then select the largest-*diameter* (not length!) speculum that will fit comfortably into his or her ear to permit full visibility. Clean the speculum thoroughly with an alcohol swab, and then attach the speculum to the battery-containing otoscope handle. Before beginning, check that the otoscope light beam is strong. (If not, obtain another otoscope or new batteries.) Some otoscopes come with disposable tips. Be sure to use a new tip for each ear examined. Dispose of these tips in an autoclave bag after use.

! 2. When you are ready to begin the examination, hold the lighted otoscope securely between your thumb and forefinger (like a pencil), and rest the little finger of the otoscope-holding hand against your partner's head. This maneuver forms a brace that allows the speculum to move as

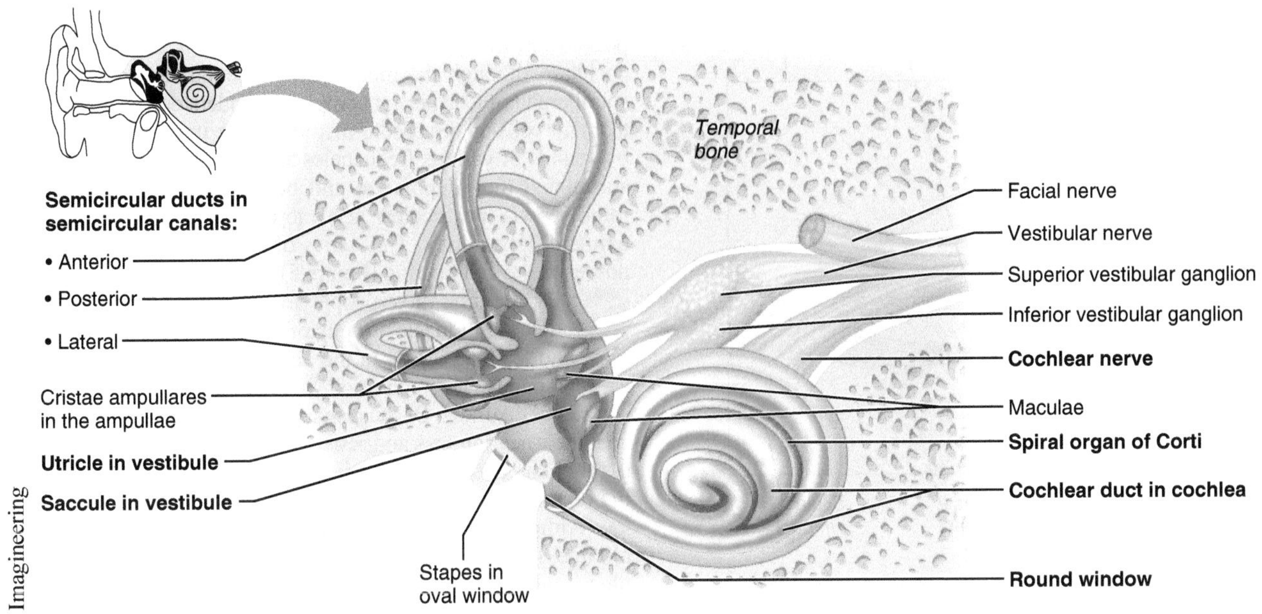

FIGURE 2 **Internal ear.** Right membranous labyrinth shown within the bony labyrinth.

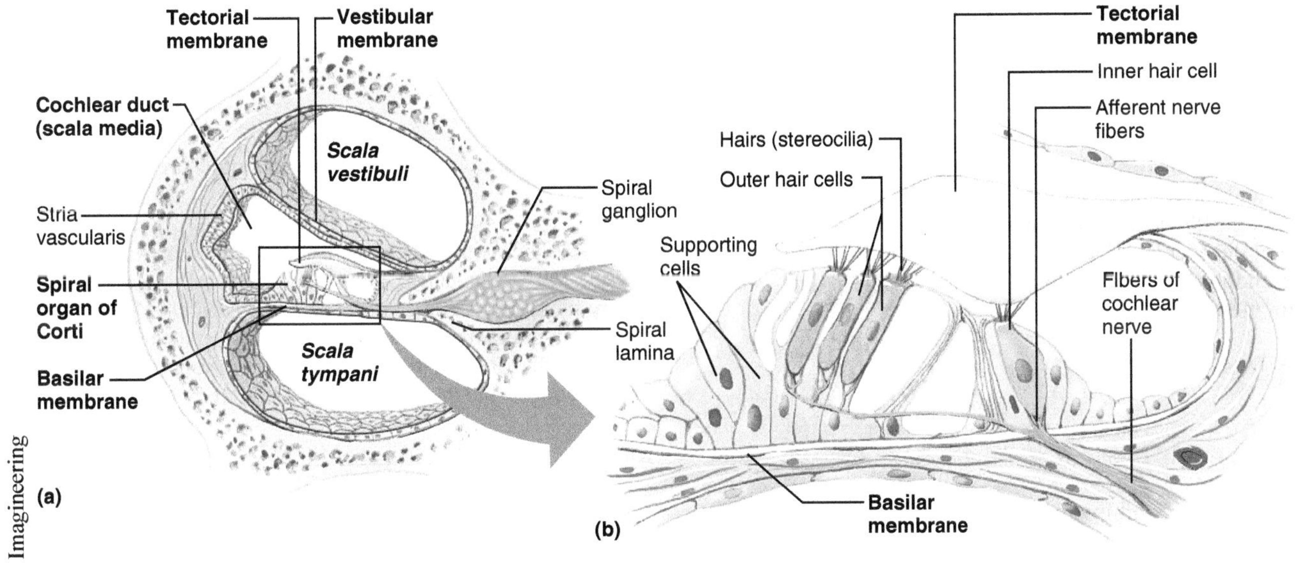

FIGURE 3 **Anatomy of the cochlea.** (**a**) Magnified cross-sectional view of one turn of the cochlea, showing the relationship of the three scalae. The scalae vestibuli and tympani contain perilymph; the cochlear duct (scala media) contains endolymph. (**b**) Detailed structure of the spiral organ of Corti.

your partner moves and prevents the speculum from penetrating too deeply into the ear canal during unexpected movements.

3. Grasp the ear pinna firmly and pull it up, back, and slightly laterally. If your partner experiences pain or discomfort when the pinna is manipulated, an inflammation or infection of the external ear may be present. If this occurs, do not attempt to examine the ear canal.

4. Carefully insert the speculum of the otoscope into the external auditory canal in a downward and forward direction only far enough to permit examination of the tympanic membrane, or eardrum. Note its shape, color, and vascular network. The healthy tympanic membrane is pearly white. During the examination, notice if there is any discharge or redness in the canal and identify earwax.

5. After the examination, thoroughly clean the speculum with the second alcohol swab before returning the otoscope to the supply area.

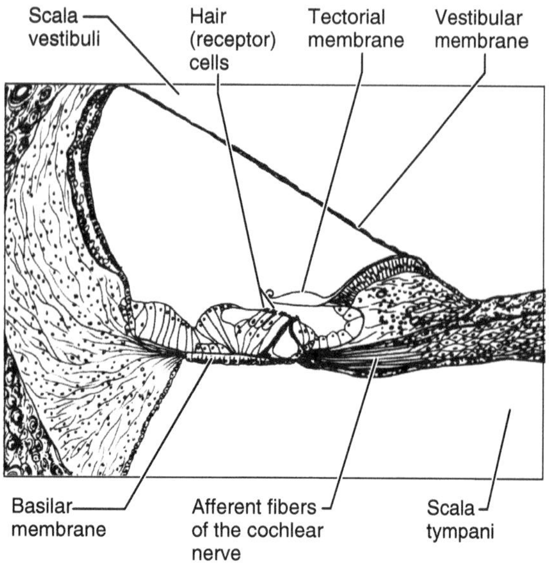
Scala vestibuli
Hair (receptor) cells
Tectorial membrane
Vestibular membrane
Basilar membrane
Afferent fibers of the cochlear nerve
Scala tympani

FIGURE 4 Microscopic view of the spiral organ of Corti.

Microscopic Anatomy of the Spiral Organ of Corti and the Mechanism of Hearing

The anatomical details of the spiral organ of Corti are shown in Figure 3. The hair (auditory receptor) cells rest on the **basilar membrane,** which forms the floor of the cochlear duct, and their "hairs" (stereocilia) project into a gelatinous membrane, the **tectorial membrane,** that overlies them. The roof of the cochlear duct is called the **vestibular membrane.** The endolymph-filled chamber of the cochlear duct is the **scala media.**

ACTIVITY 3

Examining the Microscopic Structure of the Cochlea

Obtain a compound microscope and a prepared microscope slide of the cochlea and identify the areas shown in Figure 4.

The mechanism of hearing begins as sound waves pass through the external auditory canal and through the middle ear into the internal ear, where the vibration eventually reaches the spiral organ of Corti, which contains the receptors for hearing.

The popular "traveling wave" hypothesis of von Békésy suggests that vibration of the stirrup at the oval window initiates traveling waves that cause maximal displacements of the basilar membrane where they peak and stimulate the hair cells of the spiral organ of Corti in that region. Since the area at which the traveling waves peak is a high-pressure area, the vestibular membrane is compressed at this point and, in turn, compresses the endolymph and the basilar membrane of the cochlear duct. The resulting pressure on the perilymph in the scala tympani causes the membrane of the round window to bulge outward into the middle ear chamber, thus acting as a relief valve for the compressional wave. Georg von Békésy found that high-frequency waves (high-pitched sounds) peaked close to the oval window and that low-frequency waves (low-pitched sounds) peaked farther up the basilar membrane near the apex of the cochlea. Although the mechanism of sound reception by the spiral organ of Corti is not completely understood, we do know that hair cells on the basilar membrane are uniquely stimulated by sounds of various frequencies and amplitude and that once stimulated they depolarize and begin the chain of nervous impulses via the cochlear nerve to the auditory centers of the temporal lobe cortex. This series of events results in the phenomenon we call hearing (Figure 5).

By the time most people are in their sixties, a gradual deterioration and atrophy of the spiral organ of Corti begins, and leads to a loss in the ability to hear high tones and speech sounds. This condition, **presbycusis,** is a type of sensorineural deafness. Because many elderly people refuse to accept their hearing loss and resist using hearing aids, they begin to rely more and more on their vision for clues as to what is going on around them and may be accused of ignoring people.

Although presbycusis is considered to be a disability of old age, it is becoming much more common in younger people as our world grows noisier. The damage (breakage of the "hairs" of the hair cells) caused by excessively loud sounds is progressive and cumulative. Each assault causes a bit more damage. Music played and listened to at deafening levels definitely contributes to the deterioration of hearing receptors.

ACTIVITY 4

Conducting Laboratory Tests of Hearing

Perform the following hearing tests in a quiet area.

Acuity Test

Have your lab partner pack one ear with cotton and sit quietly with eyes closed. Obtain a ticking clock or pocket watch and hold it very close to his or her *unpacked* ear. Then slowly move it away from the ear until your partner signals that the ticking is no longer audible. Record the distance in centimeters at which ticking is inaudible and then remove the cotton from the packed ear.

Right ear: ______________ Left ear: ______________

Is the threshold of audibility sharp or indefinite?

____

Sound Localization

Ask your partner to close both eyes. Hold the pocket watch at an audible distance (about 15 cm) from his or her ear, and move it to various locations (front, back, sides, and above his or her head). Have your partner locate the position by pointing in each instance. Can the sound be localized equally well at all positions?

____

If not, at what position(s) was the sound less easily located?

____

____

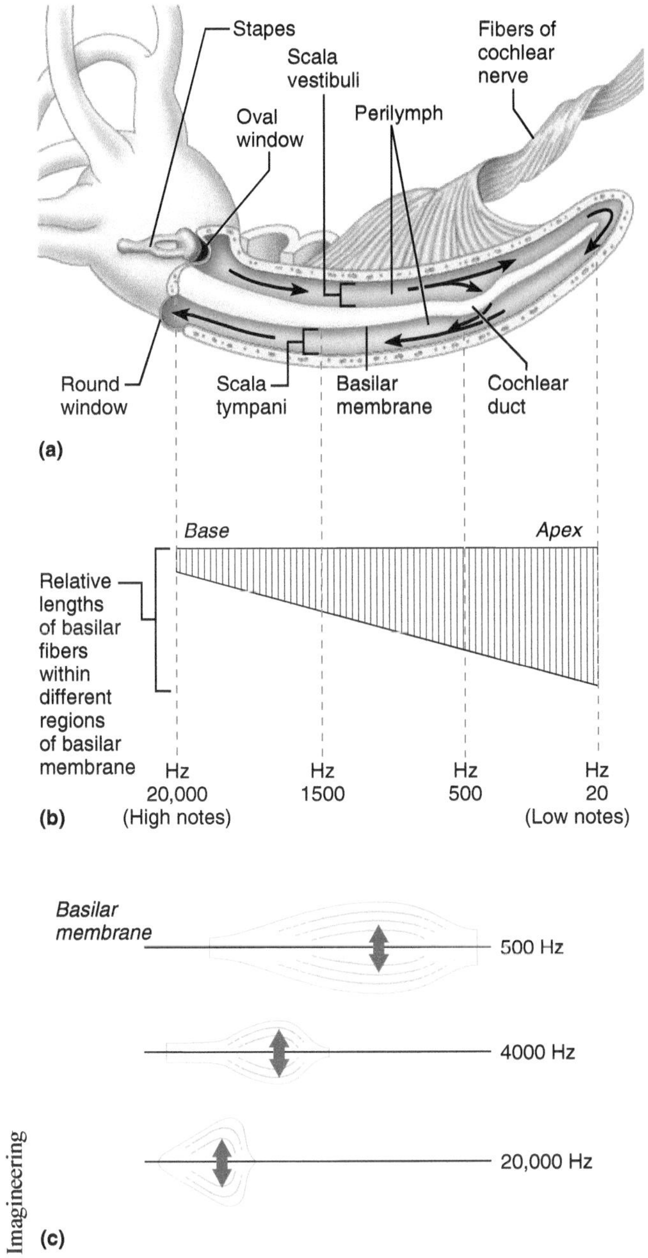

FIGURE 5 Resonance of the basilar membrane. (a) Fluid movement in the cochlea following the stirrup thrust at the oval window. Compressional wave thus created causes the round window to bulge into the middle ear. Pressure waves set up vibrations in the basilar membrane. (**b**) Fibers span the basilar membrane. The length of the fibers "tunes" specific regions to vibrate at specific frequencies. (**c**) Different frequencies of pressure waves in the cochlea stimulate particular hair cells and neurons.

The ability to localize the source of a sound depends on two factors—the difference in the loudness of the sound reaching each ear and the time of arrival of the sound at each ear. How does this information help to explain your findings?

____

____

Frequency Range of Hearing

Obtain three tuning forks: one with a low frequency (75 to 100 Hz [cps]), one with a frequency of approximately 1000 Hz, and one with a frequency of 4000 to 5000 Hz. Strike the lowest-frequency fork on the heel of your hand or with a rubber mallet, and hold it close to your partner's ear. Repeat with the other two forks.

Which fork was heard most clearly and comfortably?

_______________ Hz

Which was heard least well? _______________ Hz

Weber Test to Determine Conduction and Sensorineural Deafness

Strike a tuning fork and place the handle of the tuning fork medially on your partner's head (see Figure 6a). Is the tone equally loud in both ears, or is it louder in one ear?

____

If it is equally loud in both ears, you have equal hearing or equal loss of hearing in both ears. If sensorineural deafness is present in one ear, the tone will be heard in the unaffected ear, but not in the ear with sensorineural deafness. If conduction deafness is present, the sound will be heard more strongly in the ear in which there is a hearing loss due to sound conduction by the bone of the skull. Conduction deafness can be simulated by plugging one ear with cotton to interfere with the conduction of sound to the inner ear.

Rinne Test for Comparing Bone- and Air-Conduction Hearing

1. Strike the tuning fork, and place its handle on your partner's mastoid process (Figure 6b).

2. When your partner indicates that the sound is no longer audible, hold the still-vibrating prongs close to his auditory canal (Figure 6c). If your partner hears the fork again (by air conduction) when it is moved to that position, hearing is not impaired and the test result is to be recorded as positive (+). (Record below step 5.)

3. Repeat the test on the same ear, but this time test air-conduction hearing first.

4. After the tone is no longer heard by air conduction, hold the handle of the tuning fork on the bony mastoid process. If the subject hears the tone again by bone conduction after hearing by air conduction is lost, there is some conduction deafness and the result is recorded as negative (−).

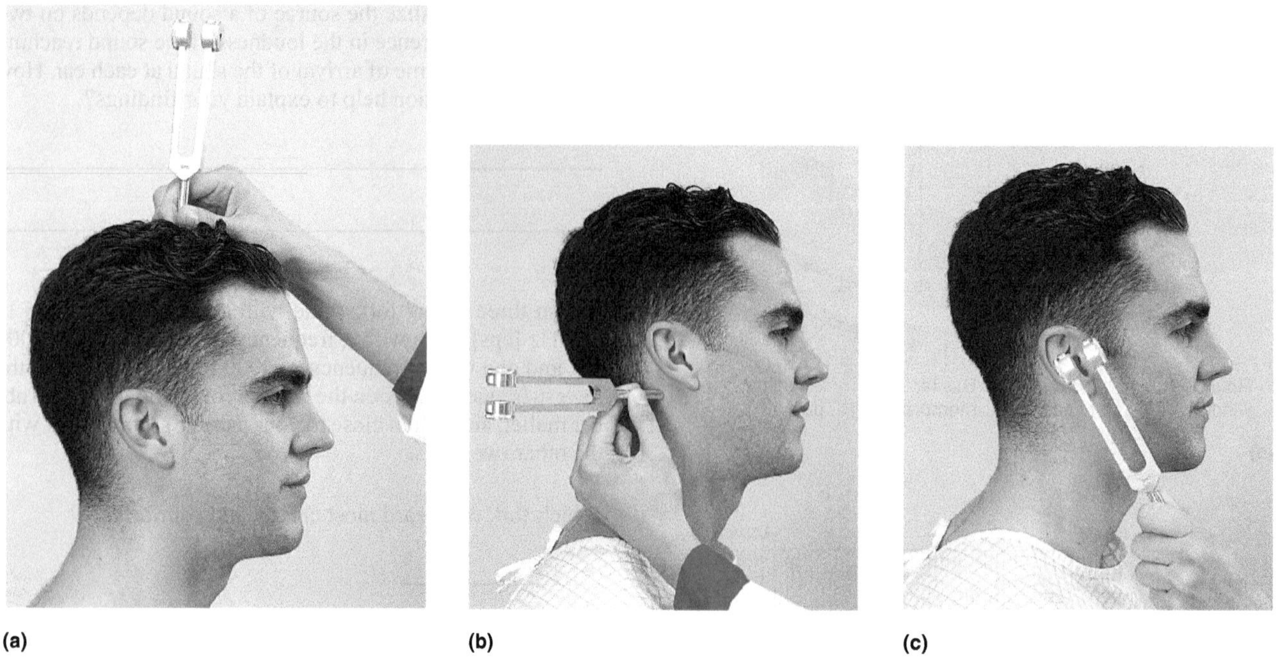

FIGURE 6 The Weber and Rinne tuning fork tests. (**a**) The Weber test to evaluate whether the sound remains centralized (normal) or lateralizes to one side or the other (indicative of some degree of conduction or sensorineural deafness). (**b** and **c**) The Rinne test to compare bone conduction and air conduction.

5. Repeat the sequence for the opposite ear.

Right ear: ________________ Left ear: ________________

Does the subject hear better by bone or by air conduction?

____

Audiometry

When the simple tuning fork tests reveal a problem in hearing, audiometer testing is usually prescribed to determine the precise nature of the hearing deficit. An *audiometer* is an instrument (specifically, an electronic oscillator with earphones) used to determine hearing acuity by exposing each ear to sound stimuli of differing *frequencies* and *intensities.* The hearing range of human beings during youth is from 20 to 20,000 Hz, but hearing acuity declines with age, with reception for the high-frequency sounds lost first. Though this loss represents a major problem for some people, such as musicians, most of us tend to be fairly unconcerned until we begin to have problems hearing sounds in the range of 125 to 8000 Hz, the normal frequency range of speech.

The basic procedure of audiometry is to initially deliver tones of different frequencies to one ear of the subject at an intensity of 0 decibels (dB). (Zero decibels is not the complete absence of sound, but rather the softest sound intensity that can be heard by a person of normal hearing at each frequency.) If the subject cannot hear a particular frequency stimulus of 0 dB, the hearing threshold level control is adjusted until the subject reports that he or she can hear the tone. The number of decibels of intensity required above 0 dB is recorded as the hearing loss. For example, if the subject cannot hear a particular frequency tone until it is delivered at 30 dB intensity, then he or she has a hearing loss of 30 dB for that frequency.

ACTIVITY 5

Audiometry Testing

1. Obtain an audiometer and earphones, and a red and a blue pencil. Before beginning the tests, examine the audiometer to identify the two tone controls: one to regulate frequency and a second to regulate the intensity (loudness) of the sound stimulus. Identify the two output control switches that regulate the delivery of sound to one ear or the other (*red* to the right ear, *blue* to the left ear). Also find the *hearing threshold level control,* which is calibrated to deliver a basal tone of 0 dB to the subject's ears.

2. Place the earphones on the subject's head so that the red cord or ear-cushion is over the right ear and the blue cord or ear-cushion is over the left ear. Instruct the subject to raise one hand when he or she hears a tone.

3. Set the frequency control at 125 Hz and the intensity control at 0 dB. Press the red output switch to deliver a tone to the subject's right ear. If the subject does not respond, raise the sound intensity slowly by rotating the hearing level control counterclockwise until the subject reports (by raising a hand) that a tone is heard. Repeat this procedure for frequencies of 250, 500, 1000, 2000, 4000, and 8000.

4. Record the results in the grid above by marking a small red circle on the grid at each frequency-dB junction at which a tone was heard. Then connect the circles with a red line to produce a hearing acuity graph for the right ear.

5. Repeat steps 3 and 4 for the left (blue) ear, and record the results with blue circles and connecting lines on the grid.

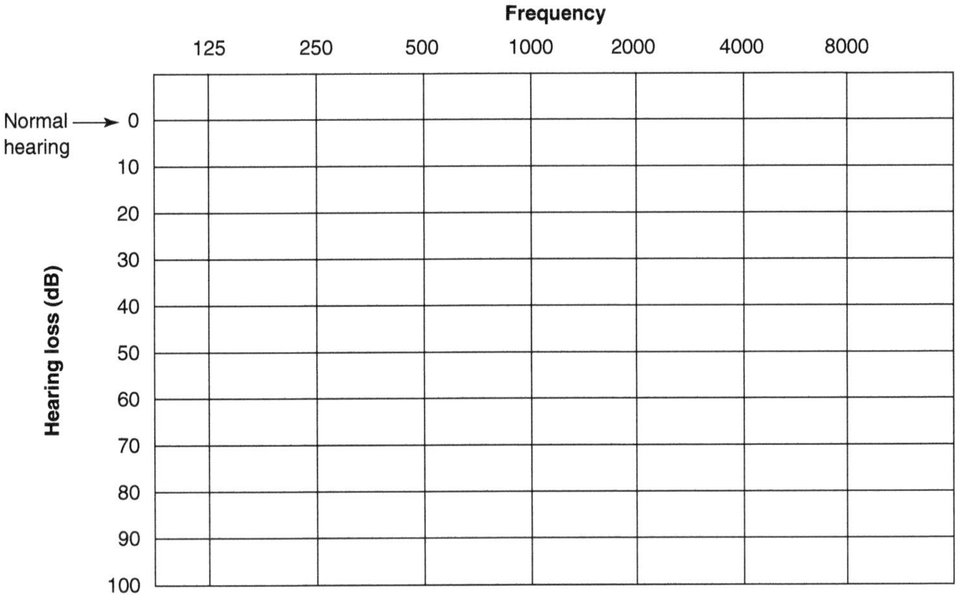

Microscopic Anatomy of the Equilibrium Apparatus and Mechanisms of Equilibrium

The equilibrium apparatus of the inner ear, the **vestibular apparatus,** is in the vestibule and semicircular canals of the bony labyrinth. Their chambers are filled with perilymph, in which membranous labyrinth structures are suspended. The vestibule contains the saclike **utricle** and **saccule,** and the semicircular chambers contain **membranous semicircular ducts.** Like the cochlear duct, these membranes are filled with endolymph and contain receptor cells that are activated by the bending of their cilia.

The semicircular canals are centrally involved in the **mechanism of dynamic equilibrium.** They are 1.2 cm in circumference and are oriented in three planes—horizontal, frontal, and sagittal. At the base of each semicircular duct is an enlarged region, the **ampulla,** which communicates with the utricle of the vestibule. Within each ampulla is a receptor region called a **crista ampullaris,** which consists of a tuft of hair cells covered with a gelatinous cap, or **cupula** (Figure 7). When your head position changes in an angular direction, as

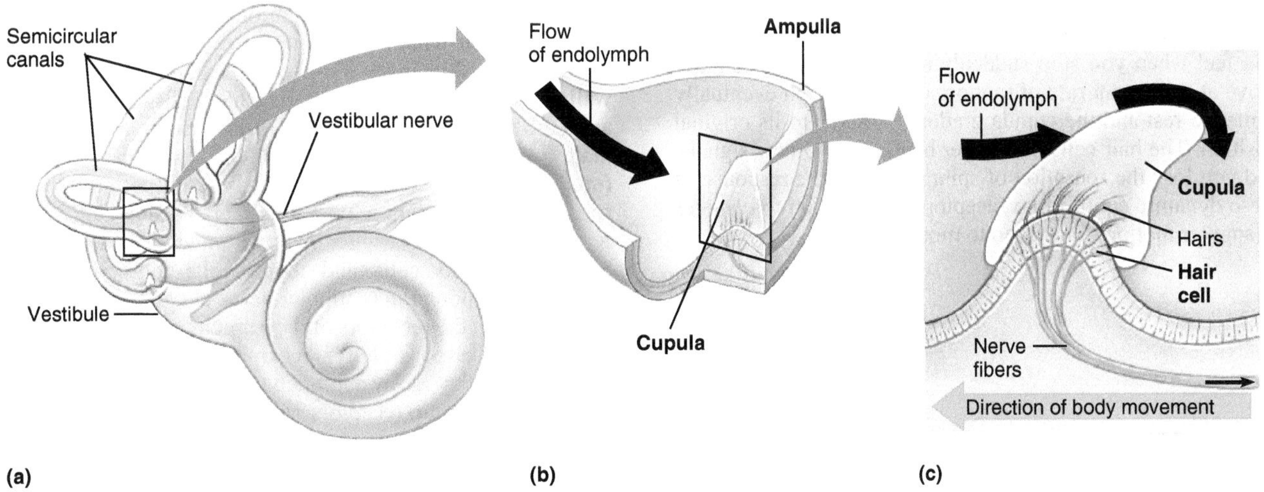

Imagineering

FIGURE 7 **Structure and function of the crista ampullaris.** (**a**) Arranged in the three spatial planes, the semicircular ducts in the semicircular canals each have a swelling called an ampulla at their base. (**b**) Each ampulla contains a crista ampullaris, a receptor that is essentially a cluster of hair cells with hairs projecting into a gelatinous cap called the cupula. (**c**) When the rate of rotation changes, inertia prevents the endolymph in the semicircular canals from moving with the head, so the fluid presses against the cupula, bending the hair cells in the opposite direction. The bending increases the frequency of action potentials in the sensory neurons in direct proportion to the amount of rotational acceleration. The mechanism adjusts quickly if rotation continues at a constant speed.

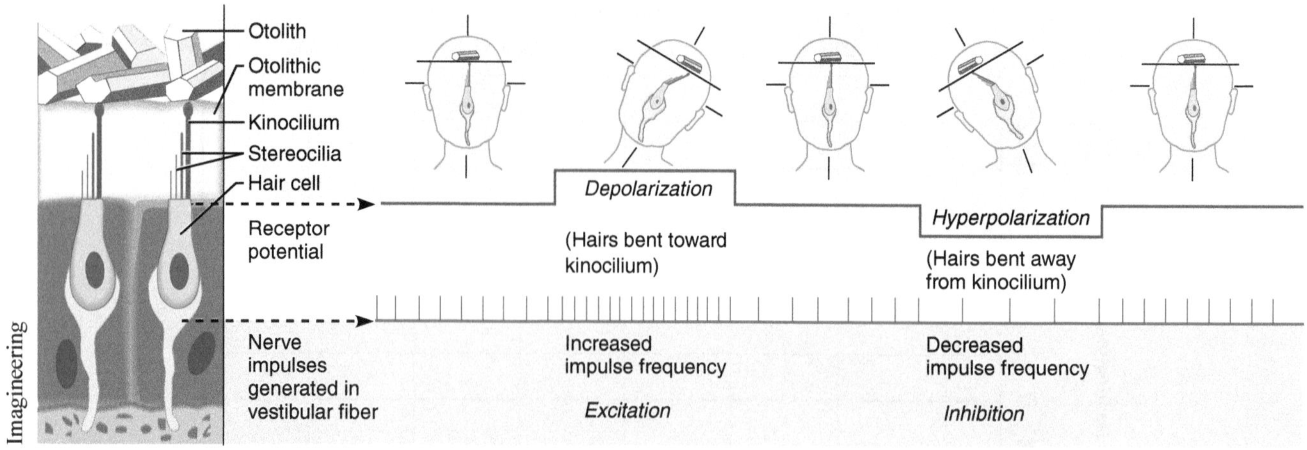

FIGURE 8 **The effect of gravitational pull on a macula receptor in the utricle.** When movement of the otolithic membrane bends the hair cells in the direction of the kinocilium, the vestibular fibers depolarize and generate action potentials more rapidly. When the hairs are bent in the direction away from the kinocilium, the hair cells become hyperpolarized, and the nerve fibers send impulses at a reduced rate (i.e., below the resting rate of discharge).

when twirling on the dance floor or when taking a rough boat ride, the endolymph in the canal lags behind, pushing the cupula—like a swinging door—in a direction opposite to that of the angular motion (Figure 7c). This movement depolarizes the hair cells, resulting in enhanced impulse transmission up the vestibular division of the eighth cranial nerve to the brain. Likewise, when the angular motion stops suddenly, the inertia of the endolymph causes it to continue to move, pushing the cupula in the same direction as the previous body motion. This movement again initiates electrical changes in the hair cells (in this case, it hyperpolarizes them). (This phenomenon accounts for the reversed motion sensation you feel when you stop suddenly after twirling.) When you move at a constant rate of motion, the endolymph eventually comes to rest and the cupula gradually returns to its original position. The hair cells, no longer bent, send no new signals, and you lose the sensation of spinning. Thus the response of these dynamic equilibrium receptors is a reaction to *changes* in angular motion rather than to motion itself.

ACTIVITY 6

Examining the Microscopic Structure of the Crista Ampullaris

Go to the demonstration area and examine the slide of a crista ampullaris. Identify the areas depicted in Figure 7b and c.

Maculae in the vestibule contain the **hair cells,** receptors that are essential to the **mechanism of static equilibrium.** The maculae respond to gravitational pull, thus providing information on which way is up or down, and to linear or straightforward changes in speed. They are located on the walls of the saccule and utricle. The hair cells in each macula are embedded in the **otolithic membrane,** a gelatinous material containing small grains of calcium carbonate **(otoliths).** When the head moves, the otoliths move in response to variations in gravitational pull. As they deflect different hair cells, they trigger hyperpolarization or depolarization of the hair cells and modify the rate of impulse transmission along the vestibular nerve (Figure 8).

Although the receptors of the semicircular canals and the vestibule are responsible for dynamic and static equilibrium respectively, they rarely act independently. Complex interaction of many of the receptors is the rule. Processing is also complex and involves the brain stem and cerebellum as well as input from proprioceptors and the eyes.

ACTIVITY 7

Conducting Laboratory Tests on Equilibrium

The function of the semicircular canals and vestibule are not routinely tested in the laboratory, but the following simple tests illustrate normal equilibrium apparatus function as well as some of the complex processing interactions.

In the first balance test and the Barany test, you will look for **nystagmus,** which is the involuntary rolling of the eyes in any direction or the trailing of the eyes slowly in one direction, followed by their rapid movement in the opposite direction. It is normal after rotation; abnormal otherwise. The direction of nystagmus is that of its quick phase on acceleration.

Balance Tests

1. Have your partner walk a straight line, placing one foot directly in front of the other.

Is he or she able to walk without undue wobbling from side to side ? ______________________________

Did he or she experience any dizziness? ______________

The ability to walk with balance and without dizziness, unless subject to rotational forces, indicates normal function of the equilibrium apparatus.

Was nystagmus present? ______________________

2. Place three coins of different sizes on the floor. Ask your lab partner to pick up the coins, and carefully observe his or her muscle activity and coordination.

Did your lab partner have any difficulty locating and picking up the coins? ______________________________

Describe your observations and your lab partner's observations during the test.

____

____

What kinds of interactions involving balance and coordination must occur for a person to move fluidly during this test?

____

____

3. If a person has a depressed nervous system, mental concentration may result in a loss of balance. Ask your lab partner to stand up and count backward from ten as rapidly as possible.

Did your lab partner lose balance? ______________

Barany Test (Induction of Nystagmus and Vertigo*)

This experiment evaluates the semicircular canals and should be conducted as a group effort to protect test subject(s) from possible injury.

! The following precautionary notes should be read before beginning:

- The subject(s) chosen should not be easily inclined to dizziness during rotational or turning movements.
- Rotation should be stopped immediately if the subject feels nauseated.
- Because the subject(s) will experience vertigo and loss of balance as a result of the rotation, several classmates should be prepared to catch, hold, or support the subject(s) as necessary until the symptoms pass.

1. Instruct the subject to sit on a rotating chair or stool, and to hold on to the arms or seat of the chair, feet on stool rungs. The subject's head should be tilted forward approximately 30 degrees (almost touching the chest). The horizontal (lateral) semicircular canal will be stimulated when the head is in this position. The subject's eyes are to remain *open* during the test.
2. Four classmates should position themselves so that the subject is surrounded on all sides. The classmate posterior to the subject will rotate the chair.
3. Rotate the chair to the subject's right approximately 10 revolutions in 10 seconds, then suddenly stop the rotation.
4. Immediately note the direction of the subject's resultant nystagmus; and ask him or her to describe the feelings of movement, indicating speed and direction sensation. Record this information below.

____

____

____

____

If the semicircular canals are operating normally, the subject will experience a sensation that the stool is still rotating immediately after it has stopped and *will* demonstrate nystagmus.

When the subject is rotated to the right, the cupula will be bent to the left, causing nystagmus during rotation in which the eyes initially move slowly to the left and then quickly to the right. Nystagmus will continue until the cupula has returned to its initial position. Then, when rotation is stopped abruptly, the cupula will be bent to the right, producing nystagmus with its slow phase to the right and its rapid phase to the left. In many subjects, this will be accompanied by a feeling of vertigo and a tendency to fall to the right.

***Vertigo** is a sensation of dizziness and rotational movement when such movement is not occurring or has ceased.

Romberg Test

The Romberg test determines the integrity of the dorsal white column of the spinal cord, which transmits impulses to the brain from the proprioceptors involved with posture.

1. Have your partner stand with his or her back to the blackboard.

2. Draw one line parallel to each side of your partner's body. He or she should stand erect, with eyes open and staring straight ahead for 2 minutes while you observe any movements. Did you see any gross swaying movements?

____

3. Repeat the test. This time the subject's eyes should be closed. Note and record the degree of side-to-side movement.

____

4. Repeat the test with the subject's eyes first open and then closed. This time, however, the subject should be positioned with his or her left shoulder toward, but not touching, the board so that you may observe and record the degree of front-to-back swaying.

____

Do you think the equilibrium apparatus of the inner ear was operating equally well in all these tests?

____

The proprioceptors? __________________________

Why was the observed degree of swaying greater when the eyes were closed?

____

____

What conclusions can you draw regarding the factors necessary for maintaining body equilibrium and balance?

____

____

____

____

Role of Vision in Maintaining Equilibrium

To further demonstrate the role of vision in maintaining equilibrium, perform the following experiment. (Ask your lab partner to record observations and act as a "spotter.") Stand erect, with your eyes open. Raise your left foot approximately 30 cm off the floor, and hold it there for 1 minute.

Record the observations: __________________________

____

____

Rest for 1 or 2 minutes; and then repeat the experiment with the same foot raised but with your eyes closed. Record the observations:

____

____

NAME ______________________

LAB TIME/DATE ______________________

REVIEW SHEET

Special Senses: Hearing and Equilibrium

Anatomy of the Ear

1. Select the terms from column B that apply to the column A descriptions. Some terms are used more than once.

Column A

_______, _______, _______ 1. structure composing the external ear

_______, _______, _______ 2. structures composing the internal ear

_______, _______, _______ 3. collectively called the ossicles

_______ 4. involved in equalizing the pressure in the middle ear with atmospheric pressure

_______ 5. vibrates at the same frequency as sound waves hitting it; transmits the vibrations to the ossicles

_______, _______ 6. contain receptors for the sense of balance

_______ 7. transmits the vibratory motion of the stirrup to the fluid in the scala vestibuli of the inner ear

_______ 8. acts as a pressure relief valve for the increased fluid pressure in the scala tympani; bulges into the tympanic cavity

_______ 9. passage between the throat and the tympanic cavity

_______ 10. fluid contained within the membranous labyrinth

_______ 11. fluid contained within the osseous labyrinth and bathing the membranous labyrinth

Column B

a. pharyngotympanic (auditory) tube

b. cochlea

c. endolymph

d. external auditory canal

e. incus (anvil)

f. malleus (hammer)

g. oval window

h. perilymph

i. pinna (auricle)

j. round window

k. semicircular canals

l. stapes (stirrup)

m. tympanic membrane

n. vestibule

2. Identify all indicated structures and ear regions in the following diagram.

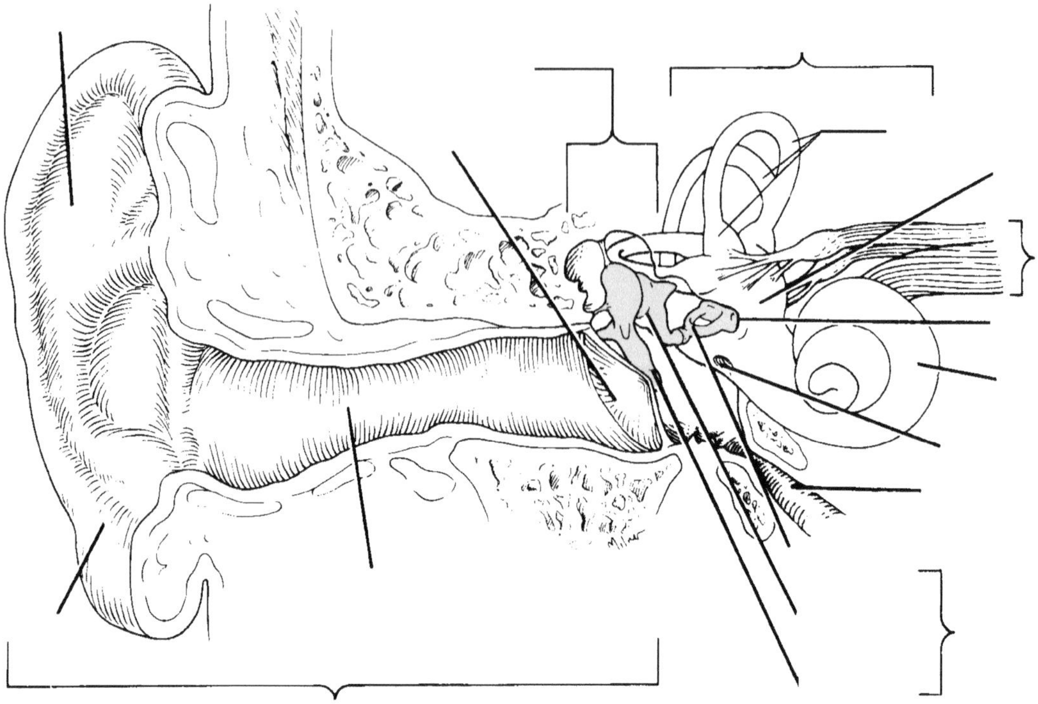

3. Match the membranous labyrinth structures listed in column B with the descriptive statements in column A.

Column A	Column B
_______, _______ 1. sacs found within the vestibule	a. ampulla
_______ 2. contains the spiral organ of Corti	b. basilar membrane
_______, _______ 3. sites of the maculae	c. cochlear duct
_______ 4. positioned in all spatial planes	d. cochlear nerve
_______ 5. hair cells of spiral organ of Corti rest on this membrane	e. cupula
_______ 6. gelatinous membrane overlying the hair cells of the spiral organ of Corti	f. otoliths
_______ 7. contains the crista ampullaris	g. saccule
_______, _______, _______, _______ 8. function in static equilibrium	h. semicircular ducts
_______, _______, _______, _______ 9. function in dynamic equilibrium	i. tectorial membrane
_______ 10. carries auditory information to the brain	j. utricle
_______ 11. gelatinous cap overlying hair cells of the crista ampullaris	k. vestibular nerve
_______ 12. grains of calcium carbonate in the maculae	

4. Sound waves hitting the tympanic membrane (eardrum) initiate its vibratory motion. Trace the pathway through which vibrations and fluid currents are transmitted to finally stimulate the hair cells in the spiral organ of Corti. (Name the appropriate ear structures in their correct sequence.)

Tympanic membrane → ______________________________

____

____

5. Describe how sounds of different frequency (pitch) are differentiated in the cochlea. ______________________________

____

____

____

6. Explain the role of the endolymph of the semicircular canals in activating the receptors during angular motion.

____

____

____

7. Explain the role of the otoliths in perception of static equilibrium (head position). ______________________________

____

____

____

Laboratory Tests

8. Was the auditory acuity measurement made during the experiment on page 386 the same or different for both ears?

______________________________ What factors might account for a difference in the acuity of the two ears?

____

____

9. During the sound localization experiment on page 386, note the position(s) in which the sound was least easily located.

How can this phenomenon be explained? ______________________________

____

10. In the frequency experiment on page 387, note which tuning fork was the most difficult to hear.

What conclusion can you draw? ______________________________

____

11. When the tuning fork handle was pressed to your forehead during the Weber test, where did the sound seem to originate?

____

Where did it seem to originate when one ear was plugged with cotton? ______________________________

How do sound waves reach the cochlea when conduction deafness is present? ______________________________

____

12. Indicate whether the following conditions relate to conduction deafness (C) or sensorineural deafness (S).

______ 1. can result from the fusion of the ossicles

______ 2. can result from a lesion on the cochlear nerve

______ 3. sound heard in one ear but not in the other during bone and air conduction

______ 4. can result from otitis media

______ 5. can result from impacted cerumen or a perforated eardrum

______ 6. can result from a blood clot in the auditory cortex

13. The Rinne test evaluates an individual's ability to hear sounds conducted by air or bone. Which is more indicative of normal hearing? ______________________________

14. Define *nystagmus.* ______________________________

____

Define *vertigo.* ______________________________

____

15. The Barany test investigated the effect that rotatory acceleration had on the semicircular canals. Explain *why* the subject still had the sensation of rotation immediately after being stopped. ______________________________

____

16. What is the usual reason for conducting the Romberg test? ______________________________

____

Was the degree of sway greater with the eyes open or closed? Why? ______________________________

____

17. Normal balance, or equilibrium, depends on input from a number of sensory receptors. Name them.

____

18. What effect does alcohol consumption have on balance and equilibrium? Explain. ______________________________

____

Special Senses: Olfaction and Taste

MATERIALS

- ☐ Prepared slides: nasal olfactory epithelium (l.s.); the tongue showing taste buds (x.s.)
- ☐ Compound microscope
- ☐ Small mirror
- ☐ Paper towels
- ☐ Packets of granulated sugar
- ☐ Disposable autoclave bag
- ☐ Paper plates
- ☐ Equal-size food cubes of cheese, apple, raw potato, dried prunes, banana, raw carrot, and hard-cooked egg white (These prepared foods should be in an opaque container; a foil-lined egg carton would work well.)
- ☐ Toothpicks
- ☐ Disposable gloves
- ☐ Cotton-tipped swabs
- ☐ Paper cups
- ☐ Flask of distilled or tap water
- ☐ Prepared vials of oil of cloves, oil of peppermint, and oil of wintergreen or corresponding flavors found in the condiment section of a supermarket
- ☐ Chipped ice
- ☐ Five numbered vials containing common household substances with strong odors (herbs, spices, etc.)
- ☐ Nose clips
- ☐ Absorbent cotton

OBJECTIVES

1. To describe the location and cellular composition of the olfactory epithelium.
2. To describe the structure and function of the taste receptors.
3. To name the five basic qualities of taste sensation, and to list the chemical substances that elicit them.
4. To explain the interdependence between the senses of smell and taste.
5. To name two factors other than olfaction that influence taste appreciation of foods.
6. To define *olfactory adaptation.*

The receptors for olfaction and taste are classified as **chemoreceptors** because they respond to chemicals in solution. Although five relatively specific types of taste receptors have been identified, the olfactory receptors are considered sensitive to a much wider range of chemical sensations. The sense of smell is the least understood of the special senses.

Location and Anatomy of the Olfactory Receptors

The **olfactory epithelium** (organ of smell) occupies an area of about 5 cm^2 in the roof of the nasal cavity (Figure 1a). Since the air entering the human nasal cavity must make a hairpin turn to enter the respiratory passages below, the nasal epithelium is in a rather poor position for performing its function. This is why sniffing, which brings more air into contact with the receptors, intensifies the sense of smell.

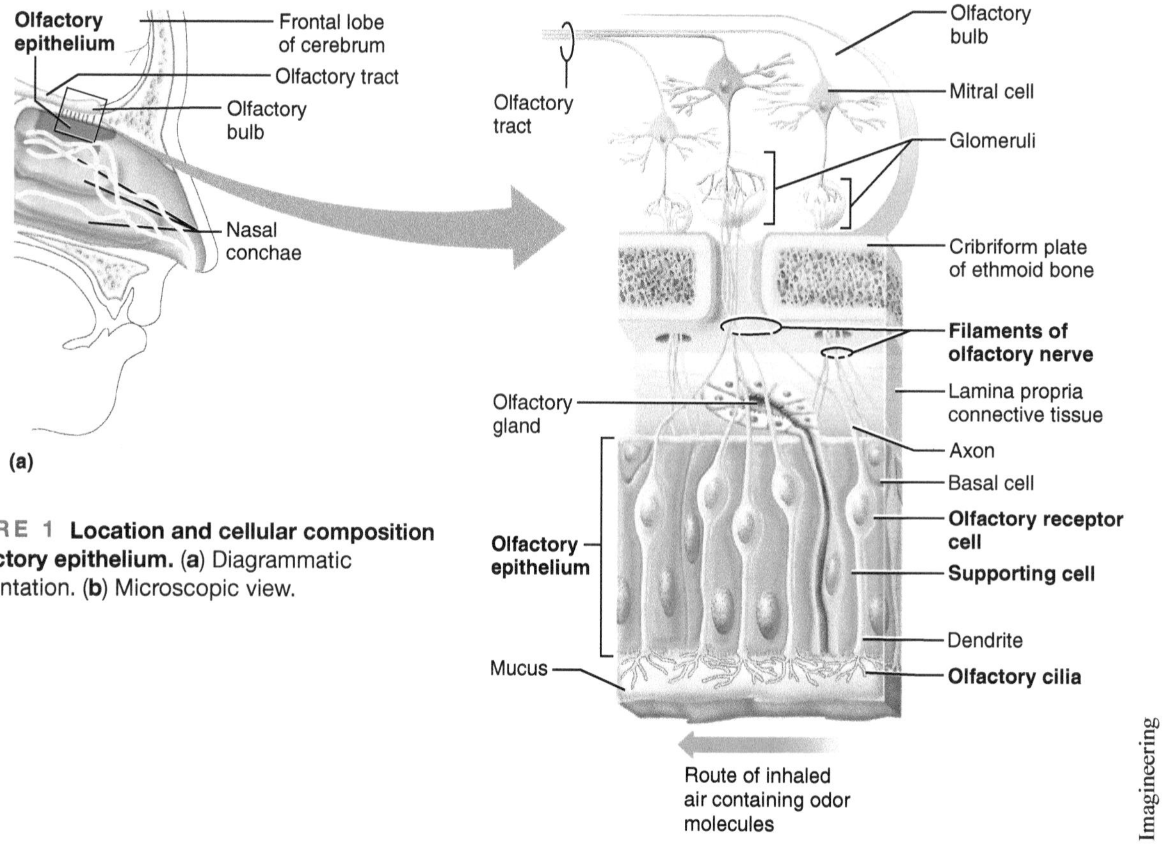

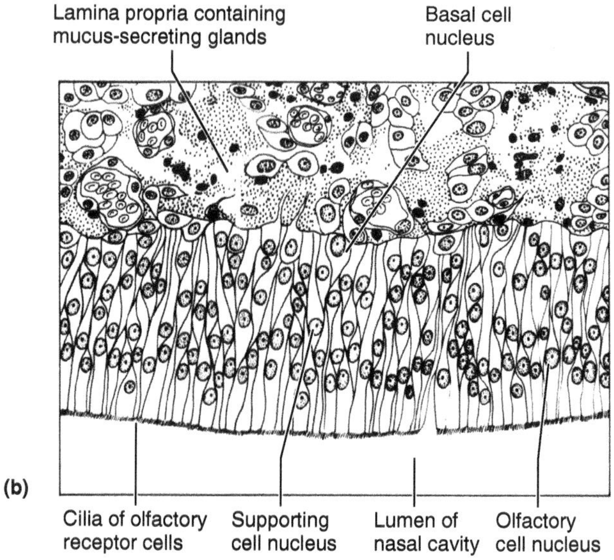

FIGURE 1 Location and cellular composition of olfactory epithelium. (**a**) Diagrammatic representation. (**b**) Microscopic view.

The specialized receptor cells in the olfactory epithelium are surrounded by **supporting cells,** non-sensory epithelial cells. The **olfactory receptor cells** are bipolar neurons whose **olfactory cilia** extend outward from the epithelium. Axonal nerve filaments emerging from their basal ends penetrate the cribriform plate of the ethmoid bone and proceed as the *olfactory nerves* to synapse in the olfactory bulbs lying on either side of the crista galli of the ethmoid bone. Impulses from neurons of the olfactory bulbs are then conveyed to the olfactory portion of the cortex (uncus) without synapsing in the thalamus.

ACTIVITY 1

Microscopic Examination of the Olfactory Epithelium

Obtain a longitudinal section of olfactory epithelium. Examine it closely using a compound microscope, comparing it to Figure 1b.

Location and Anatomy of Taste Buds

The **taste buds,** specific receptors for the sense of taste, are widely but not uniformly distributed in the oral cavity. Most are located in **papillae,** peglike projections of the mucosa, on the dorsal surface of the tongue (as described next). A few are found on the soft palate, epiglottis, pharynx, and inner surface of the cheeks.

Taste buds are located primarily on the sides of the large round **circumvallate papillae** (arranged in a V formation on the posterior surface of the tongue); in the side walls of the **foliate papillae;** and on the tops of the more numerous, mushroom-shaped fungiform papillae. (See Figure 2.)

- Use a mirror to examine your tongue. Which of the various papillae types can you pick out? ______________________

____

Each taste bud consists largely of a globular arrangement of two types of modified epithelial cells: the **gustatory,** or **taste cells,** which are the actual receptor cells, and basal cells. Several nerve fibers enter each taste bud and supply sensory nerve endings to each of the taste cells. The long microvilli of the receptor cells penetrate the epithelial surface through an opening called the **taste pore.** When these microvilli, called **gustatory hairs,** contact specific chemicals in the solution, the taste cells depolarize. The afferent fibers from the taste buds to the sensory cortex in the postcentral gyrus of the brain are carried in three cranial nerves: the *facial nerve (VII)* serves the anterior two-thirds of the tongue; the *glossopharyngeal nerve (IX)* serves the posterior third of the tongue; and the *vagus nerve (X)* carries a few fibers from the pharyngeal region.

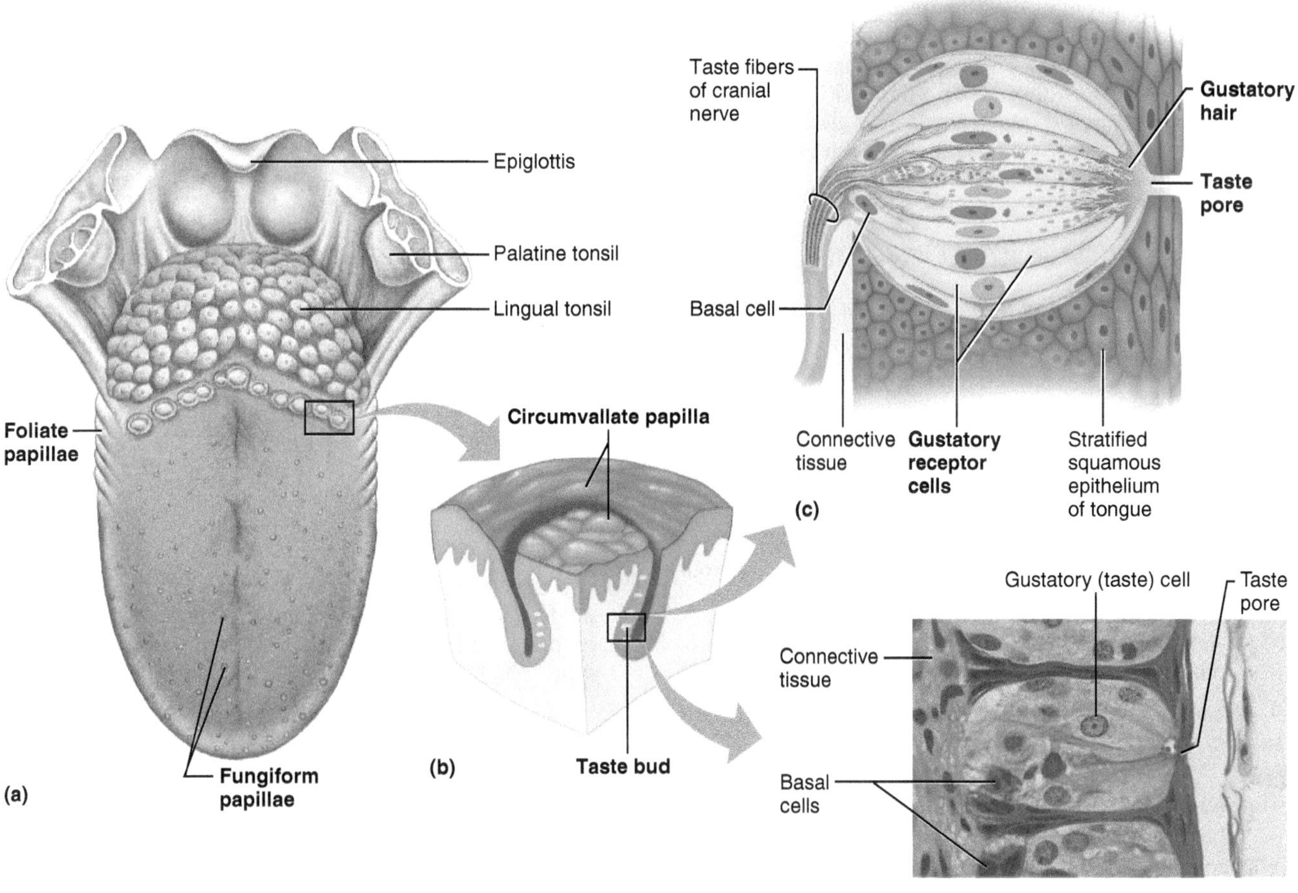

Imagineering

(d)

Carolina Biological Supply/ Phototake.

Imagineering/Adapted from Marieb and Mallatt, *Human Anatomy*, 3e, F16.1, © Benjamin Cummings 2003.

FIGURE 2 **Location and structure of taste buds.** (**a**) Taste buds on the tongue are associated with papillae, projections of the tongue mucosa. (**b**) A sectioned circumvallate papilla shows the position of the taste buds in its lateral walls. (**c**) An enlarged view of a taste bud. (**d**) Photomicrograph of a taste bud (540×).

ACTIVITY 2

Microscopic Examination of Taste Buds

Obtain a microscope and a prepared slide of a tongue cross section. Use Figure 2b as a guide to aid you in locating the taste buds on the tongue papillae. Make a detailed study of one taste bud. Identify the taste pore and gustatory hairs if observed. Compare your observations to Plate 17 in the Histology Atlas.

When taste is tested with pure chemical compounds, most taste sensations can be grouped into one of five basic qualities—sweet, sour, bitter, salty, or umami (*u-mam'e;* "delicious"). Although all taste buds are believed to respond in some degree to all five classes of chemical stimuli, each type responds optimally to only one.

The *sweet receptors* respond to a number of seemingly unrelated compounds such as sugars (fructose, sucrose, glucose), saccharine, and some amino acids. Both sweet and bitter responses are mediated by a G protein, gustducin. The sweet response causes K^+ channels to close, whereas the bitter response results in increased intracellular levels of Ca^{2+}. Activation of sour receptors is mediated by hydrogen ions (H^+) and blockade of K^+ (or Na^+) channels. Salty taste seems to be due to influx of Na^+ through Na^+ channels, while umami is elicited by the amino acid glutamate, which is responsible for the "meat taste" of beef and the flavor of monosodium glutamate (MSG).

Laboratory Experiments

! *Notify instructor of any food or scent allergies before beginning experiments.*

ACTIVITY 3

Stimulating Taste Buds

1. Obtain several paper towels, a sugar packet, and a disposable autoclave bag and bring them to your bench.

2. With a paper towel, dry the dorsal surface of your tongue.

! Immediately dispose of the paper towel in the autoclave bag.

3. Tear off a corner of the sugar packet and shake a few sugar crystals on your dried tongue. Do *not* close your mouth.

Time how long it takes to taste the sugar. ____________ sec

Why couldn't you taste the sugar immediately?

____

ACTIVITY 4

Examining the Combined Effects of Smell, Texture, and Temperature on Taste

Effects of Smell and Texture

1. Ask the subject to sit with eyes closed and to pinch his or her nostrils shut.

2. Using a paper plate, obtain samples of the food items provided by your laboratory instructor. At no time should the subject be allowed to see the foods being tested. Wear plastic gloves and use toothpicks to handle food.

3. For each test, place a cube of food in the subject's mouth and ask him or her to identify the food by using the following sequence of activities:

- First, manipulate the food with the tongue.
- Second, chew the food.
- Third, if a positive identification is not made with the first two techniques and the taste sense, ask the subject to release the pinched nostrils and to continue chewing with the nostrils open to determine if a positive identification can be made.

In the chart on page 401, record the type of food, and then put a check mark in the appropriate column for the result.

Was the sense of smell equally important in all cases?

____

Where did it seem to be important and why?

____

____

Discard gloves in autoclave bag.

Effect of Olfactory Stimulation

There is no question that what is commonly referred to as taste depends heavily on stimulation of the olfactory receptors, particularly in the case of strongly odoriferous substances. The following experiment should illustrate this fact.

1. Obtain vials of oil of wintergreen, peppermint, and cloves, paper cup, flask of water, paper towels, and some fresh cotton-tipped swabs. Ask the subject to sit so that he or she cannot see which vial is being used, and to dry the tongue and close the nostrils.

2. Use a cotton swab to apply a drop of one of the oils to the subject's tongue. Can he or she distinguish the flavor?

____

Identification by Texture and Smell

Food tested	Texture only	Chewing with nostrils pinched	Chewing with nostrils open	Identification not made

! Put the used swab in the autoclave bag. *Do not redip the swab into the oil.*

3. Have the subject open the nostrils, and record the change in sensation he or she reports.

____

4. Have the subject rinse the mouth well and dry the tongue.

5. Prepare two swabs, each with one of the two remaining oils.

6. Hold one swab under the subject's open nostrils, while touching the second swab to the tongue.

Record the reported sensations. ______________________________

____

____

! 7. Dispose of the used swabs and paper towels in the autoclave bag before continuing.

Which sense, taste or smell, appears to be more important in the proper identification of a strongly flavored volatile substance?

____

Effect of Temperature

In addition to the effect that olfaction and food texture play in determining our taste sensations, the temperature of foods also helps determine if the food is appreciated or even tasted. To illustrate this, have your partner hold some chipped ice on the tongue for approximately a minute and then close his or her eyes. Immediately place any of the foods previously identified in his or her mouth and ask for an identification.

Results? ______________________________

____

____

Identification by Mouth and Nasal Inhalation

Vial number	Identification with nose clips	Identification without nose clips	Other observations
1			
2			
3			
4			
5			

ACTIVITY 5

Assessing the Importance of Taste and Olfaction in Odor Identification

1. Go to the designated testing area. Close your nostrils with a nose clip, and breathe through your mouth. Breathing through your mouth only, attempt to identify the odors of common substances in the numbered vials at the testing area. Do not look at the substance in the container. Record your responses on the chart below.

2. Remove the nose clips, and repeat the tests using your nose to sniff the odors. Record your responses on the chart below.

3. Record any other observations you make as you conduct the tests.

4. Which method gave the best identification results?

____

What can you conclude about the effectiveness of the senses of taste and olfaction in identifying odors?

____

ACTIVITY 6

Demonstrating Olfactory Adaptation

Obtain some absorbent cotton and two of the following oils (oil of wintergreen, peppermint, or cloves). Place several drops of oil on the absorbent cotton. Press one nostril shut. Hold the cotton under the open nostril and exhale through the mouth. Record the time required for the odor to disappear (for olfactory adaptation to occur).

______________ sec

Repeat the procedure with the other nostril.

______________ sec

Immediately test another oil with the nostril that has just experienced olfactory adaptation. What are the results?

____

What conclusions can you draw? ______________

____

NAME ____________________

LAB TIME/DATE ____________________

REVIEW SHEET

Special Senses: Olfaction and Taste

Location and Anatomy of the Olfactory Receptors

1. Describe the cellular composition and the location of the olfactory epithelium. ____________________

____

____

2. How and why does sniffing improve your sense of smell? ____________________

____

Location and Anatomy of Taste Buds

3. Name five sites where receptors for taste are found, and circle the predominant site.

____________________, ____________________, ____________________,

____________________, and ____________________

4. Describe the cellular makeup and arrangement of a taste bud. (Use a diagram, if helpful.) ____________________

____

Laboratory Experiments

5. Taste and smell receptors are both classified as ____________________, because they both respond to ____________________

6. Why is it impossible to taste substances with a dry tongue? ____________________

____

7. The basic taste sensations are mediated by specific chemical substances or groups. Name them for the following taste modalities.

salt: ____________________ sour: ____________________ umami: ____________________

bitter: ____________________ sweet: ____________________

8. Name three factors that influence our appreciation of foods. Substantiate each choice with an example from the laboratory experience.

1. ______________ Substantiation: ____

____

2. ______________ Substantiation: ____

____

3. ______________ Substantiation: ____

____

Which of the factors chosen is most important? ______________________ Substantiate your choice with an example from everyday life. ____

____

Expand on your explanation and choices by explaining why a cold, greasy hamburger is unappetizing to most people.

____

____

9. How palatable is food when you have a cold? ______________________ Explain your answer. ______________

____

10. In your opinion, is olfactory adaptation desirable? ______________________________ Explain your answer.

____

____

Name: ______________________________________ Biology 2020 1A
Date:___________________________

1. STROBE LIGHT
The retina contains how many kinds of light cells? Name them.

____

____

____

_________________________.

2. ACCOMODATION
How would you expect the near point of accommodation to change as you age?

____

____

____

_________________________.

3. EYE DOMINANCE
Record which eye is dominant? Does it match our dominant hand? Give a reason as to why a left eyed dominant person might be right hand dominant.

____

____

____

_________________________.

4. VISION DISC
Using the vision disc, record your right or left peripheral vision by degrees. Why do some people have different peripheral visions, and why the variations from one side versus the other?

____

____

____

_________________________.

5. HORSE SKULL: PREY OR PREDATOR?
Is the horse a prey or predator? What are humans in the animal kingdom? How does peripheral vision versus focal vision affect the animals' survival skills?

____

____

____

____

_________________________________.

6. SHOOTING GALLERY

How does peripheral normal vision, altered focal vision, and focal vision affect the ability to "shoot the animals"?

____

____

____

____

______________________________.

7. EYE MODEL; CHART AND STUDY GUIDE
Be able to identify the structures found on the study guide list. Additionally, what are the names of the intrinsic muscles of the eye? Find out what cranial nerves innervate them. Be able to identify the lacrimal glands.

____

____

____

____

______________________________.

8. BLIND SPOT TEST
What is the cause of the blind?

____

____

____

________________________.

9. EYE SLIDE

10. ASTIGMATISM CHART
What would you see if you had astigmatism? What is the cause of astigmatism? How would it be corrected?

____

____

____

____

______________________________.

11. BRAIN MODEL: CRANIAL NERVES
Be able to identify where the olfactory bulbs, optic nerve and optic chiasm are. What are their associated cranial nerves?

____

____

____

____________________.

12. PSEUDOISOCHROMATIC PLATES
What is monochromacy? What are some of the causes of color blindness? Genetically speaking, what gender does this predominantly affect?

____

____

____

____________________.

13. EYE MODEL TEST
Identify the different structures

14. EYE CHART TEST: SCHNELLEN CHART
What does this chart test? How do you read the ability of an individual's sight using this chart?

____

____

____

____________________.

15. AFTER IMAGE
What is an after image? Why are you able to see it that way?

____

____

____

____

____________________________.

16. PURKINJE FIGURES
What are they? Why are you able to see them when you wiggle the flashlight back and forth?

____

____

____

____________________.

17. OPTICAL ILLUSIONS
How do optical illusions work?

18. DISAPPEARING GREY SPOT ILLUSION
Why do you see the grey squares appear? Why do they disappear after you attempt to touch them?

19. MOSQUITO: VARYING SOUND PITCHES FOR VARYING GENERATIONS
Why do younger people hear at higher pitches than older individuals?

20. COCHLEAR SLIDE
Be able to identify the various cross-sectional areas of the cochlea

21. EAR MODEL
Locate the different structures of the outer and inner ear.

22. BONE CONDUCTION (TUNING FORK)
Why are you able to hear sounds when the tuning fork are placed on the crown and mastoid process of the head? Where can you hear the best (in air)? Can a person with "congestion" hear better with air conduction or sound conduction? How would you know if a person has outer ear hearing loss compared to inner ear hearing loss?

____

____

____________________________________.

23. LOCATION OF SOUND

24. EAR BONES: PLASTINATED IN RESIN
Be able to identify the three ossicles in the ear. These are the smallest bones in the body. Which one is first affected with sound?

____

____

____

______________________.

25. EAR MODEL
Be able to identify the structures listed on the study guide

26. TWO POINT DISCRIMINATION
Why would you feel only "one point" after the compass ends are reduced? What mechanoreceptors are affected with light touch? Which ones are affected with deep touch?

____

____

____

____

_____________________________.

27. SKIN MODEL
Identify the structures listed.

28. TOUCH STIMULATION
Why is it important to have mechanoreceptor inhibition?

____

____

____

____

_____________________________.

29. TASTE BUD CHART
Be able to identify the different regions of taste on the tongue as specified in this lab.

Blood

MATERIALS

General supply area:*

- ☐ Disposable gloves
- ☐ Safety glasses (student-provided)
- ☐ Bucket or large beaker containing 10% household bleach solution for slide and glassware disposal
- ☐ Spray bottles containing 10% bleach solution
- ☐ Autoclave bag
- ☐ Designated lancet (sharps) disposal container
- ☐ Plasma (obtained from an animal hospital or prepared by centrifuging animal [for example, cattle or sheep] blood obtained from a biological supply house)
- ☐ Test tubes and test tube racks
- ☐ Wide-range pH paper
- ☐ Stained smears of human blood from a biological supply house or, if desired by the instructor, heparinized animal blood obtained from a biological supply house or an animal hospital (for example, dog blood), or EDTA-treated red cells (reference cells†) with blood type labels obscured (available from Immunocor, Inc.)
- ☐ Clean microscope slides
- ☐ Glass stirring rods

***Note to the Instructor:** See directions for handling of soiled glassware and disposable items.

†The blood in these kits (each containing four blood cell types—A1, A2, B, and O—individually supplied in 10-ml vials) is used to calibrate cell counters and other automated clinical laboratory equipment. This blood has been carefully screened and can be safely used by students for blood typing and determining hematocrits. It is not usable for hemoglobin determinations or coagulation studies.

Text continues on next page

OBJECTIVES

1. To name the two major components of blood, and to state their average percentages in whole blood.
2. To describe the composition and functional importance of plasma.
3. To define *formed elements* and list the cell types composing them, cite their relative percentages, and describe their major functions.
4. To identify red blood cells, basophils, eosinophils, monocytes, lymphocytes, and neutrophils when provided with a microscopic preparation or appropriate diagram.
5. To provide the normal values for a total white blood cell count and a total red blood cell count, and to state the importance of these tests.
6. To conduct the following blood test determinations in the laboratory, and to state their norms and the importance of each.

   differential white blood cell count
   hematocrit
   hemoglobin determination
   clotting time
   ABO and Rh blood typing
   plasma cholesterol concentration
7. To discuss the reason for transfusion reactions resulting from the administration of mismatched blood.
8. To define *leukocytosis, leukopenia, leukemia, polycythemia,* and *anemia* and to cite a possible reason for each condition.

In this exercise you will study plasma and formed elements of blood and conduct various hematologic tests. These tests are useful diagnostic tools for the physician because blood composition (number and types of blood cells, and chemical composition) reflects the status of many body functions and malfunctions.

! **ALERT: Special precautions when handling blood.** This exercise provides information on blood from several sources: human, animal, human treated, and artificial blood. The decision to use animal blood for testing or to have students test their own blood will be made by the instructor in accordance with the educational goals of the student group. For example, for students in the nursing or laboratory technician curricula, learning how to safely handle human blood or other human wastes is essential. Whenever blood is being handled, special attention must be paid to safety precautions. Instructors who opt to use human blood are responsible for its safe handling. Precautions should be used regardless of the source of the blood. This will both teach good technique and ensure the safety of the students.

Follow exactly the safety precautions listed below.

1. Wear safety gloves at all times. Discard appropriately.
2. Wear safety glasses throughout the exercise.
3. Handle only your own, freshly let (human) blood.

- ☐ Wright's stain in a dropper bottle
- ☐ Distilled water in a dropper bottle
- ☐ Sterile lancets
- ☐ Absorbent cotton balls
- ☐ Alcohol swabs (wipes)
- ☐ Paper towels
- ☐ Compound microscope
- ☐ Immersion oil
- ☐ Three-dimensional models (if available) and charts of blood cells
- ☐ Assorted slides of white blood count pathologies labeled "Unknown Sample ____"
- ☐ Timer

Because many blood tests are to be conducted in this exercise, it is advisable to set up a number of appropriately labeled supply areas for the various tests, as designated below. Some needed supplies are located in the general supply area.

Note: Artificial blood prepared by Ward's Natural Science can be used for differential counts, hematocrit, and blood typing.

Activity 4: Hematocrit

- ☐ Heparinized capillary tubes
- ☐ Microhematocrit centrifuge and reading gauge (if the reading gauge is not available, a millimeter ruler may be used)
- ☐ Capillary tube sealer or modeling clay

Activity 5: Hemoglobin determination

- ☐ Hemoglobinometer, hemolysis applicator, and lens paper; or Tallquist hemoglobin scale and test paper

Activity 6: Coagulation time

- ☐ Capillary tubes (nonheparinized)
- ☐ Fine triangular file

Activity 7: Blood typing

- ☐ Blood typing sera (anti-A, anti-B, and anti-Rh [anti-D])
- ☐ Rh typing box
- ☐ Wax marking pencil
- ☐ Toothpicks
- ☐ Medicine dropper
- ☐ Blood test cards or microscope slides

Activity 8: Demonstration

- ☐ Microscopes set up with prepared slides demonstrating the following bone (or bone marrow) conditions: macrocytic hypochromic anemia, microcytic hypochromic anemia, sickle cell anemia, lymphocytic leukemia (chronic), and eosinophilia

Activity 9: Cholesterol measurement

- ☐ Cholesterol test cards and color scale

PEx PhysioEx™ 7.0 Computer Simulation

4. Be sure you understand the instructions and have all supplies on hand before you begin any part of the exercise.

5. Do not reuse supplies and equipment once they have been exposed to blood.

6. Keep the lab area clean. Do not let anything that has come in contact with blood touch surfaces or other individuals in the lab. Pay attention to the location of any supplies and equipment that come into contact with blood.

7. Dispose of lancets immediately after use in a designated disposal container. Do not put them down on the lab bench, even temporarily.

8. Dispose of all used cotton balls, alcohol swabs, blotting paper, and so forth in autoclave bags and place all soiled glassware in containers of 10% bleach solution.

9. Wipe down the lab bench with 10% bleach solution when you are finished.

Composition of Blood

Circulating blood is a rather viscous substance that varies from bright scarlet to a dull brick red, depending on the amount of oxygen it is carrying. The average volume of blood in the body is about 5–6 L in adult males and 4–5 L in adult females.

Blood is classified as a type of connective tissue because it consists of a nonliving fluid matrix (the **plasma**) in which living cells (**formed elements**) are suspended. The fibers typical of a connective tissue matrix become visible in blood only when clotting occurs. They then appear as fibrin threads, which form the structural basis for clot formation.

More than 100 different substances are dissolved or suspended in plasma (Figure 1), which is over 90% water. These include nutrients, gases, hormones, various wastes and metabolites, many types of proteins, and electrolytes. The composition of plasma varies continuously as cells remove or add substances to the blood.

Three types of formed elements are present in blood (Table 1). Most numerous are **erythrocytes,** or **red blood cells (RBCs),** which are literally sacs of hemoglobin molecules that transport the bulk of the oxygen carried in the blood (and a small percentage of the carbon dioxide). **Leukocytes,** or **white blood cells (WBCs),** are part of the body's nonspecific defenses and the immune system, and **platelets** function in hemostasis (blood clot formation). Formed elements normally constitute 45% of whole blood; plasma accounts for the remaining 55%.

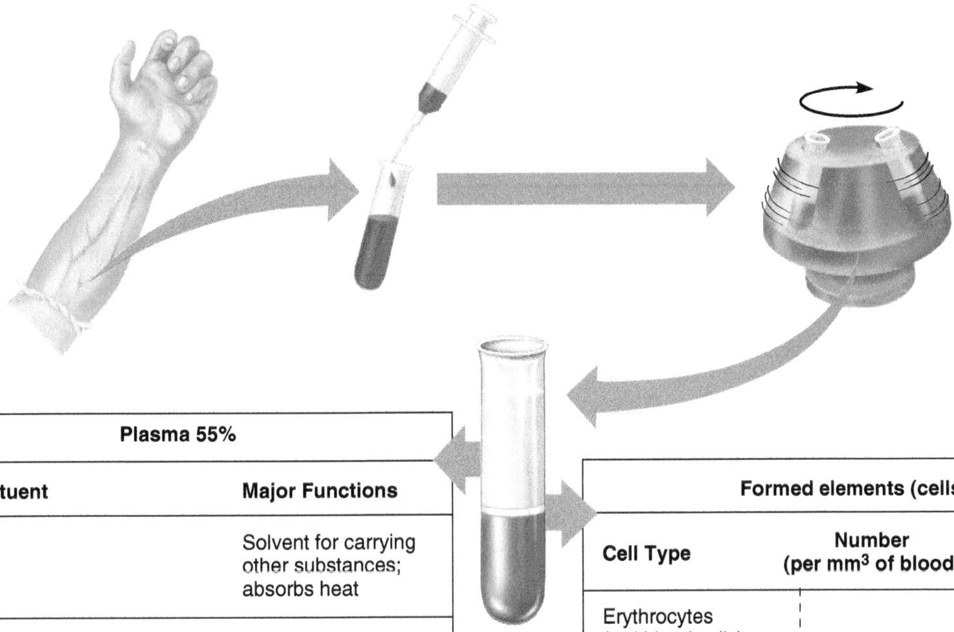

Plasma 55%	
Constituent	**Major Functions**
Water	Solvent for carrying other substances; absorbs heat
Salts (electrolytes) Sodium Potassium Calcium Magnesium Chloride Bicarbonate	Osmotic balance, pH buffering, regulation of membrane permeability
Plasma proteins Albumin	Osmotic balance, pH buffering
Fibrinogen	Clotting of blood
Globulins	Defense (antibodies) and lipid transport
Substances transported by blood Nutrients (glucose, fatty acids, amino acids, vitamins) Waste products of metabolism (urea, uric acid) Respiratory gases (O_2 and CO_2) Hormones	

Formed elements (cells) 45%		
Cell Type	**Number (per mm^3 of blood)**	**Functions**
Erythrocytes (red blood cells) 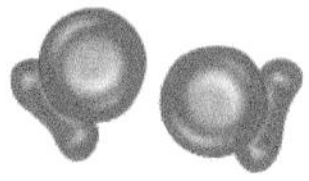	4 – 6 million	Transport oxygen and help transport carbon dioxide
Leukocytes (white blood cells) 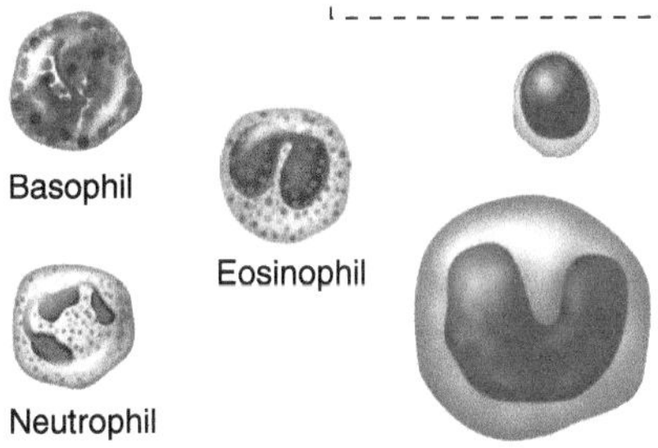 Basophil, Eosinophil, Neutrophil, Lymphocyte, Monocyte	4000 – 11,000	Defense and immunity
Platelets 	250,000 – 500,000	Blood clotting

Imagineering

FIGURE 1 The composition of blood.

ACTIVITY 1

Determining the Physical Characteristics of Plasma

Go to the general supply area and carefully pour a few milliliters of plasma into a test tube. Also obtain some wide-range pH paper, and then return to your laboratory bench to make the following simple observations.

pH of Plasma

Test the pH of the plasma with wide-range pH paper. Record

the pH observed. ____________

Color and Clarity of Plasma

Hold the test tube up to a source of natural light. Note and record its color and degree of transparency. Is it clear, translucent, or opaque?

Color ____

Degree of transparency ____________________________

TABLE 1 Summary of Formed Elements of the Blood

Cell type	Illustration	Description*	Number of cells/mm^3 (μl) of blood	Duration of development (D) and life span (LS)	Function
Erythrocytes (red blood cells, RBCs)		Biconcave, anucleate disc; salmon-colored; diameter 7–8 μm	4–6 million	D: about 15 days LS: 100–120 days	Transport oxygen and carbon dioxide
Leukocytes (white blood cells, WBCs)		Spherical, nucleated cells KNOW	4800–10,800		
• **Granulocytes** Neutrophil (most abundant)	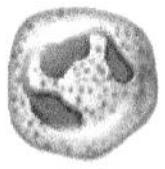	Nucleus multilobed; inconspicuous cytoplasmic granules; diameter 10–12 μm	3000–7000	D: about 14 days LS: 6 hours to a few days	Phagocytize bacteria
Eosinophil	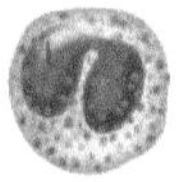	Nucleus bilobed; red cytoplasmic granules; diameter 10–14 μm	100–400	D: about 14 days LS: 8–12 days	Kill parasitic worms; destroy antigen-antibody complexes; inactivate some inflammatory chemicals of allergy
Basophil	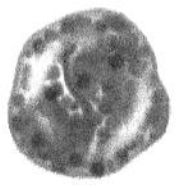	Nucleus lobed; large blue-purple cytoplasmic granules; diameter 10–14 μm	20–50	D: 1–7 days LS: ? (a few hours to a few days)	Release histamine and other mediators of inflammation; contain heparin, an anticoagulant
• **Agranulocytes** Lymphocyte		Nucleus spherical or indented; pale blue cytoplasm; diameter 5–17 μm	1500–3000	D: days to weeks LS: hours to years	Mount immune response by direct cell attack or via antibodies
Monocyte	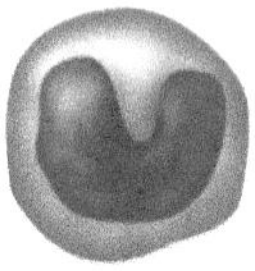	Nucleus U- or kidney-shaped; gray-blue cytoplasm; diameter 14–24 μm	100–700	D: 2–3 days LS: months	Phagocytosis; develop into macrophages in tissues
• **Platelets**	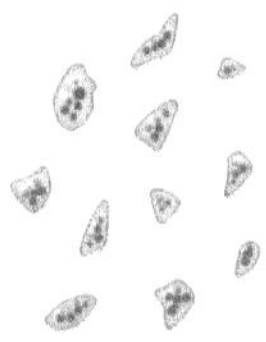	Discoid cytoplasmic fragments containing granules; stain deep purple; diameter 2–4 μm	150,000–400,000	D: 4–5 days LS: 5–10 days	Seal small tears in blood vessels; instrumental in blood clotting

*Appearance when stained with Wright's stain.

Imagineering

Consistency

While wearing gloves, dip your finger and thumb into plasma and then press them firmly together for a few seconds. Gently pull them apart. How would you describe the consistency of plasma (slippery, watery, sticky, granular)? Record your observations.

____

ACTIVITY 2

Examining the Formed Elements of Blood Microscopically

In this section, you will observe blood cells on an already prepared (purchased) blood slide or on a slide prepared from your own blood or blood provided by your instructor.

- Those using the purchased blood slide are to obtain a slide and begin their observations at step 6.

- Those testing blood provided by a biological supply source or an animal hospital are to obtain a tube of the supplied blood, disposable gloves, and the supplies listed in step 1, except for the lancets and alcohol swabs. After donning gloves, those students will go to step 3b to begin their observations.
- If you are examining your own blood, you will perform all the steps described below *except* step 3b.

1. Obtain two glass slides, a glass stirring rod, dropper bottles of Wright's stain and distilled water, two or three lancets, cotton balls, and alcohol swabs. Bring this equipment to the laboratory bench. Clean the slides thoroughly and dry them.
2. Open the alcohol swab packet and scrub your third or fourth finger with the swab. (Because the pricked finger may be a little sore later, it is better to prepare a finger on the hand used less often.) Circumduct your hand (swing it in a cone-shaped path) for 10 to 15 seconds. This will dry the alcohol and cause your fingers to become engorged with blood. Then, open the lancet packet and grasp the lancet by its blunt end. Quickly jab the pointed end into the prepared finger to produce a free flow of blood. It is *not* a good idea to squeeze or "milk" the finger, as this forces out tissue fluid as well as blood. If the blood is not flowing freely, another puncture should be made.

! *Under no circumstances is a lancet to be used for more than one puncture.* Dispose of the lancets in the designated disposal container immediately after use.

3a. With a cotton ball, wipe away the first drop of blood; then allow another large drop of blood to form. Touch the blood to one of the cleaned slides approximately 1.3 cm, or ½ inch, from the end. Then quickly (to prevent clotting) use the second slide to form a blood smear as shown in Figure 2. When properly prepared, the blood smear is uniformly thin. If the blood smear appears streaked, the blood probably began to clot or coagulate before the smear was made, and another slide should be prepared. Continue at step 4.

3b. Dip a glass rod in the blood provided, and transfer a generous drop of blood to the end of a cleaned microscope slide. For the time being, lay the glass rod on a paper towel on the bench. Then, as described in step 3a and Figure 2, use the second slide to make your blood smear.

4. Dry the slide by waving it in the air. When it is completely dry, it will look dull. Place it on a paper towel, and flood it with Wright's stain. Count the number of drops of stain used. Allow the stain to remain on the slide for 3 to 4 minutes, and then flood the slide with an equal number of drops of distilled water. Allow the water and Wright's stain mixture to remain on the slide for 4 or 5 minutes or until a metallic green film or scum is apparent on the fluid surface. Blow on the slide gently every minute or so to keep the water and stain mixed during this interval.
5. Rinse the slide with a stream of distilled water. Then flood it with distilled water, and allow it to lie flat until the slide becomes translucent and takes on a pink cast.

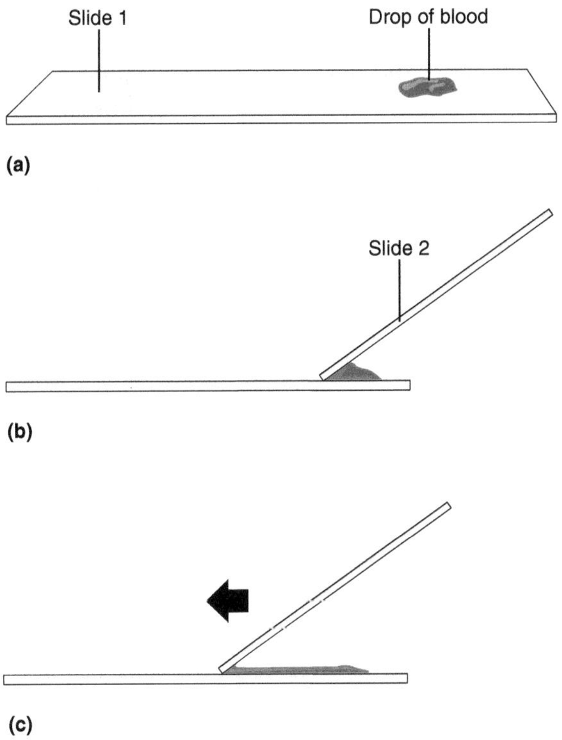

Precision Graphics

FIGURE 2 Procedure for making a blood smear. (**a**) Place a drop of blood on slide 1 approximately ½ inch from one end. (**b**) Hold slide 2 at a 30° to 40° angle to slide 1 (it should touch the drop of blood) and allow blood to spread along entire bottom edge of angled slide. (**c**) Smoothly advance slide 2 to end of slide 1 (blood should run out before reaching the end of slide 1). Then lift slide 2 away from slide 1 and place it on a paper towel.

Then stand the slide on its long edge on the paper towel, and allow it to dry completely. Once the slide is dry, you can begin your observations.

6. Obtain a microscope and scan the slide under low power to find the area where the blood smear is the thinnest. After scanning the slide in low power to find the areas with the largest numbers of nucleated WBCs, read the following descriptions of cell types, and find each one on Figure 1 and Table 1. Then, switch to the oil immersion lens, and observe the slide carefully to identify each cell type.
7. Set your prepared slide aside for use in Activity 3.

Erythrocytes

Erythrocytes, or red blood cells, which average 7.5 μm in diameter, vary in color from a salmon red color to pale pink, depending on the effectiveness of the stain. They have a distinctive biconcave disc shape and appear paler in the center than at the edge.

As you observe the slide, notice that the red blood cells are by far the most numerous blood cells seen in the field. Their number averages 4.5 million to 5.5 million cells per cubic millimeter of blood (for women and men, respectively).

Red blood cells differ from the other blood cells because they are anucleate when mature and circulating in the blood. As a result, they are unable to reproduce or repair damage and have a limited life span of 100 to 120 days, after which they begin to fragment and are destroyed in the spleen and other reticuloendothelial tissues of the body.

In various anemias, the red blood cells may appear pale (an indication of decreased hemoglobin content) or may be nucleated (an indication that the bone marrow is turning out cells prematurely). ●

Leukocytes

Leukocytes, or white blood cells, are nucleated cells that are formed in the bone marrow from the same stem cells (*hemocytoblast*) as red blood cells. They are much less numerous than the red blood cells, averaging from 4800 to 10,800 cells per cubic millimeter. Basically, white blood cells are protective, pathogen-destroying cells that are transported to all parts of the body in the blood or lymph. Important to their protective function is their ability to move in and out of blood vessels, a process called **diapedesis,** and to wander through body tissues by **amoeboid motion** to reach sites of inflammation or tissue destruction. They are classified into two major groups, depending on whether or not they contain conspicuous granules in their cytoplasm.

Granulocytes make up the first group. The granules in their cytoplasm stain differentially with Wright's stain, and they have peculiarly lobed nuclei, which often consist of expanded nuclear regions connected by thin strands of nucleoplasm. There are three types of granulocytes:

Neutrophil: The most abundant of the white blood cells (40% to 70% of the leukocyte population); nucleus consists of 3 to 7 lobes and the pale lilac cytoplasm contains fine cytoplasmic granules, which are generally indistinguishable and take up both the acidic (red) and basic (blue) dyes (*neutrophil* = neutral loving); functions as an active phagocyte. The number of neutrophils increases exponentially during acute infections.

Eosinophil: Represents 2% to 4% of the leukocyte population; nucleus is generally figure-8 or bilobed in shape; contains large cytoplasmic granules (elaborate lysosomes) that stain red-orange with the acid dyes in Wright's stain. Eosinophils are about the size of neutrophils and play a role in counterattacking parasitic worms. They also lessen allergy attacks by phagocytizing antigen-antibody complexes and inactivating some inflammatory chemicals.

Basophil: Least abundant leukocyte type representing less than 1% of the population; large U- or S-shaped nucleus with two or more indentations. Cytoplasm contains coarse, sparse granules that are stained deep purple by the basic dyes in Wright's stain. The granules contain several chemicals, including histamine, a vasodilator which is discharged on exposure to antigens and helps mediate the inflammatory response. Basophils are about the size of neutrophils.

The second group, **agranulocytes,** or **agranular leukocytes,** contains no *visible* cytoplasmic granules. Although found in the bloodstream, they are much more abundant in lymphoid tissues. Their nuclei tend to be closer to the norm, that is, spherical, oval, or kidney-shaped. Specific characteristics of the two types of agranulocytes are listed below.

Lymphocyte: The smallest of the leukocytes, approximately the size of a red blood cell. The nucleus stains dark blue to purple, is generally spherical or slightly indented, and accounts for most of the cell mass. Sparse cytoplasm appears as a thin blue rim around the nucleus. Concerned with immunologic responses in the body; one population, the *B lymphocytes,* oversees the production of antibodies that are released to blood. The second population, *T lymphocytes,* plays a regulatory role and destroys grafts, tumors, and virus-infected cells. Represents 25% or more of the WBC population.

Monocyte: The largest of the leukocytes; approximately twice the size of red blood cells. Represents 3% to 8% of the leukocyte population. Dark blue nucleus is generally kidney-shaped; abundant cytoplasm stains gray-blue. Once in the tissues, monocytes convert to macrophages, active phagocytes (the "long-term cleanup team"), increasing dramatically in number during chronic infections such as tuberculosis.

Students are often asked to list the leukocytes in order from the most abundant to the least abundant. The following silly phrase may help you with this task: *N*ever *l*et *m*onkeys *e*at *b*ananas (neutrophils, lymphocytes, monocytes, eosinophils, basophils).

Platelets

Platelets are cell fragments of large multinucleate cells (**megakaryocytes**) formed in the bone marrow. They appear as darkly staining, irregularly shaped bodies interspersed among the blood cells. The normal platelet count in blood ranges from 150,000 to 400,000 per cubic millimeter. Platelets are instrumental in the clotting process that occurs in plasma when blood vessels are ruptured.

After you have identified these cell types on your slide, observe charts and three-dimensional models of blood cells if these are available. Do not dispose of your slide, as it will be used later for the differential white blood cell count.

Hematologic Tests

When someone enters a hospital as a patient, several hematologic tests are routinely done to determine general level of health as well as the presence of pathologic conditions. You will be conducting the most common of these tests in this exercise.

! Materials such as cotton balls, lancets, and alcohol swabs are used in nearly all of the following diagnostic tests. These supplies are at the general supply area and should be properly disposed of (glassware to the bleach bucket, lancets in a designated disposal container, and disposable items to the autoclave bag) immediately after use.

Other necessary supplies and equipment are at specific supply areas marked according to the test with which they are used. Since nearly all of the tests require a finger stab, if you will be using your own blood it might be wise to quickly read through the tests to determine in which instances more than one preparation can be done from the same finger stab. A little planning will save you the discomfort of a multiple-punctured finger.

An alternative to using blood obtained from the finger stab technique is using heparinized blood samples supplied by your instructor. The purpose of using heparinized tubes is to prevent the blood from clotting. Thus blood collected and stored in such tubes will be suitable for all tests except coagulation time testing.

Total White and Red Blood Cell Counts

A **total WBC count** or **total RBC count** determines the total number of that cell type per unit volume of blood. Total WBC and RBC counts are a routine part of any physical exam. Most clinical agencies use computers to conduct these counts. Since the hand counting technique typically done in college labs is rather outdated, total RBC and WBC counts will not be done here, but the importance of such counts (both normal and abnormal values) is briefly described below.

Total White Blood Cell Count Since white blood cells are an important part of the body's defense system, it is essential to note any abnormalities in them.

Leukocytosis, an abnormally high WBC count, may indicate bacterial or viral infection, metabolic disease, hemorrhage, or poisoning by drugs or chemicals. A decrease in the white cell number below 4000/mm^3 (**leukopenia**) may indicate typhoid fever, measles, infectious hepatitis or cirrhosis, tuberculosis, or excessive antibiotic or X-ray therapy. A person with leukopenia lacks the usual protective mechanisms. **Leukemia,** a malignant disorder of the lymphoid tissues characterized by uncontrolled proliferation of abnormal WBCs accompanied by a reduction in the number of RBCs and platelets, is detectable not only by a total WBC count but also by a differential WBC count. ●

Total Red Blood Cell Count Since RBCs are absolutely necessary for oxygen transport, a doctor typically investigates any excessive change in their number immediately.

An increase in the number of RBCs (**polycythemia**) may result from bone marrow cancer or from living at high altitudes where less oxygen is available. A decrease in the number of RBCs results in anemia. (The term **anemia** simply indicates a decreased oxygen-carrying capacity of blood that may result from a decrease in RBC number or size or a decreased hemoglobin content of the RBCs.) A decrease in RBCs may result suddenly from hemorrhage or more gradually from conditions that destroy RBCs or hinder RBC production. ●

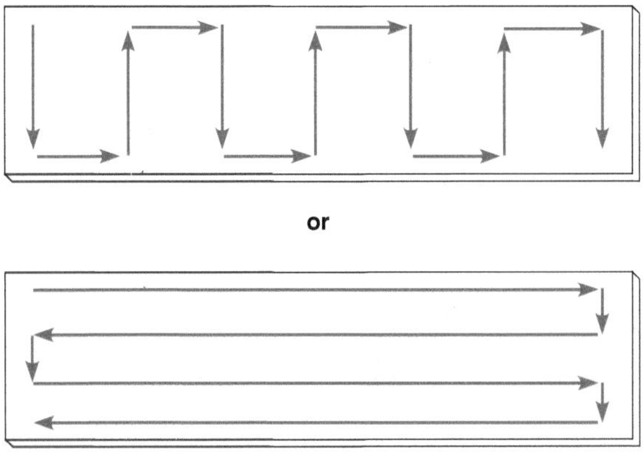

Precision Graphics

FIGURE 3 **Alternative methods of moving the slide for a differential WBC count.**

Differential White Blood Cell Count

To make a **differential white blood cell count,** 100 WBCs are counted and classified according to type. Such a count is routine in a physical examination and in diagnosing illness, since any abnormality or significant elevation in percentages of WBC types may indicate a problem or the source of pathology.

ACTIVITY 3

Conducting a Differential WBC Count

1. Use the slide prepared for the identification of the blood cells in Activity 2. Begin at the edge of the smear and move the slide in a systematic manner on the microscope stage—either up and down or from side to side as indicated in Figure 3.

2. Record each type of white blood cell you observe by making a count in the first blank column of the chart at the top of the next page (for example, 卌|| = 7 cells) until you have observed and recorded a total of 100 WBCs. Using the following equation, compute the percentage of each WBC type counted, and record the percentages on the Hematologic Test Data Sheet on the next page.

$$\text{Percent (\%)} = \frac{\text{\# observed}}{\text{Total \# counted (100)}} \times 100$$

3. Select a slide marked "Unknown sample," record the slide number, and use the count chart on the next page to conduct a differential count. Record the percentages on the data sheet at the bottom of the next page.

How does the differential count from the unknown sample slide compare to a normal count?

____

____

Count of 100 WBCs

Cell type	Number observed: Student blood smear	Number observed: Unknown sample # ___
Neutrophils		
Eosinophils		
Basophils		
Lymphocytes		
Monocytes		

Using the text and other references, try to determine the blood pathology on the unknown slide. Defend your answer.

____

____

4. How does your differential white blood cell count correlate with the percentages given earlier?

____

Hematocrit

The **hematocrit,** or **packed cell volume (PCV),** is routinely determined when anemia is suspected. Centrifuging whole blood spins the formed elements to the bottom of the tube, with plasma forming the top layer (see Figure 1). Since the blood cell population is primarily RBCs, the PCV is generally considered equivalent to the RBC volume, and this is the only value reported. However, the relative percentage of WBCs can be differentiated, and both WBC and plasma volume will be reported here. Normal hematocrit values for the male and female, respectively, are 47.0 ± 7 and 42.0 ± 5.

ACTIVITY 4

Determining the Hematocrit

The hematocrit is determined by the micromethod, so only a drop of blood is needed. If possible (and the centrifuge allows), all members of the class should prepare their capillary tubes at the same time so the centrifuge can be run only once.

1. Obtain two heparinized capillary tubes, capillary tube sealer or modeling clay, a lancet, alcohol swabs, and some cotton balls.

2. If you are using your own blood, cleanse a finger, and allow the blood to flow freely. Wipe away the first few drops

Hematologic Test Data Sheet

Differential WBC count:

WBC	Student blood smear	Unknown sample # ___
% neutrophils	________	________
% eosinophils	________	________
% basophils	________	________
% monocytes	________	________
% lymphocytes	________	________

Hematocrit (PCV):

RBC ________ % of blood volume

WBC ________ % of blood volume } not generally

Plasma ________ % of blood } reported

Hemoglobin (Hb) content:

Tallquist method: ______ g/100 ml of blood; ______ % Hb

Hemoglobinometer (type: ____________________)

________ g/100 ml of blood; ________ %Hb

Ratio (PCV to grams of Hb per 100 ml of blood): ______

Coagulation time ______

Blood typing:

ABO group ______ Rh factor ______

Cholesterol concentration ______ mg/dl of blood

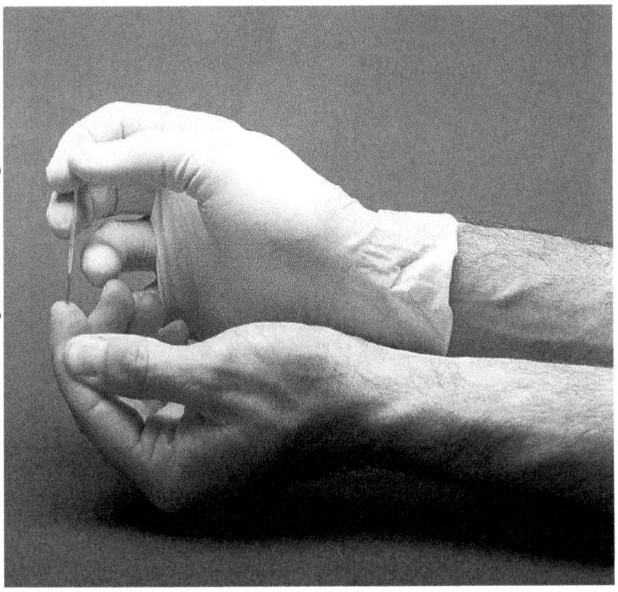

Elena Dorfman, Pearson Benjamin Cummings

(a)

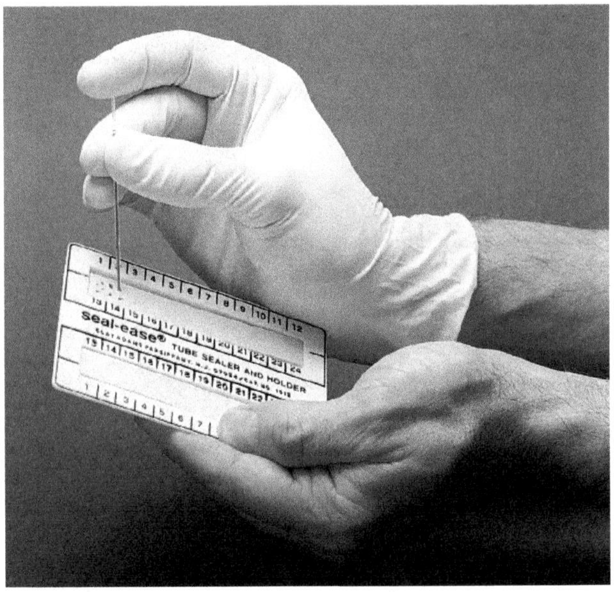

Elena Dorfman, Pearson Benjamin Cummings

(b)

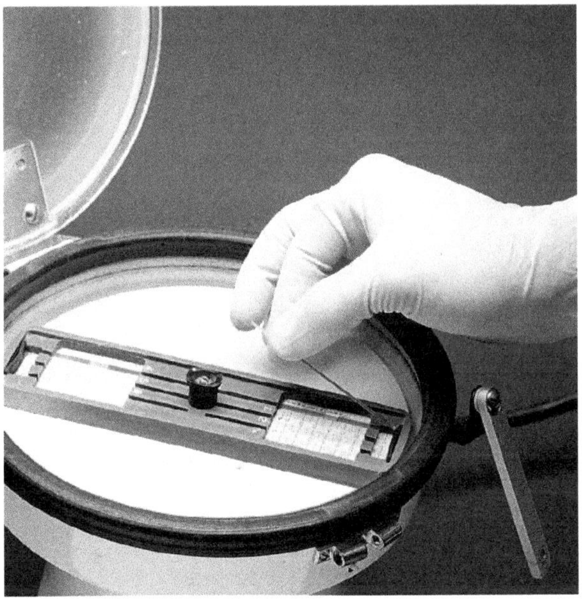

Elena Dorfman, Pearson Benjamin Cummings

(c)

FIGURE 4 **Steps in a hematocrit determination.** (**a**) Load a heparinized capillary tube with blood. (**b**) Plug the blood-containing end of the tube with clay. (**c**) Place the tube in a microhematocrit centrifuge. (Centrifuge must be balanced.)

and, holding the red-line-marked end of the capillary tube to the blood drop, allow the tube to fill at least three-fourths full by capillary action (Figure 4a). If the blood is not flowing freely, the end of the capillary tube will not be completely submerged in the blood during filling, air will enter, and you will have to prepare another sample.

If you are using instructor-provided blood, simply immerse the red-marked end of the capillary tube in the blood sample and fill it three-quarters full as just described.

3. Plug the blood-containing end by pressing it into the capillary tube sealer or clay (Figure 4b). Prepare a second tube in the same manner.

4. Place the prepared tubes opposite one another in the radial grooves of the microhematocrit centrifuge with the sealed ends abutting the rubber gasket at the centrifuge periphery (Figure 4c). This loading procedure balances the centrifuge and prevents blood from spraying everywhere by centrifugal force. *Make a note of the numbers of the grooves your tubes are in.* When all the tubes have been loaded, make sure the centrifuge is properly balanced, and secure the centrifuge cover. Turn the centrifuge on, and set the timer for 4 or 5 minutes.

5. Determine the percentage of RBCs, WBCs, and plasma by using the microhematocrit reader. The RBCs are the bottom layer, the plasma is the top layer, and the WBCs are the buff-colored layer between the two. If the reader is not available, use a millimeter ruler to measure the length of the filled capillary tube occupied by each element, and compute its percentage by using the following formula:

$$\frac{\text{Height of the column composed of the element (mm)}}{\text{Height of the original column of whole blood (mm)}} \times 100$$

Record your calculations below and on the data sheet on the previous page.

% RBC ________ % WBC ________ % plasma ________

Usually WBCs constitute 1% of the total blood volume. How do your blood values compare to this figure and to the normal percentages for RBCs and plasma?

____

As a rule, a hematocrit is considered a more accurate test than the total RBC count for determining the RBC composition of the blood. A hematocrit within the normal range generally

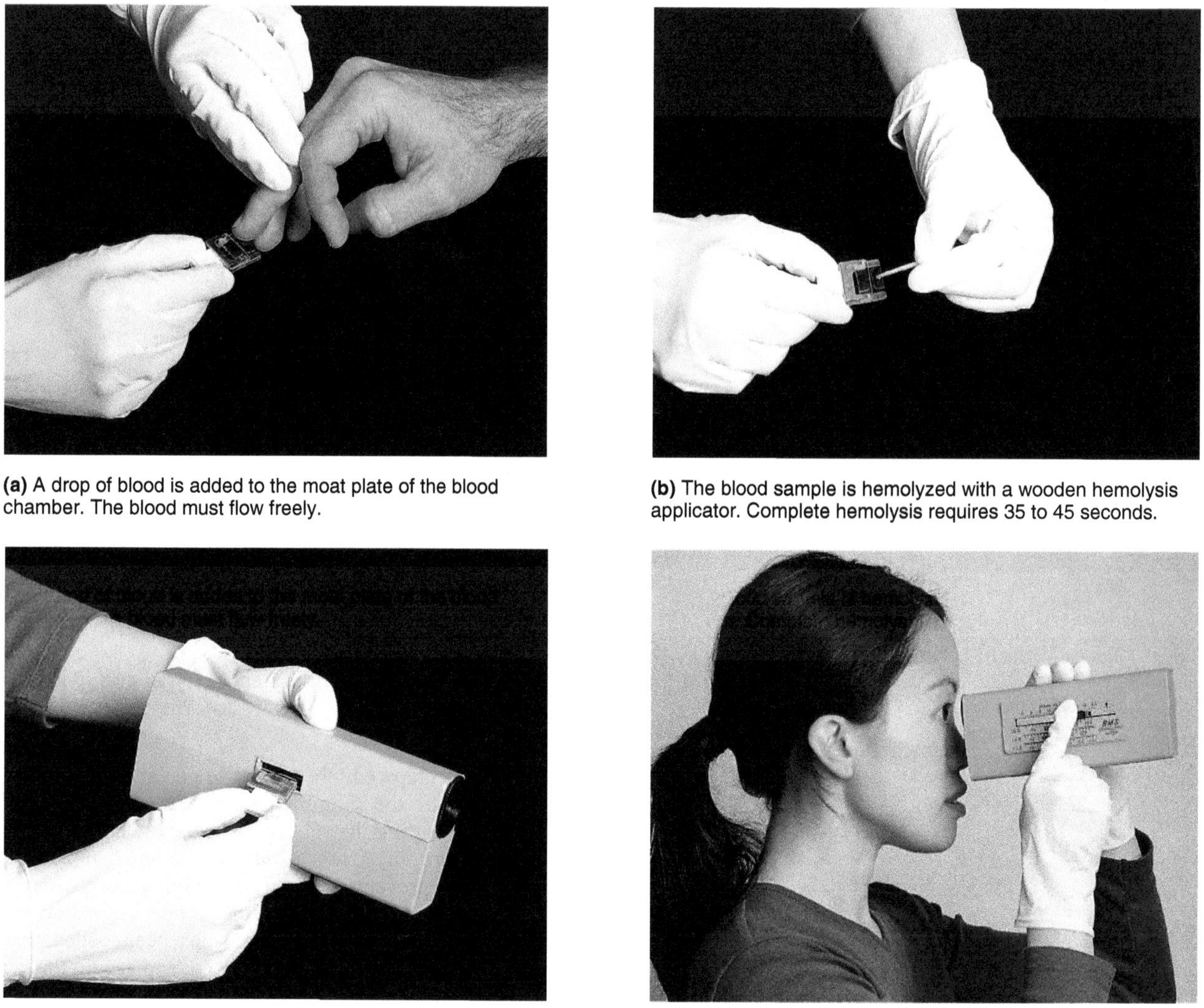

(a) A drop of blood is added to the moat plate of the blood chamber. The blood must flow freely.

(b) The blood sample is hemolyzed with a wooden hemolysis applicator. Complete hemolysis requires 35 to 45 seconds.

(c) The charged blood chamber is inserted into the slot on the side of the hemoglobinometer.

(d) The colors of the green split screen are found by moving the slide with the right index finger. When the two colors match in density, the grams/100 ml and % Hb are read on the scale.

Elena Dorfman, Pearson Benjamin Cummings
Elena Dorfman, Pearson Benjamin Cummings
Elena Dorfman, Pearson Benjamin Cummings

FIGURE 5 Hemoglobin determination using a hemoglobinometer.

indicates a normal RBC number, whereas an abnormally high or low hematocrit is cause for concern. ■

Hemoglobin Concentration

As noted earlier, a person can be anemic even with a normal RBC count. Since hemoglobin (Hb) is the RBC protein responsible for oxygen transport, perhaps the most accurate way of measuring the oxygen-carrying capacity of the blood is to determine its hemoglobin content. Oxygen, which combines reversibly with the heme (iron-containing portion) of the hemoglobin molecule, is picked up by the blood cells in the lungs and unloaded in the tissues. Thus, the more hemoglobin molecules the RBCs contain, the more oxygen they will be able to transport. Normal blood contains 12 to 18 g of hemoglobin per 100 ml of blood. Hemoglobin content in men is slightly higher (13 to 18 g) than in women (12 to 16 g).

ACTIVITY 5

Determining Hemoglobin Concentration

Several techniques have been developed to estimate the hemoglobin content of blood, ranging from the old, rather inaccurate Tallquist method to expensive colorimeters, which are precisely calibrated and yield highly accurate results. Directions for both the Tallquist method and a hemoglobinometer are provided here.

Tallquist Method

1. Obtain a Tallquist hemoglobin scale, test paper, lancets, alcohol swabs, and cotton balls.

2. Use instructor-provided blood or prepare the finger as previously described. (For best results, make sure the alcohol

evaporates before puncturing your finger.) Place one good-sized drop of blood on the special absorbent paper provided with the color scale. The blood stain should be larger than the holes on the color scale.

3. As soon as the blood has dried and loses its glossy appearance, match its color, under natural light, with the color standards by moving the specimen under the comparison scale so that the blood stain appears at all the various apertures. (The blood should not be allowed to dry to a brown color, as this will result in an inaccurate reading.) Because the colors on the scale represent 1% variations in hemoglobin content, it may be necessary to estimate the percentage if the color of your blood sample is intermediate between two color standards.

4. On the data sheet, record your results as the percentage of hemoglobin concentration and as grams per 100 ml of blood.

Hemoglobinometer Determination

1. Obtain a hemoglobinometer, hemolysis applicator, alcohol swab, and lens paper, and bring them to your bench. Test the hemoglobinometer light source to make sure it is working; if not, request new batteries before proceeding and test it again.

2. Remove the blood chamber from the slot in the side of the hemoglobinometer and disassemble the blood chamber by separating the glass plates from the metal clip. Notice as you do this that the larger glass plate has an H-shaped depression cut into it that acts as a moat to hold the blood, whereas the smaller glass piece is flat and serves as a coverslip.

3. Clean the glass plates with an alcohol swab, and then wipe them dry with lens paper. Hold the plates by their sides to prevent smearing during the wiping process.

4. Reassemble the blood chamber (remember: larger glass piece on the bottom with the moat up), but leave the moat plate about halfway out to provide adequate exposed surface to charge it with blood.

5. Obtain a drop of blood (from the provided sample or from your fingertip as before), and place it on the depressed area of the moat plate that is closest to you (Figure 5a).

6. Using the wooden hemolysis applicator, stir or agitate the blood to rupture (lyse) the RBCs (Figure 5b). This usually takes 35 to 45 seconds. Hemolysis is complete when the blood appears transparent rather than cloudy.

7. Push the blood-containing glass plate all the way into the metal clip and then firmly insert the charged blood chamber back into the slot on the side of the instrument (Figure 5c).

8. Hold the hemoglobinometer in your left hand with your left thumb resting on the light switch located on the underside of the instrument. Look into the eyepiece and notice that there is a green area divided into two halves (a split field).

9. With the index finger of your right hand, slowly move the slide on the right side of the hemoglobinometer back and forth until the two halves of the green field match (Figure 5d).

10. Note and record on the data sheet the grams of Hb (hemoglobin)/100 ml of blood indicated on the uppermost scale by the index mark on the slide. Also record % Hb, indicated by one of the lower scales.

11. Disassemble the blood chamber once again, and carefully place its parts (glass plates and clip) into a bleach-containing beaker.

Generally speaking, the relationship between the PCV and grams of hemoglobin per 100 ml of blood is 3:1—for example, a PCV of 35 with 12 g of Hb per 100 ml of blood is a ratio of 3:1. How do your values compare?

____

Record on the data sheet the value obtained from your data.

Bleeding Time

Normally a sharp prick of the finger or earlobe results in bleeding that lasts from 2 to 7 minutes (Ivy method) or 0 to 5 minutes (Duke method), although other factors such as altitude affect the time. How long the bleeding lasts is referred to as **bleeding time** and tests the ability of platelets to stop bleeding in capillaries and small vessels. Absence of some clotting factors may affect bleeding time, but prolonged bleeding time is most often associated with deficient or abnormal platelets.

Coagulation Time

Blood clotting, or **coagulation,** is a protective mechanism that minimizes blood loss when blood vessels are ruptured. This process requires the interaction of many substances normally present in the plasma (clotting factors, or procoagulants) as well as some released by platelets and injured tissues. Basically hemostasis proceeds as follows (Figure 6a): The injured tissues and platelets release **tissue factor (TF)** and **PF_3** respectively, which trigger the clotting mechanism, or cascade. Tissue factor and PF_3 interact with other blood protein clotting factors and calcium ions to form **prothrombin activator,** which in turn converts **prothrombin** (present in plasma) to **thrombin.** Thrombin then acts enzymatically to polymerize the soluble **fibrinogen** proteins (present in plasma) into insoluble **fibrin,** which forms a meshwork of strands that traps the RBCs and forms the basis of the clot (Figure 6b). Normally, blood removed from the body clots within 2 to 6 minutes.

ACTIVITY 6

Determining Coagulation Time

1. Obtain a *nonheparinized* capillary tube, a timer (or watch), a lancet, cotton balls, a triangular file, and alcohol swabs.

2. Clean and prick the finger to produce a free flow of blood. Discard the lancet in the disposal container.

3. Place one end of the capillary tube in the blood drop, and hold the opposite end at a lower level to collect the sample.

4. Lay the capillary tube on a paper towel.

Record the time. ________________

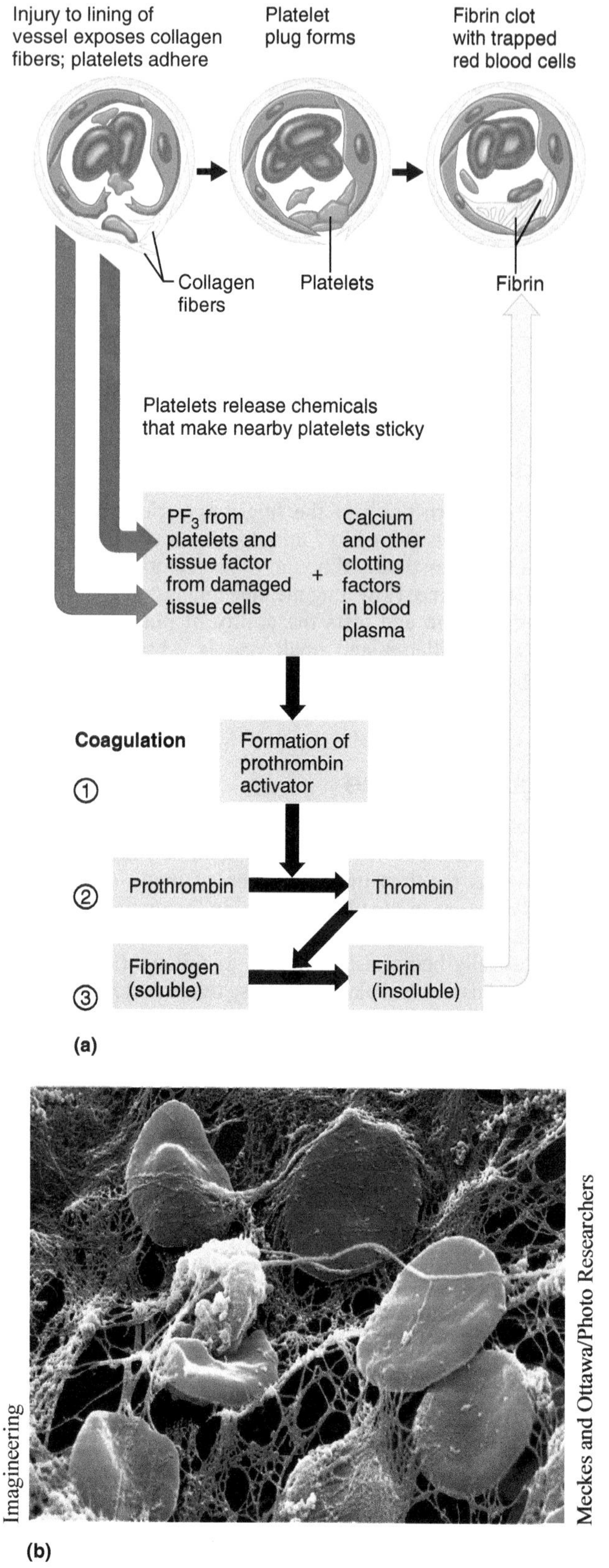

Injury to lining of vessel exposes collagen fibers; platelets adhere
Platelet plug forms
Fibrin clot with trapped red blood cells
Collagen fibers
Platelets
Fibrin
Platelets release chemicals that make nearby platelets sticky
PF3 from platelets and tissue factor from damaged tissue cells
+
Calcium and other clotting factors in blood plasma
Coagulation
Formation of prothrombin activator
①
②
Prothrombin
Thrombin
③
Fibrinogen (soluble)
Fibrin (insoluble)
(a)
Imagineering
Meckes and Ottawa/Photo Researchers
(b)

FIGURE 6 **Events of hemostasis and blood clotting.** (**a**) Simple schematic of events. Steps numbered 1–3 represent the major events of coagulation. (**b**) Photomicrograph of RBCs trapped in a fibrin mesh (3400x).

5. At 30-second intervals, make a small nick on the tube close to one end with the triangular file, and then carefully break the tube. Slowly separate the ends to see if a gel-like thread of fibrin spans the gap. When this occurs, record below and on the data sheet the time for coagulation to occur. Are your results within the normal time range?

____

6. Put used supplies in the autoclave bag and broken capillary tubes into the sharps container.

Blood Typing

Blood typing is a system of blood classification based on the presence of specific glycoproteins on the outer surface of the RBC plasma membrane. Such proteins are called **antigens,** or **agglutinogens,** and are genetically determined. In many cases, these antigens are accompanied by plasma proteins, **antibodies** or **agglutinins,** that react with RBCs bearing different antigens, causing them to be clumped, agglutinated, and eventually hemolyzed. It is because of this phenomenon that a person's blood must be carefully typed before a whole blood or packed cell transfusion.

Several blood typing systems exist, based on the various possible antigens, but the factors routinely typed for are antigens of the ABO and Rh blood groups which are most commonly involved in transfusion reactions. Other blood factors, such as Kell, Lewis, M, and N, are not routinely typed for unless the individual will require multiple transfusions. The basis of the ABO typing is shown in Table 2.

Individuals whose red blood cells carry the Rh antigen are Rh positive (approximately 85% of the U.S. population); those lacking the antigen are Rh negative. Unlike ABO blood groups, neither the blood of the Rh-positive (Rh^+) nor Rh-negative (Rh^-) individuals carries preformed anti-Rh antibodies. This is understandable in the case of the Rh-positive individual. However, Rh-negative persons who receive transfusions of Rh-positive blood become sensitized by the Rh antigens of the donor RBCs, and their systems begin to produce anti-Rh antibodies. On subsequent exposures to Rh-positive blood, typical transfusion reactions occur, resulting in the clumping and hemolysis of the donor blood cells.

Although the blood of dogs and other mammals does react with some of the human agglutinins (present in the antisera), the reaction is not as pronounced and varies with the animal blood used. Hence, the most accurate and predictable blood typing results are obtained with human blood. The artificial blood kit does not use any body fluids and produces results similar to but not identical to results for human blood.

ACTIVITY 7

Typing for ABO and Rh Blood Groups

Blood may be typed on glass slides or using blood test cards. Each method is described in this activity.

Typing Blood Using Glass Slides

1. Obtain two clean microscope slides, a wax marking pencil, anti-A, anti-B, and anti-Rh typing sera, toothpicks, lancets, alcohol swabs, medicine dropper, and the Rh typing box.

TABLE 2 ABO Blood Typing

ABO blood type	Antigens present on RBC membranes	Antibodies present in plasma	% of U.S. population White	Black	Asian
A	A	Anti-B	40	27	28
B	B	Anti-A	11	20	27
AB	A and B	None	4	4	5
O	Neither	Anti-A and anti-B	45	49	40

2. Divide slide 1 into halves with the wax marking pencil. Label the lower left-hand corner "anti-A" and the lower right-hand corner "anti-B." Mark the bottom of slide 2 "anti-Rh."

3. Place one drop of anti-A serum on the *left* side of slide 1. Place one drop of anti-B serum on the *right* side of slide 1. Place one drop of anti-Rh serum in the center of slide 2.

4. If you are using your own blood, cleanse your finger with an alcohol swab, pierce the finger with a lancet, and wipe away the first drop of blood. Obtain 3 drops of freely flowing blood, placing one drop on each side of slide 1 and a drop on slide 2. Immediately dispose of the lancet in a designated disposal container.

If using instructor-provided animal blood or EDTA-treated red cells, use a medicine dropper to place one drop of blood on each side of slide 1 and a drop of blood on slide 2.

Blood Typing

Result	Observed (+)	Not observed (−)
Presence of clumping with anti-A		
Presence of clumping with anti-B		
Presence of clumping with anti-Rh		

! 5. Quickly mix each blood-antiserum sample with a *fresh* toothpick. Then dispose of the toothpicks and used alcohol swab in the autoclave bag.

6. Place slide 2 on the Rh typing box and rock gently back and forth. (A slightly higher temperature is required for precise Rh typing than for ABO typing.)

7. After 2 minutes, observe all three blood samples for evidence of clumping. The agglutination that occurs in the positive test for the Rh factor is very fine and difficult to perceive; thus if there is any question, observe the slide under the microscope. Record your observations in the Blood Typing chart.

8. Interpret your ABO results in light of the information in Figure 7. If clumping was observed on slide 2, you are Rh positive. If not, you are Rh negative.

9. Record your blood type on the data sheet.

10. Put the used slides in the bleach-containing bucket at the general supply area; put disposable supplies in the autoclave bag.

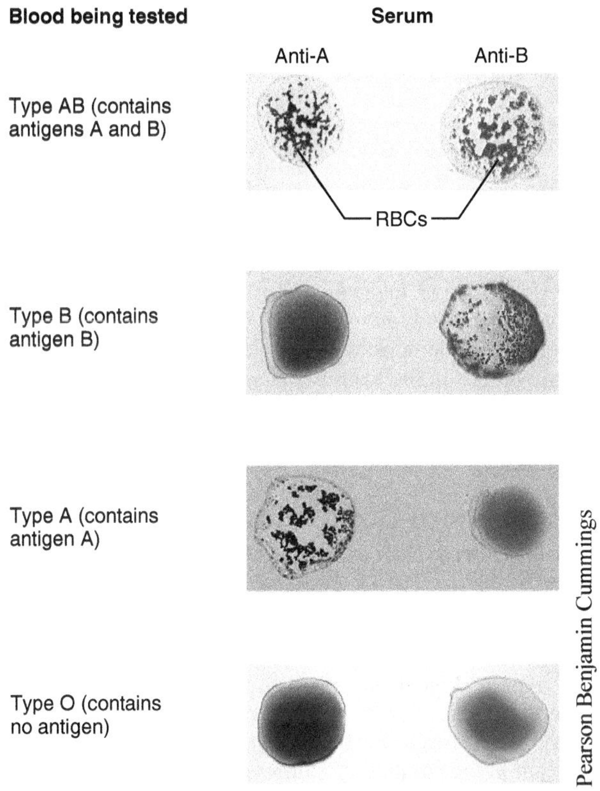

FIGURE 7 Blood typing of ABO blood types. When serum containing anti-A or anti-B antibodies (agglutinins) is added to a blood sample, agglutination will occur between the antibody and the corresponding antigen (agglutinogen A or B). As illustrated, agglutination occurs with both sera in blood group AB, with anti-B serum in blood group B, with anti-A serum in blood group A, and with neither serum in blood group O.

Using Blood Typing Cards

1. Obtain a blood typing card marked A, B, and Rh, dropper bottles of anti-A serum, anti-B serum, and anti-Rh serum, toothpicks, lancets, and alcohol swabs.

2. Place a drop of anti-A serum in the spot marked anti-A, place a drop of anti-B serum on the spot marked anti-B, and place a drop of anti-Rh serum on the spot marked anti-Rh (or anti-D).

3. Carefully add a drop of blood to each of the spots marked "Blood" on the card. If you are using your own blood, refer to step 4 in the Activity 7 section Typing Blood Using Glass Slides. Immediately discard the lancet in the designated disposal container.

4. Using a new toothpick for each test, mix the blood sample with the antibody. Dispose of the toothpicks appropriately.

5. Gently rock the card to allow the blood and antibodies to mix.

6. After 2 minutes, observe the card for evidence of clumping. The Rh clumping is very fine and may be difficult to observe. Record your observations in the Blood Typing chart. Use Figure 7 to interpret your results.

7. Record your blood type on the chart and discard the card in an autoclave bag.

ACTIVITY 8

Observing Demonstration Slides

Before continuing on to the cholesterol determination, take the time to look at the slides of *macrocytic hypochromic anemia, microcytic hypochromic anemia, sickle cell anemia, lymphocytic leukemia* (chronic), and *eosinophilia* that have been put on demonstration by your instructor. Record your observations in the appropriate section of the Review Sheet. You can refer to your notes, the text, and other references later to respond to questions about the blood pathologies represented on the slides.

Cholesterol Concentration in Plasma

Atherosclerosis is the disease process in which the body's blood vessels become increasingly occluded by plaques. Because the plaques narrow the arteries, they can contribute to hypertensive heart disease. They also serve as focal points for the formation of blood clots (thrombi), which may break away and block smaller vessels farther downstream in the circulatory pathway and cause heart attacks or strokes.

Ever since medical clinicians discovered that cholesterol is a major component of the smooth muscle plaques formed during atherosclerosis, it has had a bad press. Today, virtually no physical examination of an adult is considered complete until cholesterol levels are assessed along with other lifestyle risk factors. A normal value for plasma cholesterol in adults ranges from 130 to 200 mg per 100 ml of plasma; you will use blood to make such a determination.

Although the total plasma cholesterol concentration is valuable information, it may be misleading, particularly if a person's high-density lipoprotein (HDL) level is high and low-density lipoprotein (LDL) level is relatively low. Cholesterol, being water insoluble, is transported in the blood complexed to lipoproteins. In general, cholesterol bound into HDLs is destined to be degraded by the liver and then eliminated from the body, whereas that forming part of the LDLs is "traveling" to the body's tissue cells. When LDL levels are excessive, cholesterol is deposited in the blood vessel walls; hence, LDLs are considered to carry the "bad" cholesterol.

ACTIVITY 9

Measuring Plasma Cholesterol Concentration

1. Go to the appropriate supply area, and obtain a cholesterol test card and color scale, lancet, and alcohol swab.

2. Clean your fingertip with the alcohol swab, allow it to dry, then prick it with a lancet. Place a drop of blood on the test area of the card. Put the lancet in the designated disposal container.

3. After 3 minutes, remove the blood sample strip from the card and discard in the autoclave bag.

4. Analyze the underlying test spot, using the included color scale. Record the cholesterol level below and on the data sheet.

Cholesterol level __________ mg/dl

! 5. Before leaving the laboratory, use the spray bottle of bleach solution and saturate a paper towel to thoroughly wash down your laboratory bench.

NAME ______________________________

LAB TIME/DATE ______________________

Blood

Composition of Blood

1. What is the blood volume of an average-size adult male? __________ liters An average adult female? __________ liters

2. What determines whether blood is bright red or a dull brick-red? ______________________________

____

3. Use the key to identify the cell type(s) or blood elements that fit the following descriptive statements.

Key:

a. red blood cell	d. basophil	g. lymphocyte
b. megakaryocyte	e. monocyte	h. formed elements
c. eosinophil	f. neutrophil	i. plasma

______________ 1. most numerous leukocyte

______________, ______________, and ______________ 2. granulocytes (3)

______________ 3. also called an erythrocyte; anucleate formed element

______________, ______________ 4. actively phagocytic leukocytes

______________, ______________ 5. agranulocytes

______________ 6. ancestral cell of platelets

______________ 7. (a) through (g) are all examples of these

______________ 8. number rises during parasite infections

______________ 9. releases histamine; promotes inflammation

______________ 10. many formed in lymphoid tissue

______________ 11. transports oxygen

______________ 12. primarily water, noncellular; the fluid matrix of blood

______________ 13. increases in number during prolonged infections

______________, ______________, ______________,

______________, ______________ 14. the five types of white blood cells

4. List four classes of nutrients normally found in plasma. ____________________,

____________________, ____________________, and ____________________

Name two gases. ____________________ and ____________________

Name three ions. ____________________, ____________________, and ____________________

5. Describe the consistency and color of the plasma you observed in the laboratory. ____________________

____

6. What is the average life span of a red blood cell? How does its anucleate condition affect this life span?

____

____

____

7. From memory, describe the structural characteristics of each of the following blood cell types as accurately as possible, and note the percentage of each in the total white blood cell population.

eosinophils: ____________________

____

neutrophils: ____________________

____

lymphocytes: ____________________

____

basophils: ____________________

____

monocytes: ____________________

____

8. Correctly identify the blood pathologies described in column A by matching them with selections from column B:

	Column A	Column B
________	1. abnormal increase in the number of WBCs	a. anemia
________	2. abnormal increase in the number of RBCs	b. leukocytosis
________	3. condition of too few RBCs or of RBCs with hemoglobin deficiencies	c. leukopenia
		d. polycythemia
________	4. abnormal decrease in the number of WBCs	

Hematologic Tests

9. Broadly speaking, why are hematologic studies of blood so important in the diagnosis of disease?

____

____

10. In the chart below, record information from the blood tests you read about or conducted. Complete the chart by recording values for healthy male adults and indicating the significance of high or low values for each test.

Test	Student test results	Normal values (healthy male adults)	Significance	
			High values	Low values
Total WBC count	No data			
Total RBC count	No data			
Hematocrit				
Hemoglobin determination				
Bleeding time	No data			
Coagulation time				

11. Why is a differential WBC count more valuable than a total WBC count when trying to pin down the specific source of pathology? ____

____

____

12. What name is given to the process of RBC production? ______

What hormone acts as a stimulus for this process? ______

Why might patients with kidney disease suffer from anemia? ______

______

How can such patients be treated? ______

13. Discuss the effect of each of the following factors on RBC count. Consult an appropriate reference as necessary, and explain your reasoning.

long-term effect of athletic training (for example, running 4 to 5 miles per day over a period of six to nine months):

______

______

a permanent move from sea level to a high-altitude area: ______

______

______

14. Define *hematocrit.* ______

15. If you had a high hematocrit, would you expect your hemoglobin determination to be high or low? ______

Why? ______

______

16. What is an anticoagulant? ______

Name two anticoagulants used in conducting the hematologic tests. ______

and ______

What is the body's natural anticoagulant? ______

17. If your blood clumped with both anti-A and anti-B sera, your ABO blood type would be ______

To what ABO blood groups could you give blood? ______

From which ABO donor types could you receive blood? ______

Which ABO blood type is most common? ______ Least common? ______

18. What blood type is theoretically considered the universal donor? ______ Why? ______

______

19. Assume the blood of two patients has been typed for ABO blood type.

Typing results
Mr. Adams:

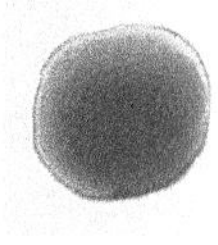

Blood drop and anti-A serum

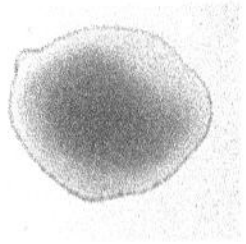

Blood drop and anti-B serum

Typing results
Mr. Calhoon:

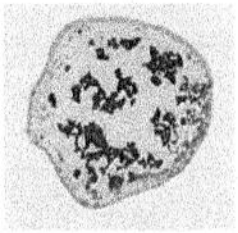

Blood drop and anti-A serum

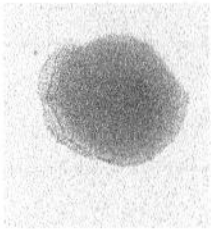

Blood drop and anti-B serum

On the basis of these results, Mr. Adams has type ______________ blood, and Mr. Calhoon has type ______________ blood.

20. Explain why an Rh-negative person does not have a transfusion reaction on the first exposure to Rh-positive blood but *does* have a reaction on the second exposure. ______________________________

____

What happens when an ABO blood type is mismatched for the first time? ______________________________

____

21. Record your observations of the five demonstration slides viewed.

a. Macrocytic hypochromic anemia: ______________________________

b. Microcytic hypochromic anemia: ______________________________

____

c. Sickle cell anemia: ______________________________

d. Lymphocytic leukemia (chronic): ______________________________

____

e. Eosinophilia: ______________________________

Which of the slides above (a through e) corresponds with the following conditions?

__________ 1. iron-deficient diet

__________ 2. a type of bone marrow cancer

__________ 3. genetic defect that causes hemoglobin to become sharp/spiky

__________ 4. lack of vitamin B_{12}

__________ 5. a tapeworm infestation in the body

__________ 6. a bleeding ulcer

22. Provide the normal, or at least "desirable," range for plasma cholesterol concentration.

____________________ mg/100 ml

23. Describe the relationship between high blood cholesterol levels and cardiovascular diseases such as hypertension, heart attacks, and strokes.

____

____

____

____

____

universal ~~donor~~ acceptor = AB^+

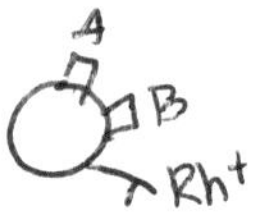

universal donor = O^-

Type	Antibodies	clumping with	can donate to	can accept	antigens
A	B	anti - A	A, AB	A, O	A
B	A	anti - B	B, AB	B, O	B
AB	none	anti - A anti - B	AB	A, B, AB, O	A & B
O	A & B	- none -	A, B, AB, O	O	none

Rh^- doesn't clump w/ antiserum
Rh^+ clumps w/ antiserum

Slides: Know hemo... ltic anemia → no RBCs
- sickle cell → mishapen RBCs

know diff types of WBCs: (p 104)

Lab 5/6 Blood and blood typing

Complete the following chart in regards to blood type

Blood Type	Antigen	Antibody	Can donate to	Can receive from
A	A	B	A, AB	A, O
B	B	A	B, AB	B, O
AB	A and B	none	AB	A, B, AB, O
O	none	A and B	A, AB, B, O	O

(clotting symbol)	Clotting reaction. Antigen is present
(solid dot symbol)	No clotting reaction. Antigen is not present

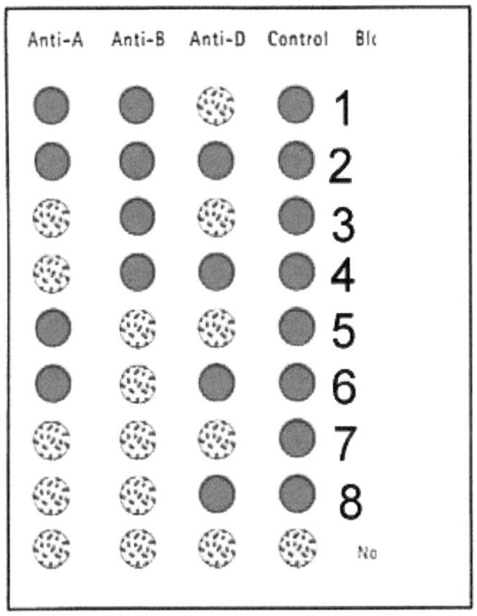

IF there is a clotting reaction, it means that antigen is present.
For the chart to the right, label what blood type each type is.

1. O+ 2. ____ 3. A+ 4. A-

5. B+ 6. B- 7. AB- 8. AB-

The following is modified from William Roan, Labtech for 2020 at CSU Eastbay.
There has been a murder. The good news is that the killer left his/her his own blood at the scene of the crime. The *Keystone Cops* were able to take blood samples of the killer's blood and the victim's blood, and the blood of 4 suspects. Unfortunately, all the blood samples were then mixed up by the *Keystone Cops.* Being cheep, the Keystone Cops have given the samples to you to type and match.
Use the blood sample kits in the front of the class to determine the killer and the victim.

Name	Anti A	Anti B	RH	Blood Type
Suspect				
Victim				
Michael Jackson.				
Bert				
PeeWee Herman				
Jed Bush's Daughter.				

Who was Killed?

Who is the murder?

Why do you think he/she did it?

physioEX version 8

EXERCISE

Blood Analysis: Computer Simulation

OBJECTIVES

1. To become familiar with the "normal" values obtained with selected blood tests.
2. To understand how common laboratory procedures for examining blood can indicate pathology, or a state of disease.
3. To learn how the following blood tests are performed:
   hematocrit (packed cell volume) determination
   erythrocyte sedimentation rate
   hemoglobin determination
   blood typing
   total blood cholesterol determination
4. To understand what each of these procedures is measuring in a sample of blood.
5. To realize the importance of proper disposal of laboratory equipment that has come in contact with blood.
6. To understand the importance of matching blood types for blood transfusions.

Blood transports soluble substances to and from all cells of the body. Blood cells are also important in defense against pathogens. Laboratory analysis of the blood gives important information about how well these functions are being carried out.

This lab exercise consists of five common laboratory tests performed on blood: hematocrit determination; erythrocyte sedimentation rate; hemoglobin determination; blood typing; and total cholesterol determination.

Hematocrit Determination

Hematocrit refers to the percentage of red blood cells (RBCs) in a sample of whole blood. A hematocrit of 48 means that 48% of the volume of blood is red blood cells. Since the function of red blood cells is the transport of oxygen to the cells of the body, the higher the hematocrit, the more red blood cells are available to carry oxygen.

Hematocrit values are determined by spinning a microcapillary tube filled with a whole blood sample in a special microhematocrit centrifuge. This procedure separates the blood cells from the blood plasma and leaves a "buffy coat" layer of white blood cells between the heavier red blood cell layer and the lighter plasma.

The hematocrit value can be determined after centrifuging by measuring the height of the layer of red cells in millimeters and dividing that number by the height of the initial column of blood to obtain the percentage of red blood cells.

The percentage of white blood cells (WBCs) can also be determined after centrifuging by comparing the height of the buffy coat to the initial height of the blood column.

The average hematocrit value for males is 47%, and the average for females is 42%. The normal upper limit is 55%. A lower-than-normal hematocrit indicates *anemia*. A higher-than-normal hematocrit indicates *polycythemia*.

From Exercise 29B in *Human Anatomy and Physiology Lab Manual with PhysioEx 8.0 Media Update*, Eighth Edition, Elaine N. Marieb, Susan J. Mitchell.

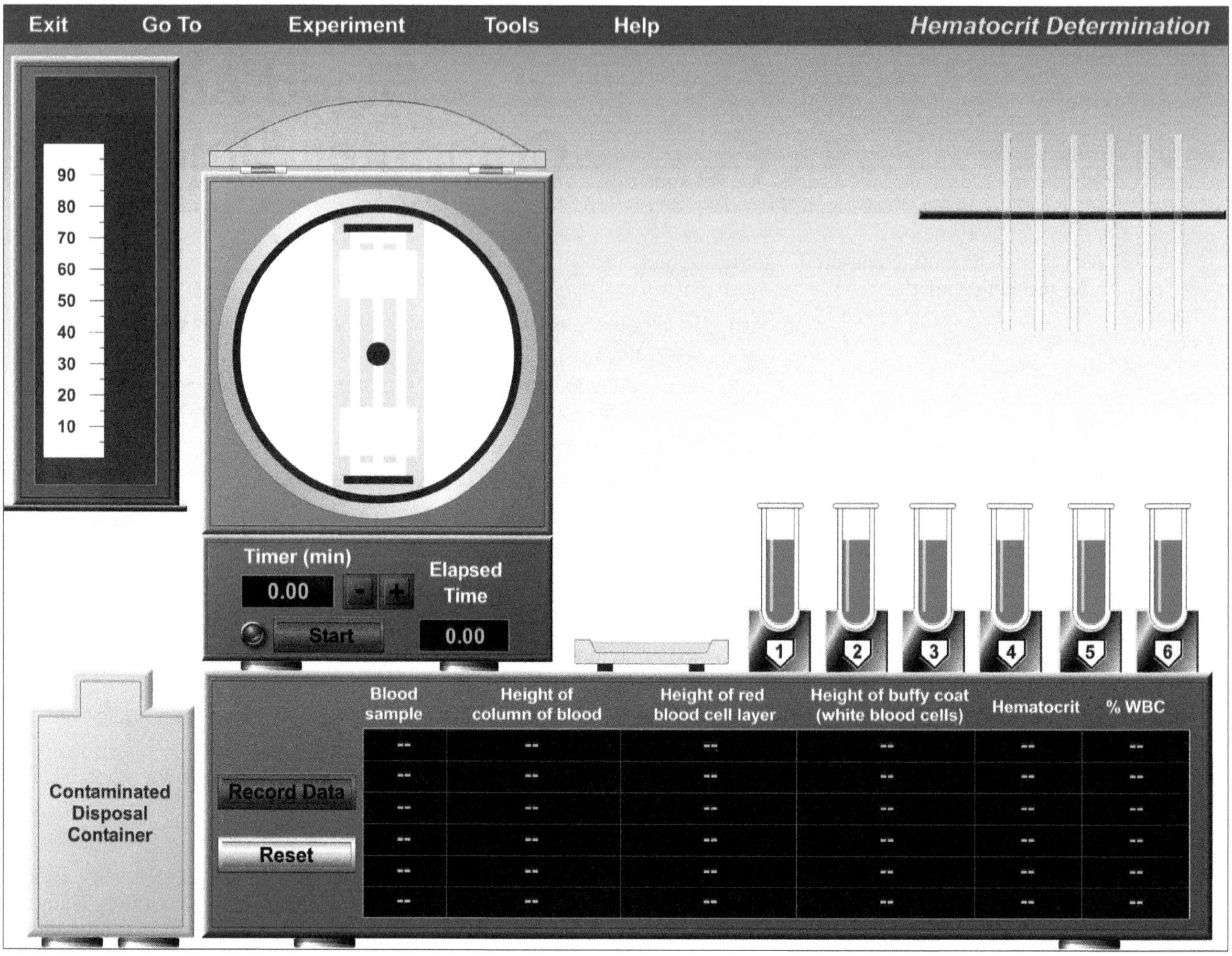

FIGURE 1 Opening screen of the Hematocrit Determination experiment.

Anemia is a condition in which insufficient oxygen is transported to the body's cells. There are many possible causes for anemia, including inadequate numbers of red blood cells, decreased amount of the oxygen-carrying pigment hemoglobin, and abnormal hemoglobin. The heme portion of hemoglobin molecules contains an atom of iron. If adequate iron is not available, the body cannot manufacture hemoglobin. This results in a condition called *iron-deficiency anemia. Aplastic anemia* is the result of the failure of the bone marrow to produce adequate blood cells. *Pernicious anemia* is due to a lack of vitamin B_{12}, which is necessary for cell division. Intrinsic factor, produced by the stomach, allows absorption of vitamin B_{12}. Individuals who do not produce adequate intrinsic factor, or individuals who do not have adequate vitamin B_{12} in their diet, will suffer from pernicious anemia. *Sickle cell anemia* is an inherited condition in which the protein portion of hemoglobin molecules is folded incorrectly. As a result, oxygen molecules cannot fit with the misshapen hemoglobin, and anemia results.

Polycythemia refers to a significant increase in red blood cells. There are many possible causes of polycythemia, including living at high altitudes, strenuous athletic training, and tumors in the bone marrow.

In the following activity, we will simulate the blood test that is used to determine hematocrit. From the drop-down menu, select **Experiment 29B: Blood Analysis** and click **GO.** Before you perform the activities, watch the video **Blood Typing** to see how similar the simulation is to actual blood typing. Then click **Hematocrit Determination.** You will see the opening screen for the Hematocrit Determination experiment (Figure 1).

To familiarize yourself with the equipment, select **Help** from the menu bar and then select **Balloons On/Off.** This feature allows you to scroll around the screen and view equipment labels. You can turn the feature off by returning to **Help** and then selecting **Balloons On/Off.**

In the upper right portion of the screen is a dispenser containing six thin tubes, which are *heparinized capillary tubes.* Heparin is a substance that keeps blood from clotting. Below the capillary tubes are six test tubes containing samples of blood to be tested. When a capillary tube is dragged to a test tube of blood, it partially fills by fluid capillary action.

To the left of the samples of blood is a container of *capillary tube sealer* (a clay material, shown on-screen as an orange-yellow substance). The capillary tubes must be sealed on one end with this tube sealer so that the blood sample can be centrifuged without spraying out the blood.

When the tubes have been sealed, they are moved to slots in the *microhematocrit centrifuge*. When the **Start** button is clicked, the centrifuge will rotate at 14,500 revolutions per minute.

After the centrifuge stops and opens, the capillary tubes are moved, one at a time, next to the metric ruler on the upper left of the screen. When you click on the **Record Data** button next to the data table at the bottom of the screen, the following information about the sample will be recorded: the height of the column of blood in millimeters, the height of the red blood cell layer, the height of the buffy coat (white blood cells), the hematocrit (percentage of red blood cells) and the percentage of white blood cells.

In the lower left corner of the screen is a contaminated disposal container. Every piece of glassware that has come in contact with the blood must be disposed of by dragging it to this container for proper disposal.

ACTIVITY 1

Hematocrit Determination

The following individuals have contributed their blood for this test:

Sample 1: healthy male, living in Boston

Sample 2: healthy female, living in Boston

Sample 3: healthy male, living in Denver

Sample 4: healthy female, living in Denver

Sample 5: male with aplastic anemia

Sample 6: female with iron-deficiency anemia

1. Click and drag one heparinized capillary tube over to the test tube containing blood sample 1. Make sure the capillary tube is touching the blood. The capillary tube will fill itself by fluid capillary action.
2. Drag the capillary tube containing sample 1 to the container of capillary tube sealer to "seal" one end of the tube.
3. Drag the capillary tube to the microhematocrit centrifuge.
4. Repeat steps 1–3 for the remaining five samples of blood.
5. Set the timer for the centrifuge for 5 minutes by clicking the **(+)** button, and then click the **Start** button.
6. When the centrifuge stops and opens, click and drag capillary tube 1 to the metric ruler.
7. Click **Record Data** to record the information about sample 1.
8. Click and drag capillary tube 1 to the contaminated disposal container.
9. Repeat steps 6–8 for the remaining five capillary tubes in the centrifuge.
10. Click **Tools,** then **Print Data** to print the data from the table (or fill in Chart 1).

If you wish to restart or repeat the lab, click the **Reset** button next to the data table.

CHART 1 **Blood Analysis Results**

Blood Sample	Total Height of Column of Blood (mm)	Height of Red Blood Cell Layer (mm)	Height of Buffy Coat (White Blood Cells) (mm)	Hematocrit	% WBC
Healthy male, living in Boston					
Healthy female, living in Boston					
Healthy male, living in Denver					
Healthy female, living in Denver					
Male with aplastic anemia					
Female with iron-deficiency anemia					

What is the hematocrit value of a healthy male living at sea level in Boston?

____

What is the hematocrit value of a healthy male living at one mile elevation in Denver?

____

Is there as much oxygen in the air in Denver as there is in Boston?

____

How do your kidneys respond to a decrease in blood oxygen? (Review this section in your textbook if necessary.)

____

____

If your bone marrow is producing an elevated number of red blood cells, what happens to your hematocrit?

____

What is the hematocrit value of the male with aplastic anemia?

____

Would the red blood cell count for an individual with aplastic anemia be higher, lower, or the same as the red blood cell count of a healthy individual?

____

What is the hematocrit value of a healthy female living in Boston?

____

Explain the difference in hematocrit values obtained from a healthy female living in Boston and a female with iron-deficiency anemia.

____

____

Erythrocyte Sedimentation Rate

The **erythrocyte sedimentation rate (ESR)** measures the settling of red blood cells in a vertical, stationary tube of blood during one hour.

In a healthy individual, red blood cells do not settle very much in an hour. In some disease conditions, increased production of fibrinogen and immunoglobulins cause the red blood cells to clump together, stack up, and form a column (called a *rouleaux formation*). Grouped like this, red blood cells are heavier and settle faster.

This test is not a very specific or diagnostic test, but it can be used to follow the progression of certain disease conditions such as sickle cell anemia, certain cancers, and inflammatory diseases such as rheumatoid arthritis. When the disease worsens, the ESR increases; and when the disease improves, the ESR decreases. The ESR is elevated in iron-deficiency anemia. Sometimes a menstruating female will develop anemia and show an increase in ESR.

The ESR can be used to evaluate a patient with chest pains: the ESR is elevated in established myocardial infarction (heart attack) but normal in angina pectoris. Similarly, it can be useful in screening a female patient with severe abdominal pains because the ESR is not elevated within the first 24 hours of acute appendicitis but is elevated in the early stage of acute pelvic inflammatory disease (PID) or ruptured ectopic pregnancy.

Click **Experiment** on the menu bar, then select **Erythrocyte Sedimentation Rate.** You will see the opening screen for the Erythrocyte Sedimentation Rate lab (Figure 2). Use the **Balloons On/Off** feature from the **Help** menu to familiarize yourself with the equipment on the screen.

In the upper left portion of the screen is a shelf with six samples of blood that have been treated with the anticoagulant heparin. Also on the shelf is a dropper bottle of sodium citrate. The sodium citrate is used to bind with calcium to prevent the blood samples from clotting so they can easily be poured into the narrow sedimentation rate tubes (used later in the lab).

Below the shelf is a test tube dispenser and a test tube rack. To the right of the test tube rack is a cabinet that contains six sedimentation tubes. This cabinet will open when all six blood samples have been added to the test tubes and diluted with sodium citrate. Below this cabinet is a timer, a window showing elapsed time, and a **Start** button to start the timer.

In the upper right portion of the screen is a magnifying chamber that will help you read the millimeter markings on the sedimentation tubes.

In the lower right portion of the screen is a contaminated disposal container. All glassware that has come in contact with the blood must be placed in this container for proper disposal.

When you click on the **Record Data** button next to the data table at the bottom of the screen, the following information about the sample will be recorded: the distance that the RBCs have settled, time elapsed, and sedimentation rate.

ACTIVITY 2

Erythrocyte Sedimentation Rate

The following individuals have contributed their blood for this test:

Sample 1: healthy individual

Sample 2: menstruating female

Sample 3: person with sickle cell anemia

Sample 4: person with iron-deficiency anemia

Sample 5: person suffering from a myocardial infarction

Sample 6: person suffering from angina pectoris

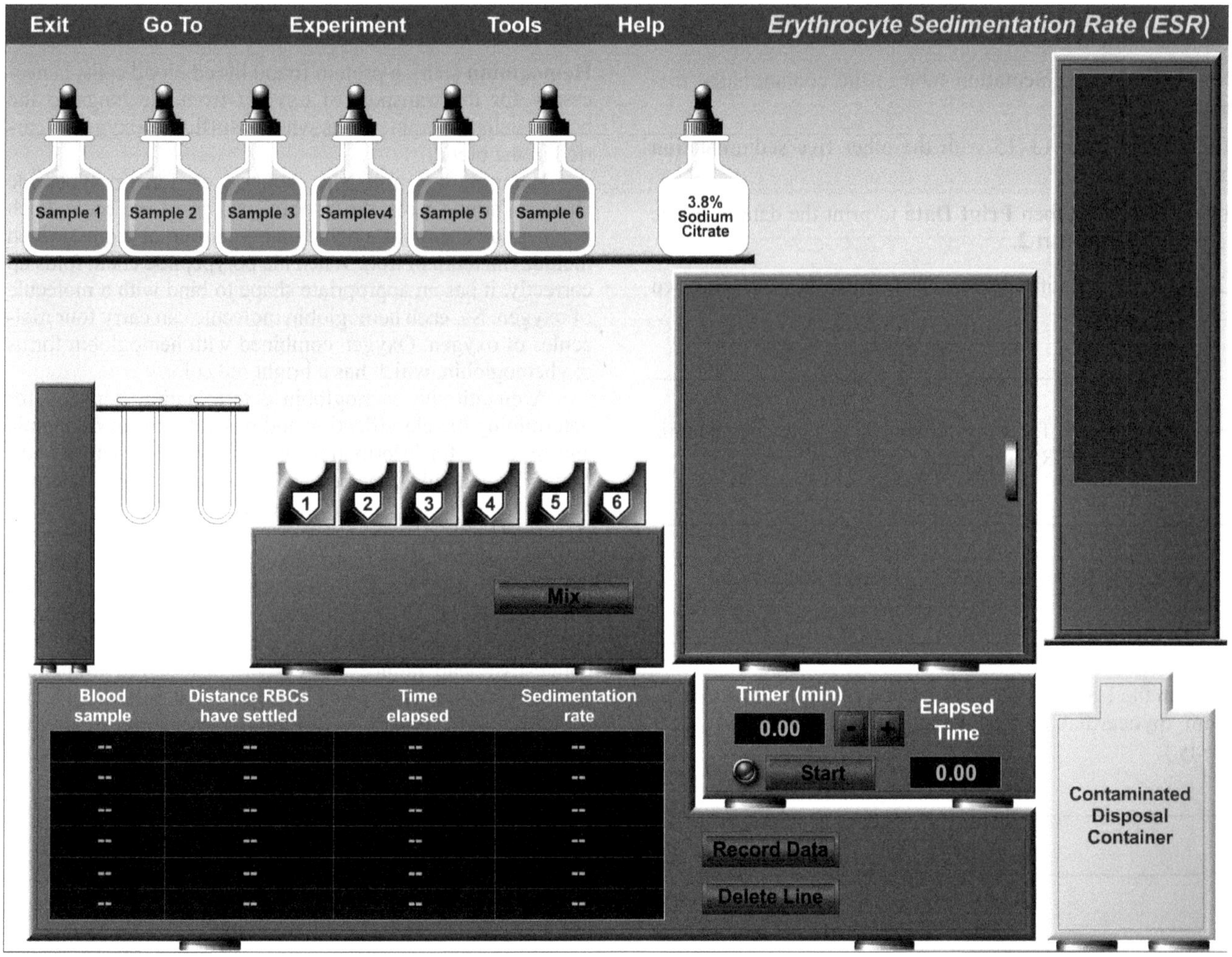

FIGURE 2 **Opening screen of the Erythrocyte Sedimentation Rate experiment.**

1. Individually click and drag six test tubes from the dispenser to the test tube rack.

2. Click on the dropper for blood sample 1, and drag it to the first test tube. One milliliter of blood will be dispensed into the tube.

3. Repeat step 2 for the remaining five samples of blood, using a different test tube for each sample.

4. Click on the dropper for the **3.8% sodium citrate,** and drag it over the test tube containing blood sample 1; 0.5 milliliter of sodium citrate will be dispensed into the tube.

5. The dropper will automatically slide over to each of the remaining samples.

6. Click on the **Mix** button. The samples will automatically mix for a few seconds.

7. After the samples have been mixed, the cabinet with six sedimentation tubes will open.

8. Click on the tube containing blood sample 1. Notice that the pointer is now a small test tube pointed to the left.

9. While still holding the mouse button down, move the mouse pointer to the first sedimentation tube in the cabinet. The contents of the small test tube will pour into the sedimentation tube.

10. Click and drag the now empty test tube to the contaminated disposal container.

11. Repeat steps 8–10 with the other five samples of blood.

12. When the six sedimentation tubes are filled, set the timer for 60 minutes by clicking the **(+)** button, and then click the **Start** button.

13. After 60 minutes have elapsed, drag sedimentation tube 1 to the magnifying chamber at the top right of the screen. Examine the tube. The tube is marked in millimeters, and the distance between two marks is 5 mm. How many millimeters has the blood settled?

____

What is in the beige-colored portion of the tube? __________

14. Click the **Record Data** button next to the data table. The distance in millimeters that the red blood cells have

settled, the elapsed time, and the sedimentation rate will be entered in the table.

15. Drag the sedimentation tube to the contaminated disposal container.

16. Repeat steps 13–15 with the other five sedimentation tubes.

17. Click **Tools,** then **Print Data** to print the data from the table, or fill in Chart 2.

Did the person with sickle cell anemia show an elevated ESR?

____

How did the ESR for a person with iron-deficiency anemia compare to the ESR for a healthy individual?

____

Explain the ESR for sample 2, the menstruating female.

____

Explain the ESRs for samples 5 and 6 (the patients suffering from myocardial infarction and angina pectoris, respectively.)

____

____

Hemoglobin

Hemoglobin (Hb), a protein found in red blood cells, is necessary for the transport of oxygen from the lungs to the body's cells. Anemia results when insufficient oxygen is carried in the blood.

Hemoglobin molecules consist of four polypeptide chains of amino acids, the "globin" part of the molecule. Each polypeptide chain has a heme unit—a group of atoms, which includes an atom of iron. When the polypeptide chain folds up correctly, it has an appropriate shape to bind with a molecule of oxygen. So, each hemoglobin molecule can carry four molecules of oxygen. Oxygen combined with hemoglobin forms oxyhemoglobin, which has a bright red color.

A quantitative hemoglobin determination is useful for determining the classification and possible causes of anemia and gives useful information on some other disease conditions. For example, a person can have anemia with a normal red blood cell count, if there is inadequate hemoglobin in the red blood cells.

Normal blood contains an average of 12 to 18 grams of hemoglobin per 100 milliliters of blood. A healthy male has 13.5 to 18 g/100 ml; a healthy female has 12 to 16 g/100 ml. Hemoglobin values increase in patients with polycythemia, congestive heart failure, and chronic obstructive pulmonary disease (COPD). They also increase at high altitudes. Hemoglobin values decrease in patients with anemia, hyperthyroidism, cirrhosis of the liver, renal disease, systemic lupus erythematosus, and severe hemorrhage.

The hemoglobin content of a sample of blood can be determined by stirring the blood with a wooden stick to rupture, or lyse, the cells. The intensity of the color of the lysed blood

CHART 2 **Erythrocyte Sedimentation Rate Results**

Blood Sample	Distance RBCs Have Settled (mm)	Elapsed Time	Sedimentation Rate
Healthy individual			
Menstruating female			
Person with sickle cell anemia			
Person with iron-deficiency anemia			
Person suffering from a myocardial infarction			
Person suffering from angina pectoris			

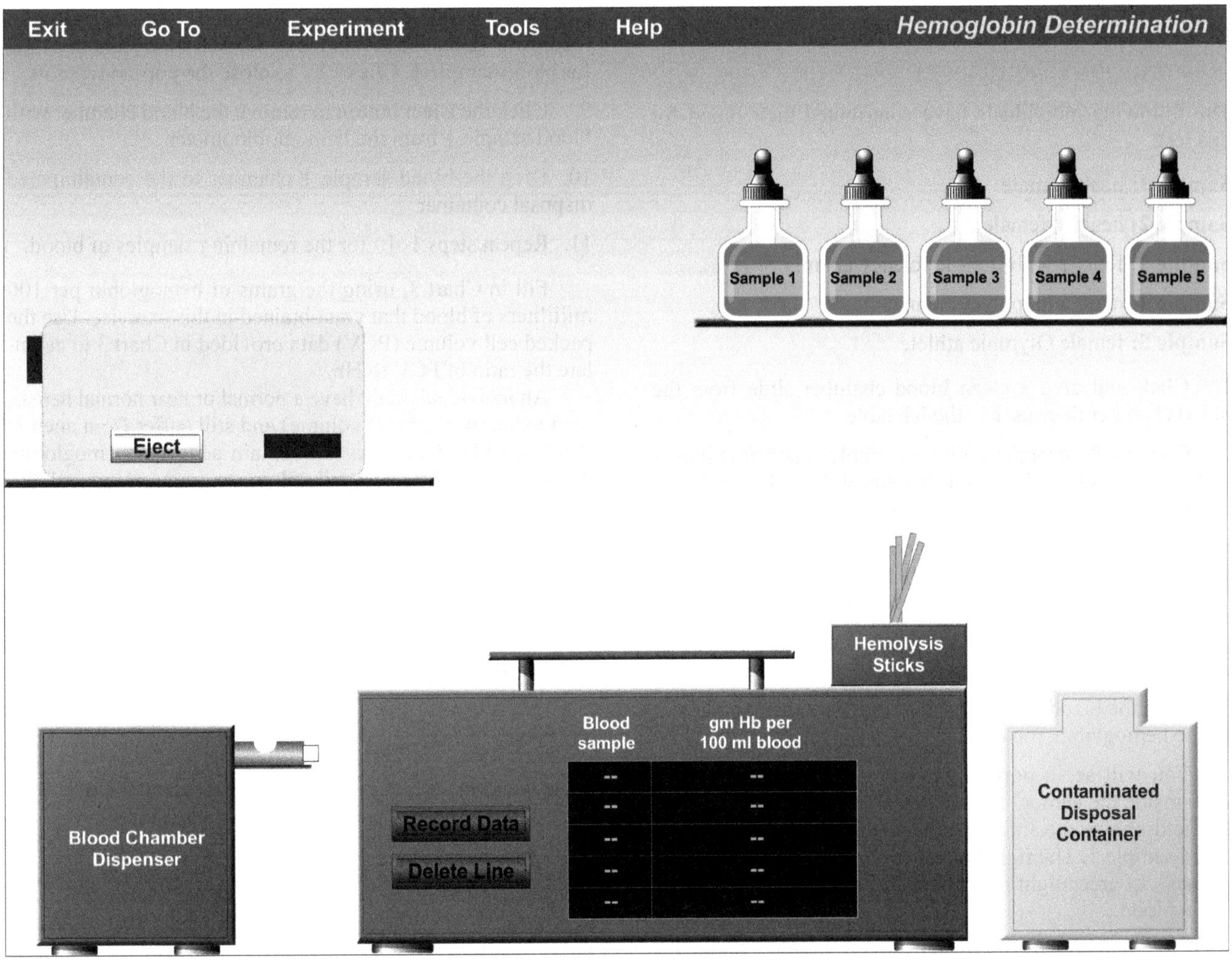

FIGURE 3 Opening screen of the Hemoglobin Determination experiment.

is a result of the amount of hemoglobin present. A *hemoglobinometer* compares the color of the sample to standard values to determine the hemoglobin content of the sample. The hemoglobinometer transmits green light through the hemolyzed blood sample. The amount of light that passes through the sample is compared to standard color intensities. Green light is used because the human eye is able to easily detect subtle differences in green colors.

From the **Experiment** menu, select **Hemoglobin Determination.** You will see the opening screen for the Hemoglobin Determination lab (Figure 3). Use the **Balloons On/Off** feature from the **Help** menu to familiarize yourself with the equipment on the screen.

In the upper right portion of the screen is a shelf with five samples of blood.

In the middle of the screen is a lab table and a container of hemolysis sticks. The hemolysis sticks will be used to stir the blood samples to lyse the red blood cells, thereby releasing their hemoglobin.

At the bottom left of the screen is a blood chamber dispenser that provides a slide with a depression to receive the blood sample.

Above the blood chamber dispenser is a hemoglobinometer. The hemoglobinometer has a black rectangular slot to receive the blood chamber and an **Eject** button to remove the blood chamber. When the loaded blood chamber is inserted into the slot, the hemoglobinometer view will change to show a split screen that compares the color of the hemolyzed blood sample to a standard color for which given levels of hemoglobin are already known. A window on the hemoglobinometer displays the grams of hemoglobin per 100 milliliters of blood. A small handle on the top right of the hemoglobinometer can be slid down until the colors shown on the device match the colors of the sample of blood to be tested.

When you click on the **Record Data** button next to the data table at the bottom of the screen, the grams of hemoglobin per 100 milliliters of blood will be recorded.

In the lower right portion of the screen is a contaminated disposal container. All glassware and hemolysis sticks that have come in contact with the blood must be placed in this container for proper disposal.

ACTIVITY 3

Hemoglobin (Hb) Determination

The following individuals have contributed their blood for this test:

Sample 1: healthy male

Sample 2: healthy female

Sample 3: female with iron-deficiency anemia

Sample 4: male with polycythemia

Sample 5: female Olympic athlete

1. Click and drag a clean blood chamber slide from the blood chamber dispenser to the lab table.
2. Click on the dropper for blood sample 1, and drag it over to the depression on the blood chamber slide. A drop of blood will be dispensed into the depression.
3. Click a hemolysis stick, and drag it to the drop of blood. The stick will stir the blood sample for 45 seconds, lysing the red blood cells and releasing their hemoglobin.
4. Drag the hemolysis stick to the contaminated disposal container.
5. Drag the blood chamber slide to the dark rectangular slot on the hemoglobinometer.
6. You will see a pop-up window appear, displaying the view inside the hemoglobinometer. The left half of the circular field shows the intensity of green light transmitted by blood sample 1. The right half of the circular field shows the intensity of green light for known levels of hemoglobin present in blood.
7. Click and hold the lever on the top right of the hemoglobinometer, and slowly drag it downward until the right half of the field matches the shade of green on the left side of the field.
8. Click the **Record Data** button next to the data table to record the grams of hemoglobin per 100 milliliters of blood for blood sample 1. Click "X" to close the pop-up window.
9. Click the **Eject** button to remove the blood chamber with blood sample 1 from the hemoglobinometer.
10. Drag the blood sample 1 chamber to the contaminated disposal container.
11. Repeat steps 1–10 for the remaining samples of blood.

Fill in Chart 3, using the grams of hemoglobin per 100 milliliters of blood that you obtained in this exercise. Use the packed cell volume (PCV) data provided in Chart 3 to calculate the ratio of PCV to Hb.

An individual might have a normal or near normal hematocrit value (packed cell volume) and still suffer from anemia if the red blood cells do not contain adequate hemoglobin. A normal ratio of packed cell volume to grams of hemoglobin is approximately 3:1.

What is the hematocrit value for the healthy male?

____

What is the hematocrit value for the healthy female?

____

What does the ratio of PCV to Hb tell you about the red blood cells of the female with iron-deficiency anemia?

____

Does the male with polycythemia have a normal ratio of PCV to Hb? ____

CHART 3 Hemoglobin Determination

Blood Sample	Hb in grams per 100 ml of blood	Hematocrit (PCV)	Ratio of PCV to Hb
Healthy male		48	
Healthy female		44	
Female with iron-deficiency anemia		40	
Male with polycythemia		60	
Female Olympic athlete		60	

Based on these results, do you think his red blood cells contain adequate quantities of hemoglobin molecules? Why?

____

____

Does the female Olympic athlete have a normal ratio of PCV to Hb? ______________________________

Based on these results, do you think her red blood cells contain adequate quantities of hemoglobin molecules? Why?

____

____

Blood Typing

All of the cells in the human body, including the red blood cells, are surrounded by a *plasma (cell) membrane*. The plasma membrane contains genetically determined glycoproteins, called antigens, that identify the cells. On red blood cell membranes, these antigens are called *agglutinogens.*

It is important to determine blood types before performing blood transfusions in order to avoid mixing incompatible blood. Although many different antigens are present on red blood cell membranes, the ABO and Rh antigens cause the most vigorous and potentially fatal transfusion reactions. If a blood transfusion recipient has antibodies (called *agglutinins*) to the antigens present on the transfused cells, the red blood cells will be clumped together, or *agglutinated,* and then lysed. This results in a potentially life-threatening blood transfusion reaction.

The ABO blood groups are determined by the presence or absence of two antigens: type A and type B (see Figure 4b). These antigens are genetically determined so a person has two copies (alleles) of the gene for these proteins, one copy from each parent. The presence of these antigens is due to a dominant gene, and their absence is due to a recessive gene.

- A person with type A blood can have two gene alleles for the A antigen, or that person could have one gene allele for type A antigen and the other allele for the absence of either A or B antigen.
- A person with type B blood can have two gene alleles for the B antigen, or that person could have one gene allele for type B antigen and the other allele for the absence of either A or B antigen.
- A person with type AB blood has one gene allele for the A antigen and the other allele for the B antigen.
- A person with type O blood will have inherited two recessive gene alleles and has neither type A nor type B antigen.

Antibodies to the A and B antigens are found preformed in the blood plasma. A person has antibodies only for the antigens not on his or her red blood cells, so a person with type A blood will have anti-B antibodies. This is summarized in Chart 4.

CHART 4 **ABO Blood Types**

Blood Type	Antigens on RBCs	Antibodies Present in Plasma
A	A	anti-B
B	B	anti-A
AB	A and B	none
O	none	anti-A and anti-B

The Rh factor is another genetically determined protein that may be present on red blood cell membranes. Approximately 85% of the population is Rh positive and has this protein. Antibodies to the Rh factor are not found preformed in the plasma. These antibodies are produced only after exposure to the Rh factor by persons who are Rh negative.

Separate drops of a blood sample are mixed with antisera containing antibodies to the types A and B antigens and antibodies to the Rh factor. An agglutination reaction (showing clumping) indicates the presence of the agglutinogen.

In this experiment, we will conduct blood typing tests on six blood samples. From the **Experiment** menu, select **Blood Typing.** You will see the opening screen for the Blood Typing lab (Figure 4a). Use the **Balloons On/Off** feature from the **Help** menu to familiarize yourself with the equipment on the screen.

In the upper right portion of the screen is a shelf with six samples of blood.

In the upper left portion of the screen is a shelf containing bottles of anti-A serum (blue color), anti-B serum (yellow color), and anti-Rh serum (white color). These bottles contain antibodies to the A antigen, B antigen, and Rh antigen, respectively.

In the center of the screen is a lab table for performing the blood typing. To the left of the lab table is a blood typing slide dispenser.

Above the blood typing slide dispenser is a container of stirring sticks. These sticks are color coded: the blue stick is to be used with the anti-A serum, the yellow stick is to be used with the anti-B serum, and the white stick is to be used with the anti-Rh serum.

To the right of the lab table is a *light box* for viewing the blood type samples. When you click on the **Light** button, the screen above unrolls to display the blood types.

To the left of the light box is a data table to record your results.

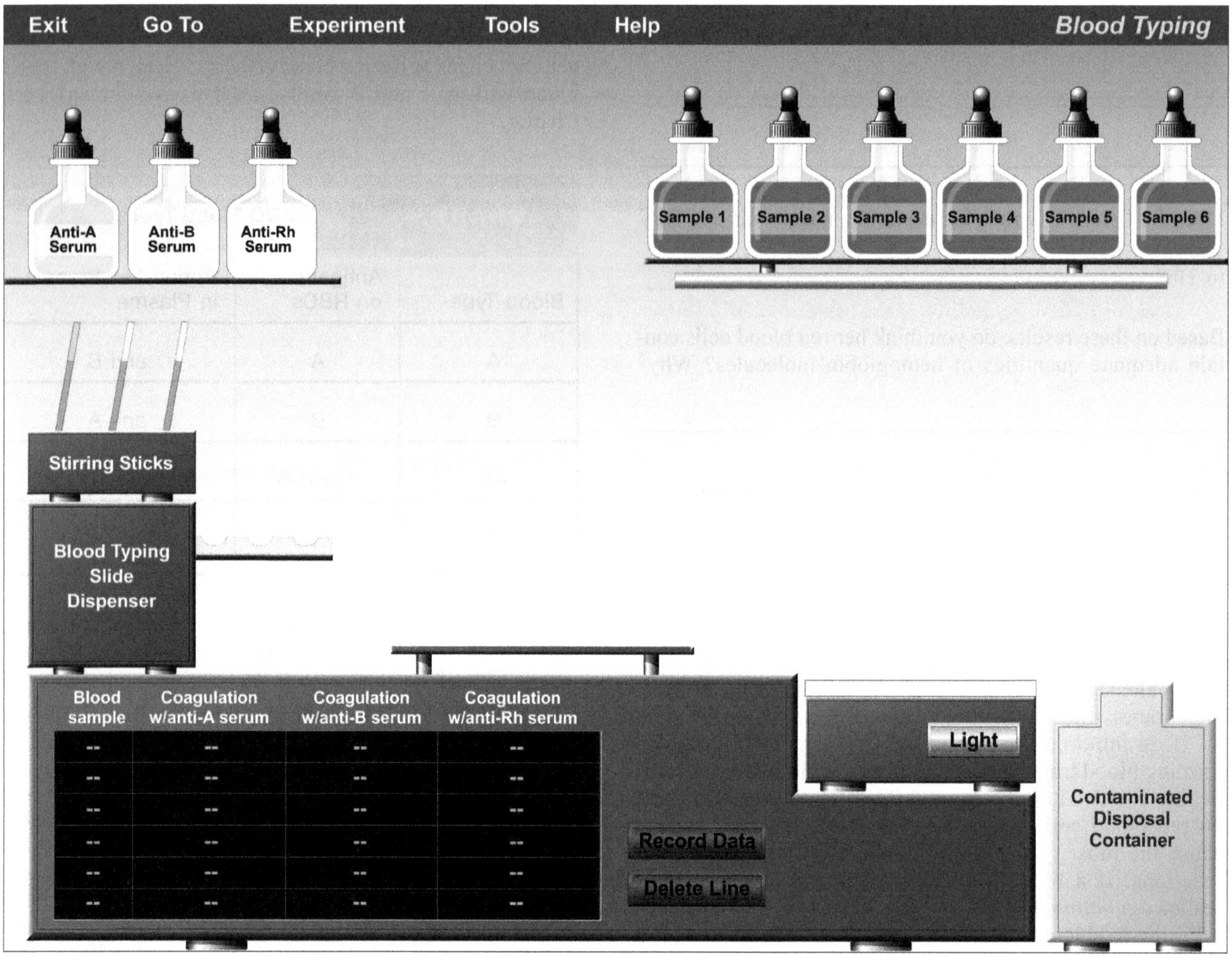

(a)

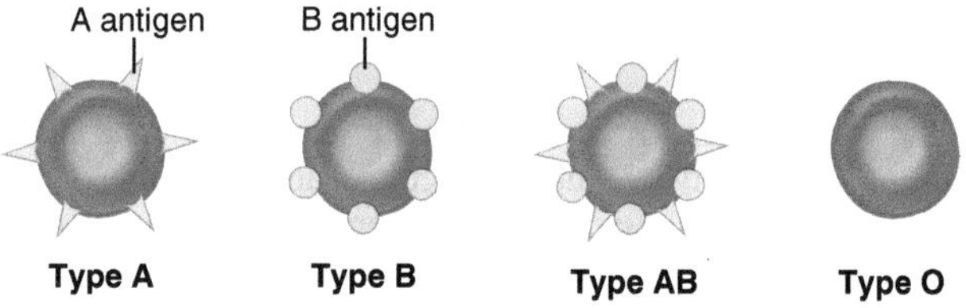

(b) Blood type surface antigens

FIGURE 4 **Blood typing.** (**a**) Opening screen of the Blood Typing experiment. (**b**) Antigens determining ABO blood type, found on the surface of red blood cells.

In the bottom right portion of the screen is a contaminated disposal container. All glassware and sticks that have come in contact with blood must be placed in this container for proper disposal.

ACTIVITY 4

Blood Typing

Six individuals with different blood types have donated their blood for this exercise.

1. Click and drag a blood typing slide from the blood typing slide dispenser to the lab table. Note that the three wells on the slide are labeled "A," "B," and "Rh."

2. Click on the dropper for blood sample 1, and drag it over the well labeled A on the blood typing slide. A drop of blood will be dispensed into the well.

3. The dropper will automatically slide over to each of the remaining wells.

4. Click on the dropper for anti-A serum, and drag it over the well labeled A on the blood typing slide. A drop of anti-A serum will be dispensed into the well.

5. Repeat step 4 with the anti-B serum. Be sure to dispense it into the well labeled B.

6. Repeat step 4 with the anti-Rh serum. Be sure to dispense it into the well labeled Rh.

7. Obtain a blue-tipped stirring stick, and drag it to well A. It will mix the blood and anti-A serum.

8. Dispose of the stirring stick in the contaminated disposal container.

9. Select a yellow-tipped stirring stick, and drag it to well B.

10. Dispose of the stirring stick in the contaminated disposal container.

11. Select a white-tipped stirring stick, and drag it to well Rh.

12. Dispose of the stirring stick in the contaminated disposal container.

13. Drag the blood typing slide to the light box, and click the **Light** button. The screen will unroll, displaying the results of the blood typing.

14. Examine the results labeled A on the screen. If coagulation (agglutination, or "clumpiness") is present, click on **Positive.** If no coagulation is present (the sample will look smooth), click on **Negative.**

15. Repeat step 14 for the results labeled B and Rh. In each case, choose **Positive** if the sample is coagulated and **Negative** if the sample is not coagulated.

16. Click the **Record Data** button on the data table to record the results of blood sample 1.

17. Click and drag the blood typing slide to the contaminated disposal container.

18. Click the **X** at the top right of the scroll to close the scroll.

19. Repeat steps 1–18 for the remaining samples of blood.

Using the data you have collected in this activity, fill in Chart 5. (Indicate coagulation as either "positive" or "negative.")

Determine the blood type of each sample and fill in the last column. For Rh positive or negative, add $^+$ or $^-$ to the blood type; for example, AB^+.

If the anti-A antibody causes the blood to coagulate, which antigen would be present on the blood cells?

____

If a person has type AB blood, which antigens are present on the red blood cells?

____

Which antibodies are present in the plasma of a person with type AB blood?

____

Does a person with type O blood have A or B antigens on the red blood cells?

____

Blood Cholesterol

Cholesterol is a lipid substance that is essential for life. It is an important component of all cell membranes and is the basis for making steroid hormones, vitamin D, and bile salts.

Cholesterol is produced in the human liver and is present in some foods of animal origin, such as milk, meat, and eggs. Since cholesterol is a water-insoluble lipid, it needs to be wrapped in protein packages, called lipoproteins, to travel in the watery blood from the liver and digestive organs to the cells of the body.

CHART 5 Blood Typing Results

Blood Sample	Agglutination with Anti-A Serum	Agglutination with Anti-B Serum	Agglutination with Anti-Rh Serum	Blood Type
1				
2				
3				
4				
5				
6				

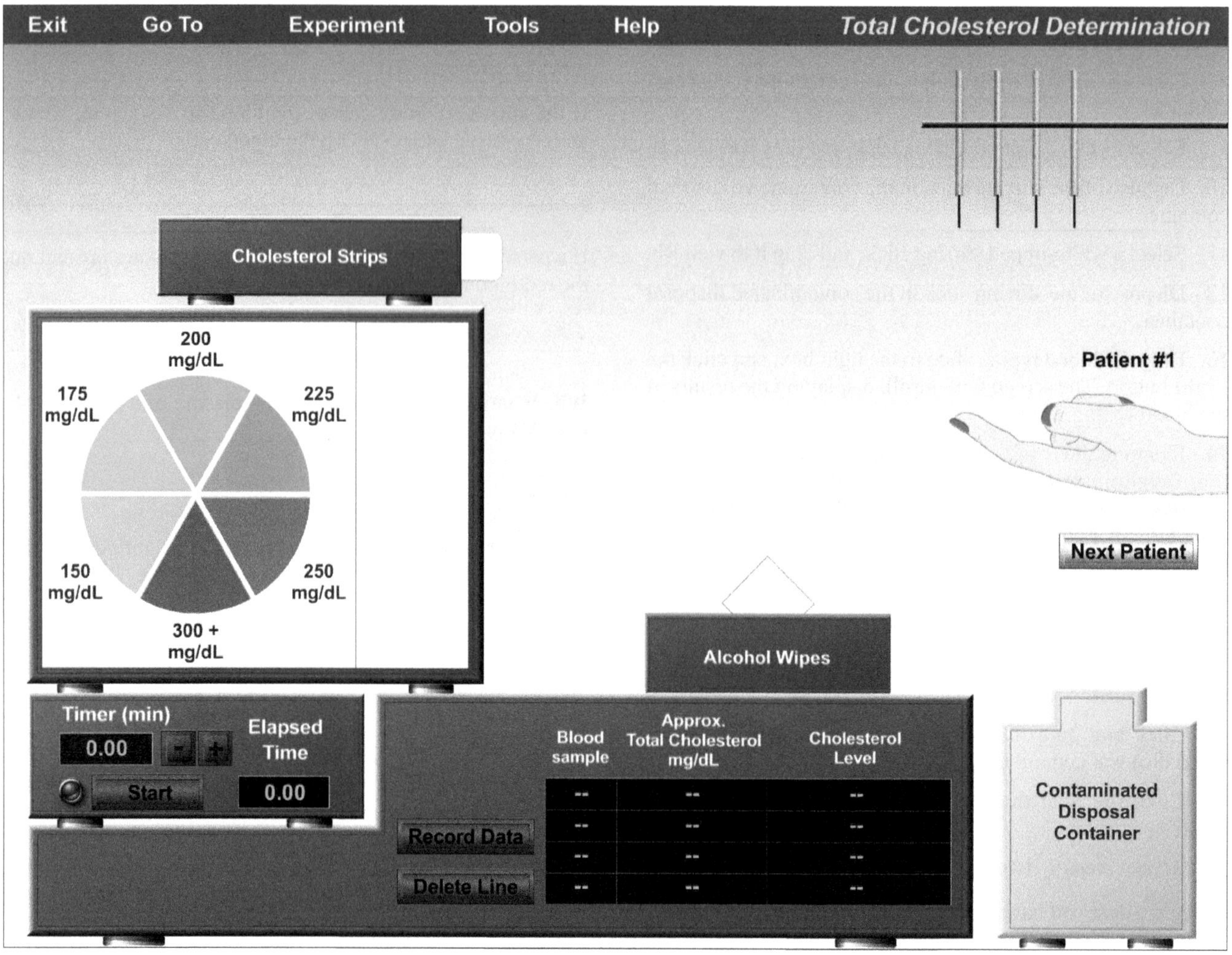

FIGURE 5 **Opening screen of the Total Cholesterol Determination experiment.**

One type of lipoprotein package, called LDL (low-density liproprotein), has been identified as a potential source of damage to the interior of arteries because it can contribute to atherosclerosis, the buildup of plaque, in these blood vessels. A total blood cholesterol determination does not measure the level of LDLs, but it does provide valuable information about the total amount of cholesterol in the blood.

Less than 200 milligrams of total cholesterol per deciliter of blood is considered desirable. Between 200 and 239 mg/dl is considered borderline high cholesterol. Over 240 mg/dl is considered high blood cholesterol and is associated with increased risk of cardiovascular disease. Abnormally low blood levels of cholesterol (total cholesterol lower than 100 mg/dl) can also be a problem. Low levels may indicate hyperthyroidism (overactive thyroid gland), liver disease, inadequate absorption of nutrients from the intestine, or malnutrition. Other reports link hypocholesterolemia (low blood cholesterol) to depression, anxiety, and mood disturbances, which are thought to be controlled by the level of available serotonin, a neurotransmitter. There is evidence of a relationship between low levels of blood cholesterol and low levels of serotonin in the brain.

In this test for total blood cholesterol, a sample of blood is mixed with enzymes that produce a colored reaction with cholesterol. The intensity of the color indicates the amount of cholesterol present. The cholesterol tester compares the color of the sample to the colors of known levels of cholesterol (standard values).

From the **Experiment** menu, select **Total Cholesterol Determination.** You will see the opening screen for the Total Cholesterol Determination lab (Figure 5). Use the **Balloons On/Off** feature from the **Help** menu to familiarize yourself with the equipment on the screen.

In the upper right portion of the screen is a dispenser of *lancets,* sharp needlelike instruments that are used to prick the finger to obtain a drop of blood.

Beneath the lancet dispenser is a patient's finger. The patient can be changed by clicking the **Next Patient** button beneath the finger.

On top of the data table is a container of alcohol wipes for cleansing the fingertip before it is punctured with the lancet.

The left portion of the screen shows a cabinet containing a *color wheel* that is divided into sections showing different intensities of green. Each shade of green corresponds to a range of total cholesterol levels. Below the cabinet is a timer that can be set for 1 to 3 minutes.

In the upper left portion of the screen is a cholesterol strip dispenser. These cholesterol strips contain chemicals that convert, by a series of reactions, the cholesterol in the blood sample into a green-colored solution. These reactions take 3 minutes. By matching the color of the cholesterol strip to a color on the color wheel, we can determine the cholesterol level of a given blood sample. Higher levels of cholesterol will result in a deeper green color.

The bottom of the screen has a data table for recording the total cholesterol level of the blood samples.

In the lower right portion of the screen is a contaminated disposal container. Any piece of equipment that has come into contact with the blood must be disposed of properly by dragging it to this contaminated disposal container.

ACTIVITY 5

Total Cholesterol Determination

1. Click and drag an alcohol wipe over the end of patient 1's finger.
2. Click and drag a lancet to the tip of the finger. The lancet will prick the finger to obtain a drop of blood.
3. Drag the lancet to the contaminated disposal container.
4. Drag a cholesterol strip to the finger. The blood should transfer to the strip.
5. Drag the cholesterol strip to the rectangular area to the right of the color wheel.
6. Set the timer for 3 minutes, and click **Start.** Notice that the strip begins to change color.
7. After 3 minutes, decide which color on the color wheel most closely matches the color on the cholesterol test strip. Click on that color. It is sometimes difficult to match the color on the cholesterol strip with the appropriate color on the color wheel. If the color you have chosen is not an exact match, you will see a pop-up window asking you to try again.
8. Click on **Record Data** to record this information in the data table.
9. Drag the cholesterol test strip for patient 1 to the contaminated disposal container. Record your results in Chart 6.
10. There are a total of four patients. Click **Next Patient** and repeat steps 1–9 until you have collected data for all four patients.

What health problems might be in store for patient 2, based on these results?

___

What advice about diet and exercise would you give patient 4?

___

CHART 6 Total Cholesterol Determination

Blood Sample	Approximate Total Cholesterol	Cholesterol Level
1		
2		
3		
4		

NAME ______________________

LAB TIME/DATE ______________________

Blood Analysis: Computer Simulation

Hematocrit Determination

The following questions refer to Activity 1: Hematocrit Determination.

1. List the following values from Chart 1:

   Hematocrit value for healthy male living at sea level in Boston = ______________________

   Hematocrit value for healthy female living at sea level in Boston = ______________________

2. Were the values listed in question 1 within normal range? ______________________

3. Describe the difference between the male and the female hematocrit for an individual living in Boston. ______________________

   ____

4. List the following values from Chart 1:

   Hematocrit value for healthy male living in Denver = ______________________

   Hematocrit value for healthy female living in Denver = ______________________

5. How did these values differ from the values for Boston? ______________________

   ____

6. Describe the effect of living at high elevations on a person's hematocrit. ______________________

   ____

7. Describe how the kidneys respond to a decrease in oxygen and what effect this has on hematocrit. ______________________

   ____

8. List the following values from Chart 1:

   Hematocrit value for male with aplastic anemia = ______________________

   % WBC for male with aplastic anemia = ______________________

9. Were the values listed in question 8 within the normal range? Why or why not?

   ____

   ____

10. List the following value from Chart 1:

Hematocrit for female with iron-deficiency anemia = ______

11. Was the value in question 10 normal or not? Explain. ______

______

Erythrocyte Sedimentation Rate

The following questions refer to Activity 2: Erythrocyte Sedimentation Rate.

12. Describe the effect that sickle cell anemia has on the sedimentation rate. ______

______

13. Why do you think that it has this effect? Hint: Sickle cell anemia alters the shape of red blood cells. ______

______

14. Record the sedimentation rate for a menstruating female. ______

15. How did this value compare to the healthy individual? Why? ______

______

16. What was the sedimentation rate for the iron-deficient individual? ______

17. What effect does iron deficiency have on ESR? ______

______

18. Record the following values from Chart 2:

ESR for person suffering from a myocardial infarction = ______

ESR for person suffering from angina pectoris = ______

19. Compare the values in question 18 and explain how they might be used to monitor heart conditions. ______

______

20. List some other conditions that ESR is used to monitor. ______

______

Hemoglobin

The following questions refer to Activity 3: Hemoglobin (Hb) Determination.

21. Describe the ratio of packed cell volume to Hb (hemoglobin) obtained for the healthy male and female subjects. ______

______

22. Describe the ratio of packed cell volume to Hb (hemoglobin) for the female with iron-deficiency anemia. ________________

23. Is the female with iron-deficiency anemia deficient in hemoglobin? ________________

24. Is the male with polycythemia deficient in hemoglobin? ________________

25. Is the female Olympic athlete deficient in hemoglobin? ________________

26. List conditions in which Hb would decrease. ________________

____

27. List conditions in which Hb would increase. ________________

____

Blood Typing

The following questions refer to Activity 4: Blood Typing.

28. Which blood sample contained the rarest blood type? ________________

29. Which blood sample contained the universal donor? ________________

30. Which blood sample contained the universal recipient? ________________

31. Which blood sample did not coagulate with any of the antibodies tested? ________________

Why? ________________

32. What antibodies would be found in the plasma of blood sample 1? ________________

33. When transfusing an individual with blood that is compatible but not the same type, it is important to separate packed cells from the plasma and administer only the packed cells. Why do you think this is done? ________________

____

34. List which blood samples in this experiment represent people who could donate blood to a person with type B^+. ________________

____

Blood Cholesterol

The following questions refer to Activity 5: Total Cholesterol Determination.

35. Which patient had desirable cholesterol levels? ________________

36. Which patient(s) had an elevated cholesterol level? ________________

37. Describe the risks for the patient identified in question 36. ______________________

____

38. Which advice would you give patient 4? Why? ______________________

____

39. Describe some reasons why a patient might have abnormally low blood cholesterol.

____

____

Urinary system

BB for diagram

* homeostatic organs of body
* Reg BP, Blood fluid vol, solute conc, etc
* filters out about 200L blood/day
* nephrons filter blood & drain into major/minor calyx
* renal pelvis = all major calyx
* renal artery: takes blood to kidney
  " " vein: away
* cortical neph: filtration of blood
  juxtamedullary: water
* renal corpuscle: house of glomerulus
* glomerulus sits inside Bowman's capsule
* vasa recta: bloodstream w/in nephron

major calyx = minor calyxs meeting

NEPHRON
1. glomerulus
2. prox convoluted tubule
3. loop of Henle ↓↑
4. distal conv. tubule
5. collecting duct

Urinalysis

- pH 5~7
- color due to BILIRUBIN (prod from metabolized RBCs)
- normal contents
  - ions (Ca^{2+}, Mg^{2+}, K^+, Na^+, Cl^-)
  - 95% H_2O
- Dont want to find
  - Albumin - common body pro[illegible]
  - Ketones (good diagnostic for diabetes) → breakdown of fat
  - Excess glucose
  - Blood

Anatomy of the Urinary System

MATERIALS

- ☐ Human dissectible torso model, three-dimensional model of the urinary system, and/or anatomical chart of the human urinary system
- ☐ Dissecting instruments and tray
- ☐ Pig or sheep kidney, doubly or triply injected
- ☐ Disposable gloves
- ☐ Three-dimensional models of the cut kidney and of a nephron (if available)
- ☐ Compound microscope
- ☐ Prepared slides of a longitudinal section of kidney and cross sections of the bladder

AIA This exercise uses the A.D.A.M.® Interactive Anatomy program.

OBJECTIVES

1. To describe the function of the urinary system.
2. To identify, on an appropriate diagram or torso model, the urinary system organs and to describe the general function of each.
3. To compare the course and length of the urethra in males and females.
4. To identify these regions of the dissected kidney (longitudinal section): hilum, cortex, medulla, medullary pyramids, major and minor calyces, pelvis, renal columns, and fibrous and perirenal fat capsules.
5. To trace the blood supply of the kidney from the renal artery to the renal vein.
6. To define the nephron as the physiological unit of the kidney, and to describe its anatomy.
7. To define *glomerular filtration, tubular reabsorption,* and *tubular secretion,* and to indicate the nephron areas involved in these processes.
8. To define *micturition,* and to explain pertinent differences in the control of the two bladder sphincters (internal and external).
9. To recognize microscopic or diagrammatic views of the histologic structure of the kidney and bladder.

Metabolism of nutrients by the body produces wastes (carbon dioxide, nitrogenous wastes, ammonia, and so on) that must be eliminated from the body if normal function is to continue. Although excretory processes involve several organ systems (the lungs excrete carbon dioxide and skin glands excrete salts and water), it is the **urinary system** that is primarily concerned with the removal of nitrogenous wastes from the body. In addition to this purely excretory function, the kidney maintains the electrolyte, acid-base, and fluid balances of the blood and is thus a major, if not *the* major, homeostatic organ of the body.

To perform its functions, the kidney acts first as a blood filter, and then as a blood processor. It allows toxins, metabolic wastes, and excess ions to leave the body in the urine, while retaining needed substances and returning them to the blood. Malfunction of the urinary system, particularly of the kidneys, leads to a failure in homeostasis which, unless corrected, is fatal.

Gross Anatomy of the Human Urinary System

The urinary system (Figure 1) consists of the paired kidneys and ureters and the single urinary bladder and urethra. The **kidneys** perform the functions described above and manufacture urine in the process. The remaining organs of the system provide temporary storage reservoirs or transportation channels for urine.

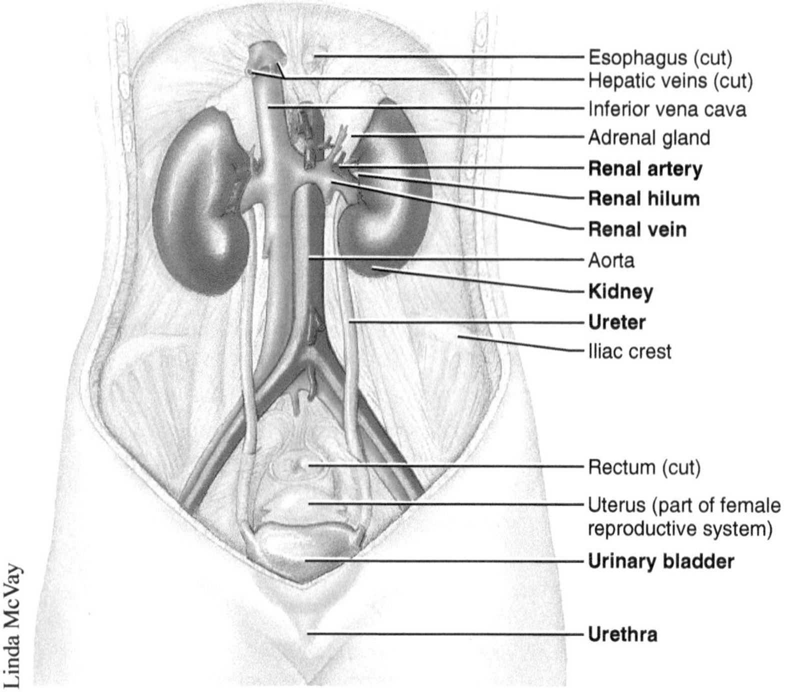
Esophagus (cut)
Hepatic veins (cut)
Inferior vena cava
Adrenal gland
Renal artery
Renal hilum
Renal vein
Aorta
Kidney
Ureter
Iliac crest
Rectum (cut)
Uterus (part of female reproductive system)
Urinary bladder
Urethra
Linda McVay

(a)

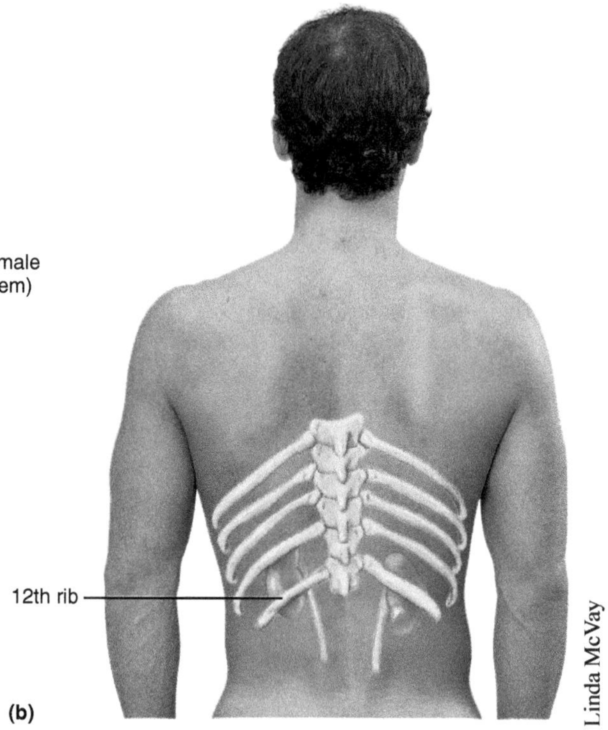
12th rib
Linda McVay

(b)

FIGURE 1 Organs of the urinary system. **(a)** Anterior view of the female urinary organs. Most unrelated abdominal organs have been removed. **(b)** Posterior in situ view showing the position of the kidneys relative to the twelfth rib pair. **(c)** Transverse section of the abdomen showing the kidneys in retroperitoneal position.

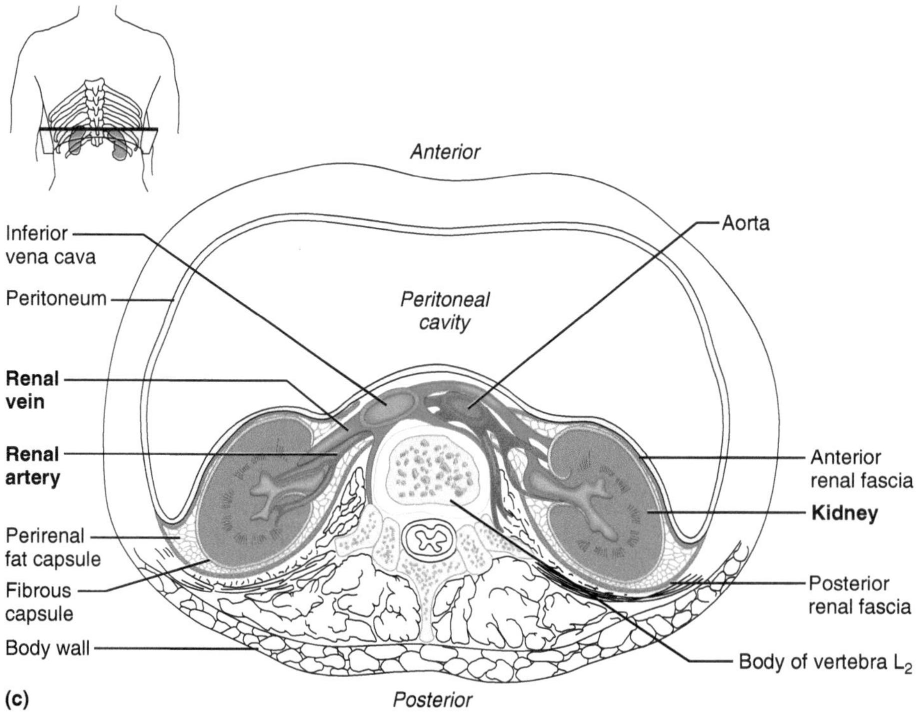
Anterior
Inferior vena cava
Peritoneum
Renal vein
Renal artery
Perirenal fat capsule
Fibrous capsule
Body wall
Aorta
Peritoneal cavity
Anterior renal fascia
Kidney
Posterior renal fascia
Body of vertebra L_2
Posterior

(c)

Imagineering

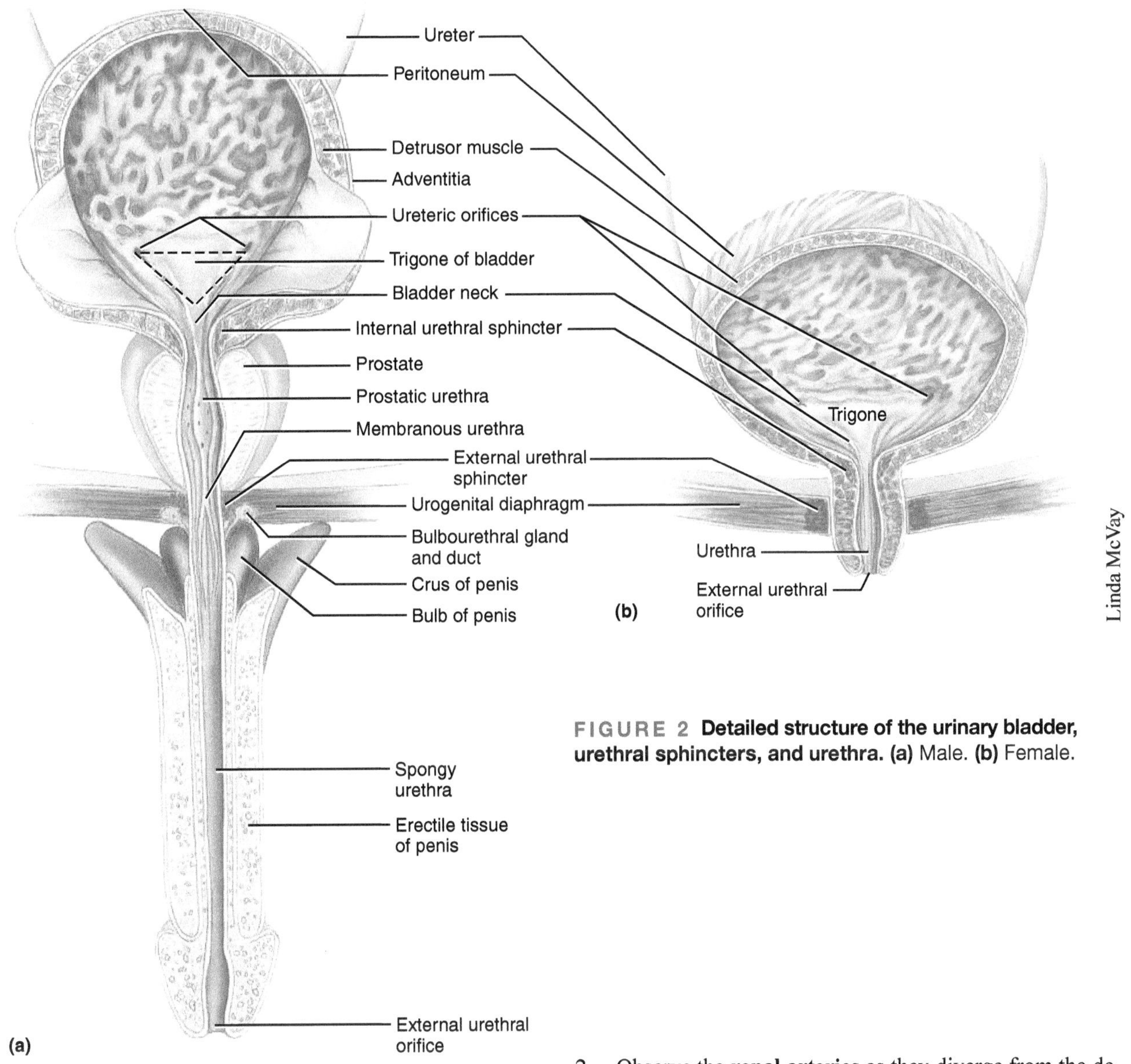
Ureter
Peritoneum
Detrusor muscle
Adventitia
Ureteric orifices
Trigone of bladder
Bladder neck
Internal urethral sphincter
Prostate
Prostatic urethra
Membranous urethra
External urethral sphincter
Urogenital diaphragm
Bulbourethral gland and duct
Crus of penis
Bulb of penis
Spongy urethra
Erectile tissue of penis
External urethral orifice
(a)
Trigone
Urethra
External urethral orifice
(b)
Linda McVay

FIGURE 2 Detailed structure of the urinary bladder, urethral sphincters, and urethra. (a) Male. **(b)** Female.

ACTIVITY 1

Identifying Urinary System Organs

Examine the human torso model, a large anatomical chart, or a three-dimensional model of the urinary system to locate and study the anatomy and relationships of the urinary organs.

1. Locate the paired kidneys on the dorsal body wall in the superior lumbar region. Notice that they are not positioned at exactly the same level. Because it is crowded by the liver, the right kidney is slightly lower than the left kidney. In a living person, a transparent membrane (the fibrous capsule), fat deposits (the *perirenal fat capsules*), and the fibrous renal fascia surround and hold the kidneys in place in a retroperitoneal position.

When the fatty material surrounding the kidneys is reduced or too meager in amount (in cases of rapid weight loss or in very thin individuals), the kidneys are less securely anchored and may drop to a more inferior position in the abdominal cavity. This phenomenon is called **ptosis.** ●

2. Observe the **renal arteries** as they diverge from the descending aorta and plunge into the indented medial region **(hilum)** of each kidney. Note also the **renal veins,** which drain the kidneys (circulatory drainage) and the two **ureters,** which drain urine from the kidneys and conduct it by peristalsis to the bladder for temporary storage.

3. Locate the **urinary bladder,** and observe the point of entry of the two ureters into this organ. Also locate the single **urethra,** which drains the bladder. The triangular region of the bladder delineated by these three openings (two ureteral and one urethral orifice) is referred to as the **trigone** (Figure 2).

4. Follow the course of the urethra to the body exterior. In the male, it is approximately 20 cm (8 inches) long, travels the length of the **penis,** and opens at its tip. Its three named regions—the *prostatic, membranous,* and *spongy urethrae*. The male urethra has a dual function: it is a urine conduit to the body exterior, and it provides a passageway for semen ejaculation. Thus in the male, the urethra is part of both the urinary and reproductive systems. In females, the urethra is very short, approximately 4 cm (1½ inches) long (see Figure 2).

capillaries send at nutrients

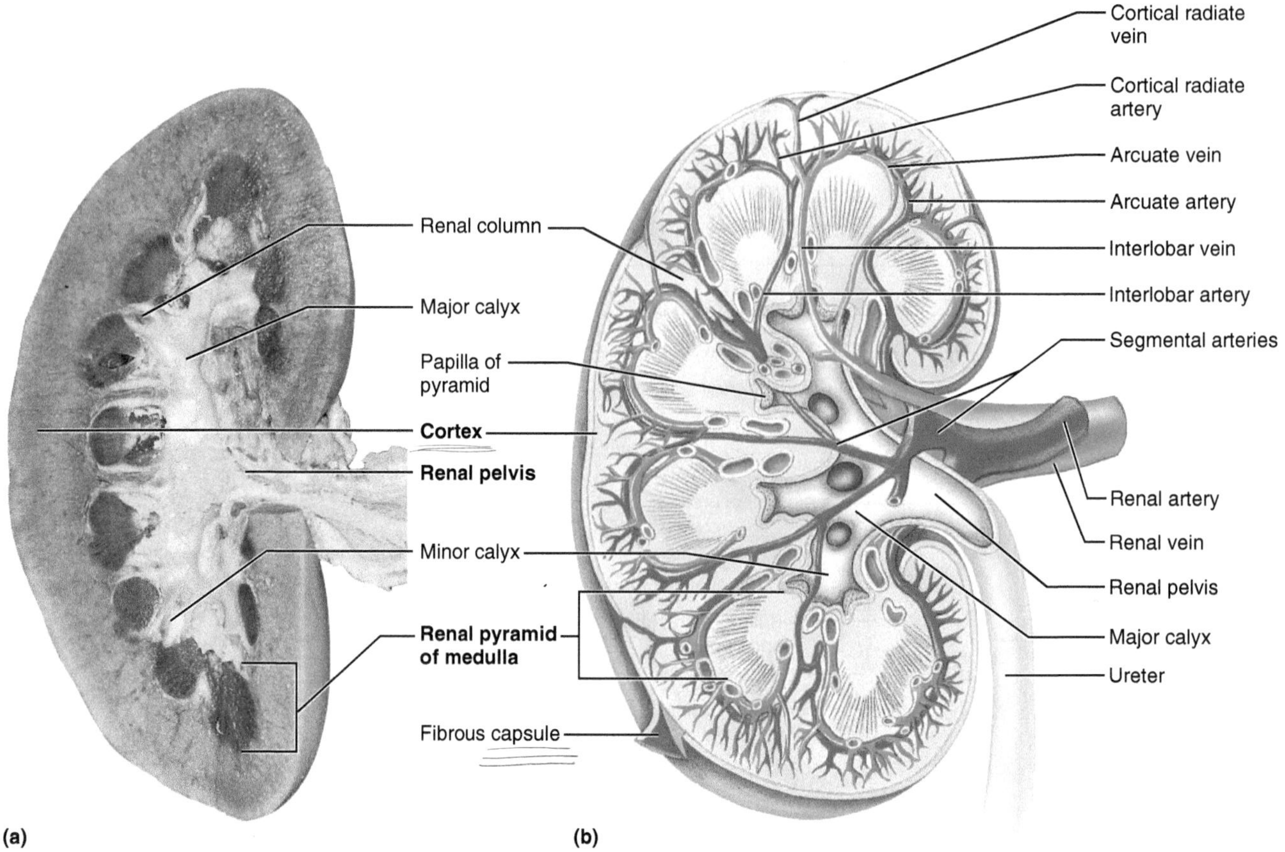

From *A Stereoscopic Atlas of Human Anatomy* by David L. Bassett

Imagineering

FIGURE 3 **Frontal section of a kidney. (a)** Photograph of a triple-injected pig kidney. Arteries and veins injected with red and blue latex respectively; pelvis and ureter injected with yellow latex. **(b)** Diagrammatic view showing the larger arteries supplying the kidney tissue.

There are no common urinary-reproductive pathways in the female, and the female's urethra serves only to transport urine to the body exterior. Its external opening, the **external urethral orifice,** lies anterior to the vaginal opening.

DISSECTION:

Gross Internal Anatomy of the Pig or Sheep Kidney

1. In preparation for dissection, don gloves. Obtain a preserved sheep or pig kidney, dissecting tray, and instruments. Observe the kidney to identify the **fibrous capsule,** a smooth, transparent membrane that adheres tightly to the external aspect of the kidney.

2. Find the ureter, renal vein, and renal artery at the hilum (indented) region. The renal vein has the thinnest wall and will be collapsed. The ureter is the largest of these structures and has the thickest wall.

3. Make a cut through the longitudinal axis (frontal section) of the kidney and locate the anatomical areas described below and depicted in Figure 3.

Kidney cortex: The superficial kidney region, which is lighter in color. If the kidney is doubly injected with latex, you will see a predominance of red and blue latex specks in this region indicating its rich vascular supply.

Medullary region: Deep to the cortex; a darker, reddish-brown color. The medulla is segregated into triangular regions that have a striped, or striated, appearance—the **medullary (renal) pyramids.** The base of each pyramid faces toward the cortex. Its more pointed **papilla,** or **apex,** points to the innermost kidney region.

Renal columns: Areas of tissue which are more like the cortex in appearance, which segregate and dip inward between the pyramids.

Renal pelvis: Medial to the hilum; a relatively flat, basinlike cavity that is continuous with the **ureter,** which exits from the hilum region. Fingerlike extensions of the pelvis should be visible. The larger, or primary, extensions are called the **major calyces** (singular: *calyx*); subdivisions of the major calyces are the **minor calyces.** Notice that the minor calyces terminate in cuplike areas that enclose the apexes of the medullary pyramids and collect urine draining from the pyramidal tips into the pelvis.

4. If the preserved kidney is doubly or triply injected, follow the renal blood supply from the renal artery to the **glomeruli.** The glomeruli appear as little red and blue specks in the cortex region. (See Figures 3 and 4.)

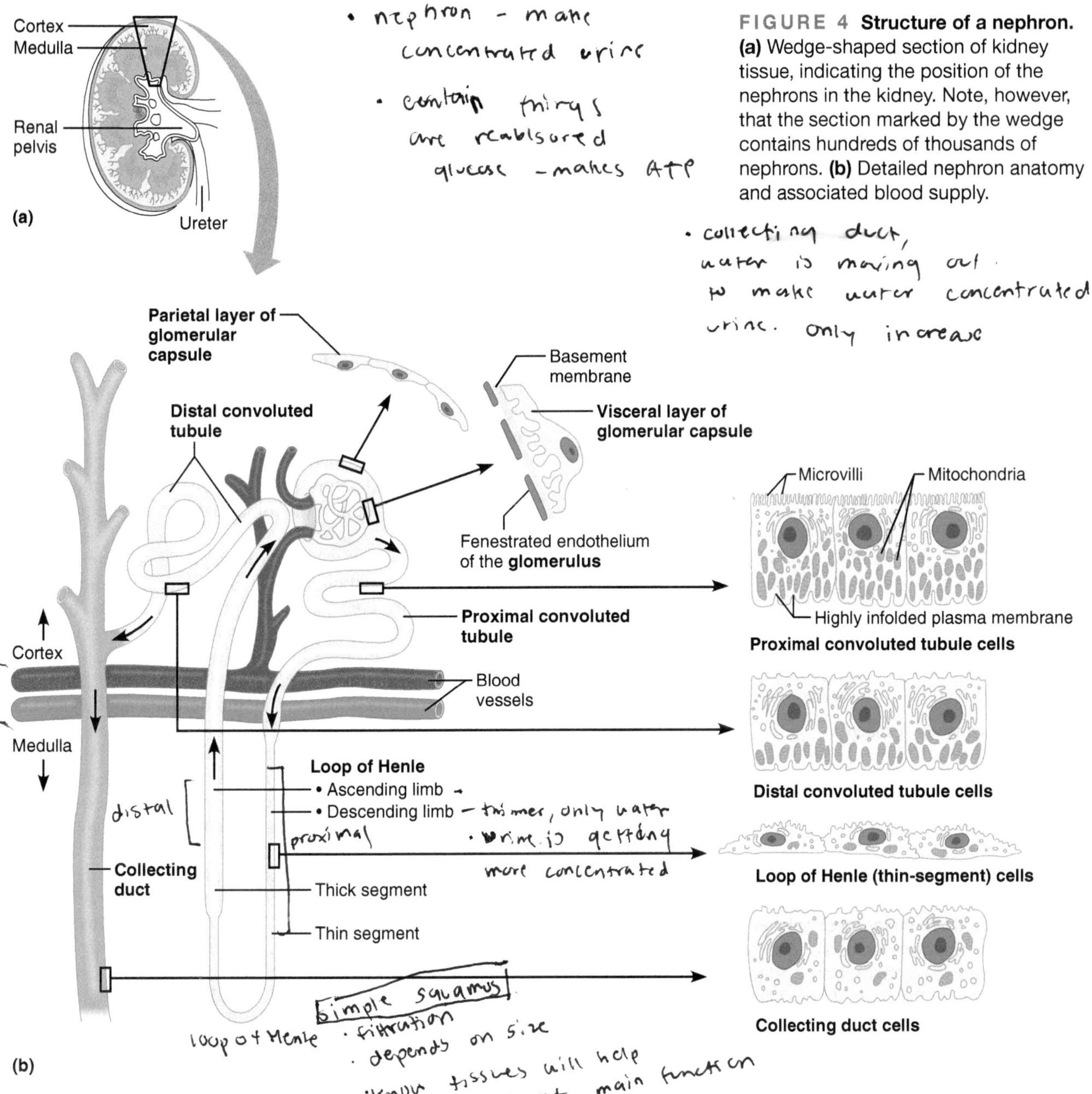
Cortex
Medulla
Renal pelvis
Ureter
(a)
Parietal layer of glomerular capsule
Basement membrane
Visceral layer of glomerular capsule
Distal convoluted tubule
Fenestrated endothelium of the glomerulus
Proximal convoluted tubule
Microvilli
Mitochondria
Highly infolded plasma membrane
Proximal convoluted tubule cells
Cortex
Blood vessels
Medulla
Distal convoluted tubule cells
Loop of Henle
• Ascending limb
• Descending limb
Collecting duct
Thick segment
Thin segment
Loop of Henle (thin-segment) cells
Collecting duct cells
(b)

FIGURE 4 Structure of a nephron. **(a)** Wedge-shaped section of kidney tissue, indicating the position of the nephrons in the kidney. Note, however, that the section marked by the wedge contains hundreds of thousands of nephrons. **(b)** Detailed nephron anatomy and associated blood supply.

Approximately a fourth of the total blood flow of the body is delivered to the kidneys each minute by the large **renal arteries.** As a renal artery approaches the kidney, it breaks up into branches called **segmental arteries,** which enter the hilum. Each segmental artery, in turn, divides into several **interlobar arteries,** which ascend toward the cortex in the renal column areas. At the top of the medullary region, these arteries give off arching branches, the **arcuate arteries,** which curve over the bases of the medullary pyramids. Small **cortical radiate arteries** branch off the arcuate arteries and ascend into the cortex, giving off the individual **afferent arterioles,** which provide the capillary networks (glomeruli and peritubular capillary beds) that supply the nephrons, or functional units, of the kidney. Blood draining from the nephron capillary networks in the cortex enters the **cortical radiate veins** and then drains through the **arcuate veins** and the **interlobar veins** to finally enter the **renal vein** in the pelvis region. (There are no segmental veins.)

Dispose of the kidney specimen as your instructor specifies.

Functional Microscopic Anatomy of the Kidney and Bladder

Kidney

Each kidney contains over a million nephrons, which are the anatomical units responsible for forming urine. Figure 4 depicts the detailed structure and the relative positioning of the nephrons in the kidney.

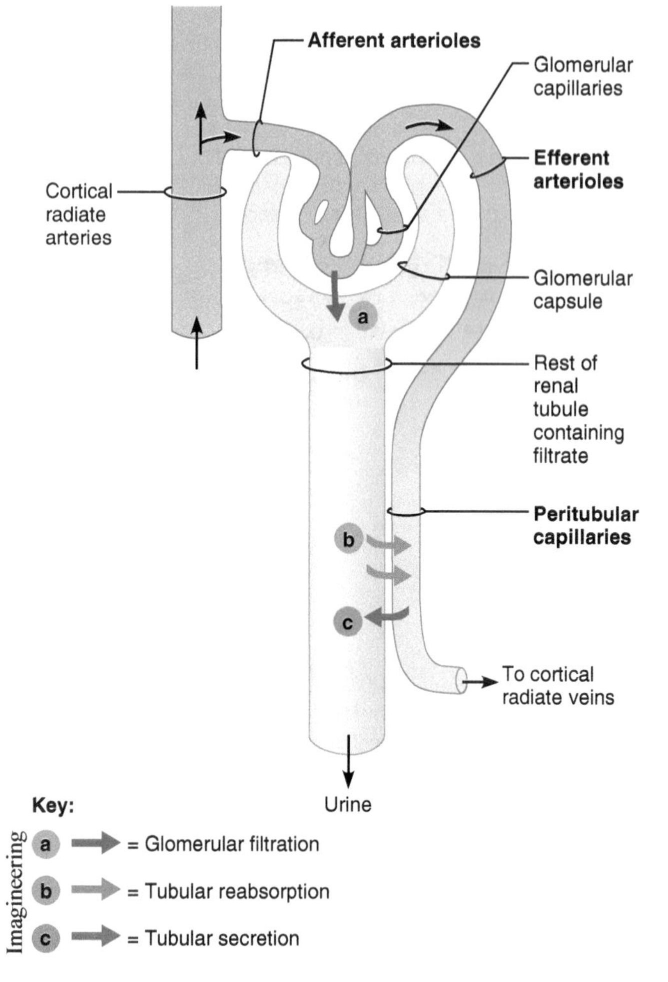

FIGURE 5 **The kidney depicted as a single, large nephron.** A kidney actually has millions of nephrons acting in parallel. The three major mechanisms by which the kidneys adjust the composition of plasma are **(a)** glomerular filtration, **(b)** tubular reabsorption, and **(c)** tubular secretion. Black arrows show the path of blood flow through the renal microcirculation.

Each nephron consists of two major structures: a **glomerulus** (a capillary knot) and a renal tubule. During embryologic development, each **renal tubule** begins as a blind-ended tubule that gradually encloses an adjacent capillary cluster, or glomerulus. The enlarged end of the tubule encasing the glomerulus is the **glomerular (Bowman's) capsule,** and its inner, or visceral, wall consists of highly specialized cells called **podocytes.** Podocytes have long, branching processes *(foot processes)* that interdigitate with those of other podocytes and cling to the endothelial wall of the glomerular capillaries, thus forming a very porous epithelial membrane surrounding the glomerulus. The glomerulus-capsule complex is sometimes called the **renal corpuscle.**

The rest of the tubule is approximately 3 cm (1.25 inches) long. As it emerges from the glomerular capsule, it becomes highly coiled and convoluted, drops down into a long hairpin loop, and then again coils and twists before entering a collecting duct. In order from the glomerular capsule, the anatomical areas of the renal tubule are: the **proximal convoluted tubule, loop of Henle** (descending and ascending limbs), and the **distal convoluted tubule.** The wall of the renal tubule is composed almost entirely of cuboidal epithelial cells, with the exception of part of the descending limb (and sometimes part of the ascending limb) of the loop of Henle, which is simple squamous epithelium. The lumen surfaces of the cuboidal cells in the proximal convoluted tubule have dense microvilli (a cellular modification that greatly increases the surface area exposed to the lumen contents, or filtrate). Microvilli also occur on cells of the distal convoluted tubule but in greatly reduced numbers, revealing its less significant role in reclaiming filtrate contents.

Most nephrons, called **cortical nephrons,** are located entirely within the cortex. However, parts of the loops of Henle of the **juxtamedullary nephrons** (located close to the cortex-medulla junction) penetrate well into the medulla. The **collecting ducts,** each of which receives urine from many nephrons, run downward through the medullary pyramids, giving them their striped appearance. As the collecting ducts approach the renal pelvis, they fuse together and empty the final urinary product into the minor calyces via the papillae of the pyramids.

The function of the nephron depends on several unique features of the renal circulation (see Figure 5). The capillary vascular supply consists of two distinct capillary beds, the *glomerulus* and the *peritubular capillary bed.* Vessels leading to and from the glomerulus, the first capillary bed, are both arterioles: the **afferent arteriole** feeds the bed while the **efferent arteriole** drains it. The glomerular capillary bed has no parallel elsewhere in the body. It is a high-pressure bed along its entire length. Its high pressure is a result of two major factors: (1) the bed is *fed and drained* by arterioles (arterioles are high-resistance vessels as opposed to venules, which are low-resistance vessels), and (2) the afferent feeder arteriole is larger in diameter than the efferent arteriole draining the bed. The high hydrostatic pressure created by these two anatomical features forces out fluid and blood components smaller than proteins from the glomerulus into the glomerular capsule. That is, it forms the filtrate which is processed by the nephron tubule.

The **peritubular capillary bed** arises from the efferent arteriole draining the glomerulus. This set of capillaries clings intimately to the renal tubule and empties into the cortical radiate veins that leave the cortex. The peritubular capillaries are *low-pressure,* porous capillaries adapted for absorption rather than filtration and readily take up the solutes and water reabsorbed from the filtrate by the tubule cells. The juxtamedullary nephrons have additional looping vessels, called the **vasa recta** (straight vessels), that parallel the long loops of Henle in the medulla. Hence, the two capillary beds of the nephron have very different, but complementary, roles: The glomerulus produces the filtrate and the peritubular capillaries reclaim most of that filtrate.

Additionally, each nephron has a region called a **juxtaglomerular apparatus (JGA),** which plays an important role in forming concentrated urine. The JGA consists of (1) *juxtaglomerular (JG) cells* (also called *granular cells*), which function as blood pressure sensors in the walls of the arterioles near the glomerulus, and (2) a *macula densa,* a specialized group of columnar chemoreceptor cells in the distal convoluted tubule abutting the JG cells (Figure 6a and Plate 2 in the Histology Atlas).

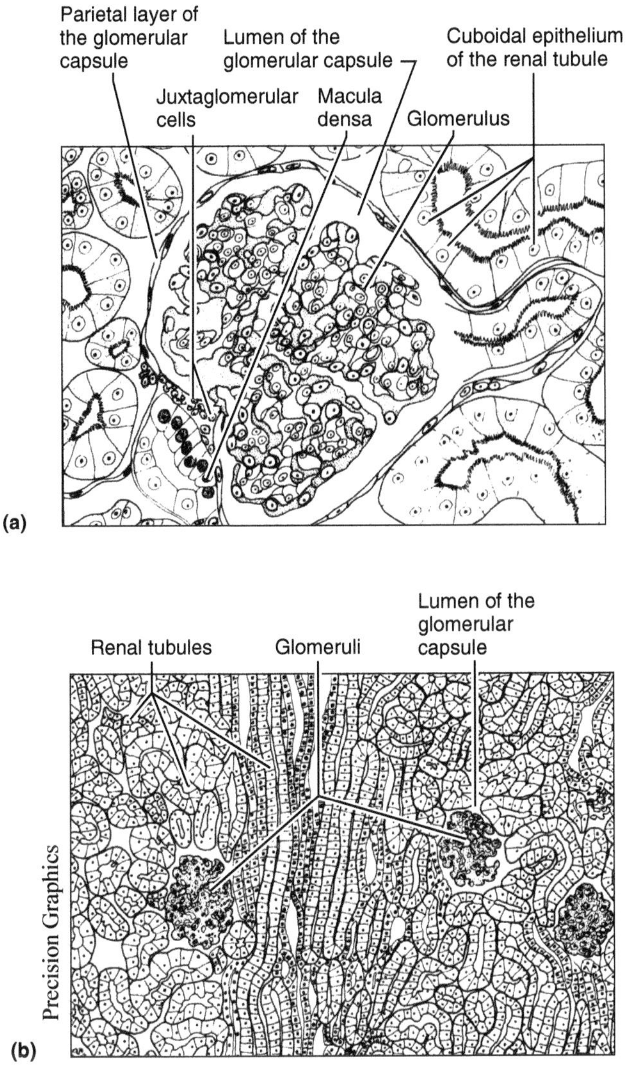
Parietal layer of the glomerular capsule
Lumen of the glomerular capsule
Cuboidal epithelium of the renal tubule
Juxtaglomerular cells
Macula densa
Glomerulus
(a)
Renal tubules
Glomeruli
Lumen of the glomerular capsule
Precision Graphics
(b)

FIGURE 6 Microscopic structure of kidney tissue. (a) Detailed structure of the glomerulus. **(b)** Low-power view of the renal cortex. (See also Plates 41 and 42 in the Histology Atlas.)

Urine formation is a result of three processes: *filtration, reabsorption,* and *secretion* (see Figure 5). **Filtration,** the role of the glomerulus, is largely a passive process in which a portion of the blood passes from the glomerular bed into the glomerular capsule. This filtrate then enters the proximal convoluted tubule where tubular reabsorption and secretion begin. During **tubular reabsorption,** many of the filtrate components move through the tubule cells and return to the blood in the peritubular capillaries. Some of this reabsorption is passive, such as that of water which passes by osmosis, but the reabsorption of most substances depends on active transport processes and is highly selective. Which substances are reabsorbed at a particular time depends on the composition of the blood and needs of the body at that time. Substances that are almost entirely reabsorbed from the filtrate include water, glucose, and amino acids. Various ions are selectively reabsorbed or allowed to go out in the urine according to what is required to maintain appropriate blood pH and electrolyte composition. Waste products (urea, creatinine, uric acid, and drug metabolites) are reabsorbed to a much lesser degree or not at all. Most (75% to 80%) of tubular reabsorption occurs in the proximal convoluted tubule. The balance occurs in other areas, especially the distal convoluted tubules and collecting ducts.

Tubular secretion is essentially the reverse process of tubular reabsorption. Substances such as hydrogen and potassium ions and creatinine move either from the blood of the peritubular capillaries through the tubular cells or from the tubular cells into the filtrate to be disposed of in the urine. This process is particularly important for the disposal of substances not already in the filtrate (such as drug metabolites), and as a device for controlling blood pH.

ACTIVITY 2

Studying Nephron Structure

1. Begin your study of nephron structure by identifying the glomerular capsule, proximal and distal convoluted tubule regions, and the loop of Henle on a model of the nephron. Then, obtain a compound microscope and a prepared slide of kidney tissue to continue with the microscope study of the kidney.

2. Hold the longitudinal section of the kidney up to the light to identify cortical and medullary areas. Then secure the slide on the microscope stage, and scan the slide under low power.

3. Move the slide so that you can see the cortical area. Identify a glomerulus, which appears as a ball of tightly packed material containing many small nuclei (Figures 6b and 7, and Plate 41 in the Histology Atlas). It is usually delineated by a vacant-appearing region (corresponding to the space between the visceral and parietal layers of the glomerular capsule) that surrounds it.

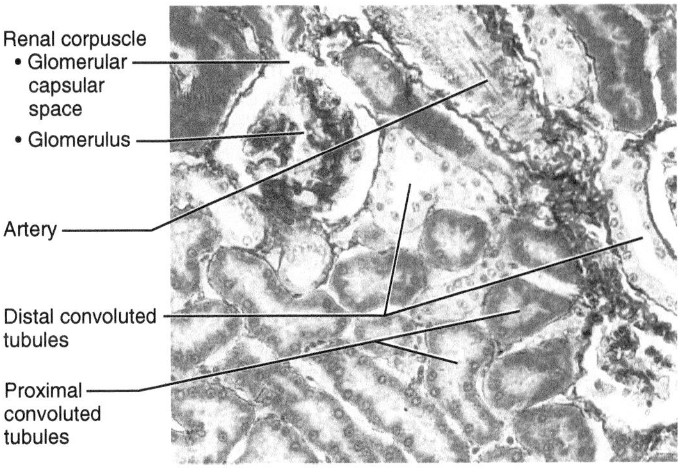
Renal corpuscle
• Glomerular capsular space
• Glomerulus
Artery
Distal convoluted tubules
Proximal convoluted tubules

FIGURE 7 Photomicrograph of renal cortical tissue. Notice the renal corpuscles and the sections through the various tubules. In the proximal convoluted tubules, the lumens appear "fuzzy" because they are filled with the long microvilli of the epithelial cells that form the tubule walls. In the distal tubules, by contrast, the lumens are clear (200×).

4. Notice that the renal tubules are cut at various angles. Try to differentiate between the fuzzy cuboidal epithelium of the proximal convoluted tubule, which has dense microvilli, and that of the distal convoluted tubule with sparse microvilli (Figure 7). Also identify the thin-walled loop of Henle.

Bladder

Although urine production by the kidney is a continuous process, urine is usually removed from the body when voiding is convenient. In the meantime the **urinary bladder,** which receives urine via the ureters and discharges it via the urethra, stores it temporarily.

Voiding, or **micturition,** is the process in which urine empties from the bladder. Two sphincter muscles or valves (see Figure 2), the **internal urethral sphincter** (more superiorly located) and the **external urethral sphincter** (more inferiorly located) control the outflow of urine from the bladder. Ordinarily, the bladder continues to collect urine until about 200 ml have accumulated, at which time the stretching of the bladder wall activates stretch receptors. Impulses transmitted to the central nervous system subsequently produce reflex contractions of the bladder wall through parasympathetic nervous system pathways (in other words, via the pelvic splanchnic nerves). As contractions increase in force and frequency, stored urine is forced past the internal sphincter, which is a smooth muscle involuntary sphincter, into the superior part of the urethra. It is then that a person feels the urge to void. The inferior external sphincter consists of skeletal muscle and is voluntarily controlled. If it is not convenient to void, the opening of this sphincter can be inhibited. Conversely, if the time is convenient, the sphincter may be relaxed and the stored urine flushed from the body. If voiding is inhibited, the reflex contractions of the bladder cease temporarily and urine continues to accumulate in the bladder. After another 200 to 300 ml of urine have been collected, the *micturition reflex* will again be initiated.

Lack of voluntary control over the external sphincter is referred to as **incontinence.** Incontinence is normal in children 2 years old or younger, as they have not yet gained control over the voluntary sphincter. In adults and older children, incontinence is generally a result of spinal cord injury, emotional problems, bladder irritability, or some other pathology of the urinary tract. ●

ACTIVITY 3

Studying Bladder Structure

1. Return the kidney slide to the supply area, and obtain a slide of bladder tissue. Scan the bladder tissue. Identify its three layers: mucosa, muscular layer, and fibrous adventitia.

2. Study the mucosa with its highly specialized transitional epithelium. The plump, transitional epithelial cells have the ability to slide over one another, thus decreasing the thickness of the mucosa layer as the bladder fills and stretches to accommodate the increased urine volume. Depending on the degree of stretching of the bladder, the mucosa may be three to eight cell layers thick. Compare the transitional epithelium of the mucosa to that shown in Figure 3h of the Classification of Tissues lab, if you have completed it.

3. Examine the heavy muscular wall (detrusor muscle), which consists of three irregularly arranged muscular layers. The innermost and outermost muscle layers are arranged longitudinally; the middle layer is arranged circularly. Attempt to differentiate the three muscle layers.

4. Draw a small section of the bladder wall, and label all regions or tissue areas.

5. Compare your sketch of the bladder wall to the structure of the ureter wall shown in Plate 43 in the Histology Atlas. How are the two organs similar histologically?

____

____

____

What is/are the most obvious differences?

____

____

NAME ______________________

LAB TIME/DATE ______________________

REVIEW SHEET

Anatomy of the Urinary System

Gross Anatomy of the Human Urinary System

1. Complete the following statements.

The kidney is referred to as an excretory organ because it excretes __1__ wastes. It is also a major homeostatic organ because it maintains the electrolyte, __2__ , and __3__ balance of the blood.

Urine is continuously formed by the __4__ and is routed down the __5__ by the mechanism of __6__ to a storage organ called the __7__ . Eventually, the urine is conducted to the body __8__ by the urethra. In the male, the urethra is __9__ centimeters long and transports both urine and __10__ . The female urethra is __11__ centimeters long and transports only urine.

Voiding or emptying the bladder is called __12__ . Voiding has both voluntary and involuntary components. The voluntary sphincter is the __13__ sphincter. An inability to control this sphincter is referred to as __14__ .

1. ______________________
2. ______________________
3. ______________________
4. ______________________
5. ______________________
6. ______________________
7. ______________________
8. ______________________
9. ______________________
10. ______________________
11. ______________________
12. ______________________
13. ______________________
14. ______________________

2. What is the function of the fat cushion that surrounds the kidneys in life? ______________________

____

3. Define *ptosis.* ______________________

____

4. Why is incontinence a normal phenomenon in the child under 1½ to 2 years old? ______________________

____

What events may lead to its occurrence in the adult? ______________________

____

____

5. Complete the labeling of the diagram to correctly identify the urinary system organs.

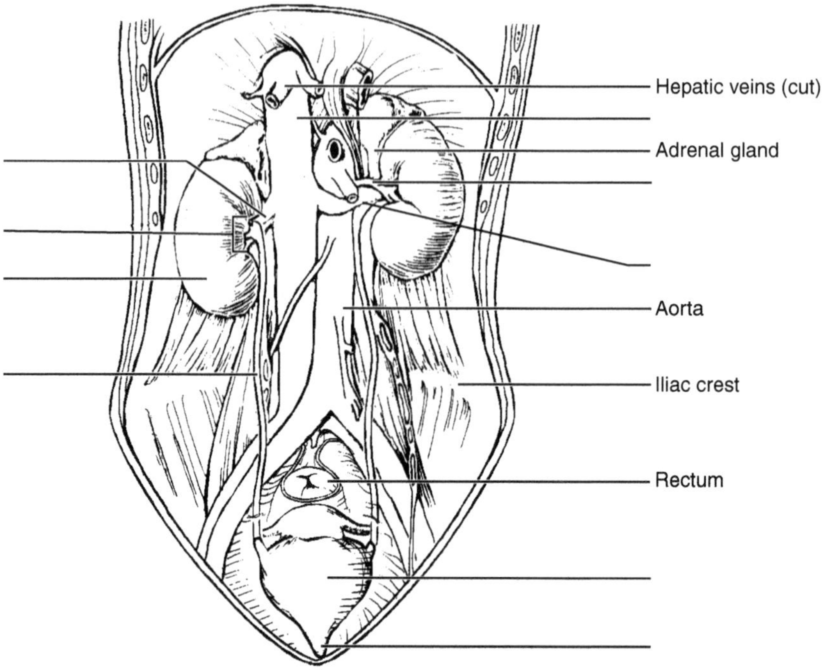
Hepatic veins (cut)
Adrenal gland
Aorta
Iliac crest
Rectum

Gross Internal Anatomy of the Pig or Sheep Kidney

6. Match the appropriate structure in column B to its description in column A.

	Column A	Column B
_______	1. smooth membrane, tightly adherent to the kidney surface	a. cortex
_______	2. portion of the kidney containing mostly collecting ducts	b. medulla
_______	3. portion of the kidney containing the bulk of the nephron structures	c. minor calyx
_______	4. superficial region of kidney tissue	d. fibrous capsule
_______	5. basinlike area of the kidney, continuous with the ureter	e. renal column
_______	6. a cup-shaped extension of the pelvis that encircles the apex of a pyramid	f. renal pelvis
_______	7. area of cortical tissue running between the medullary pyramids	

Functional Microscopic Anatomy of the Kidney and Bladder

7. Match each lettered structure in the diagram of the nephron (and associated renal blood supply) with the correct name in the numbered list.

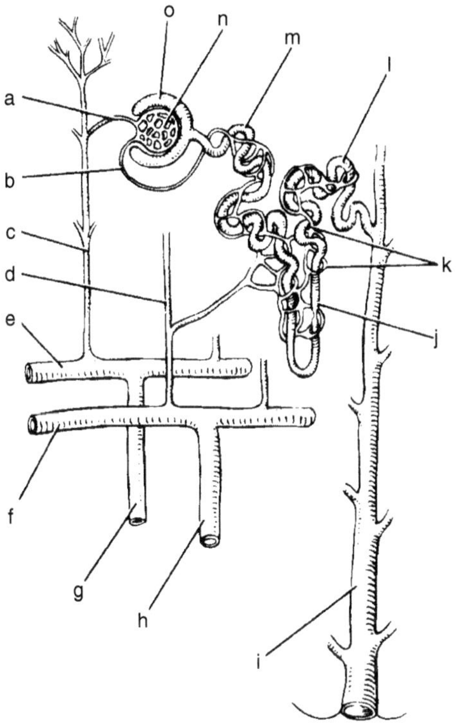

_______ 1. afferent arteriole

_______ 2. arcuate artery

_______ 3. arcuate vein

_______ 4. collecting duct

_______ 5. cortical radiate artery

_______ 6. cortical radiate vein

_______ 7. distal convoluted tubule

_______ 8. efferent arteriole

_______ 9. glomerular capsule

_______ 10. glomerulus

_______ 11. interlobar artery

_______ 12. interlobar vein

_______ 13. loop of Henle

_______ 14. peritubular capillaries

_______ 15. proximal convoluted tubule

8. Use the terms provided in question 7 to identify the following descriptions.

_______________ 1. site of filtrate formation

_______________ 2. primary site of tubular reabsorption

_______________ 3. secondarily important site of tubular reabsorption

_______________ 4. structure that conveys the processed filtrate (urine) to the renal pelvis

_______________ 5. blood supply that directly receives substances from the tubular cells

_______________ 6. its inner (visceral) membrane forms part of the filtration membrane

9. Explain *why* the glomerulus is such a high-pressure capillary bed. _______________

____

How does its high-pressure condition aid its function of filtrate formation? _______________

____

10. What structural modification of certain tubule cells enhances their ability to reabsorb substances from the filtrate?

____

11. Explain the mechanism of tubular secretion, and explain its importance in the urine formation process. ______________

____

____

12. Compare and contrast the composition of blood plasma and glomerular filtrate. ______________

____

13. Trace a drop of blood from the time it enters the kidney via the renal artery until it leaves the kidney through the renal vein.

Renal artery → ____

____

____ → renal vein

14. Define *juxtaglomerular apparatus.* ______________________________

____

15. Label the figure using the key letters of the correct terms.

Key: a. juxtaglomerular cells

b. cuboidal epithelium

c. macula densa

d. glomerular capsule (parietal layer)

e. distal convoluted tubule

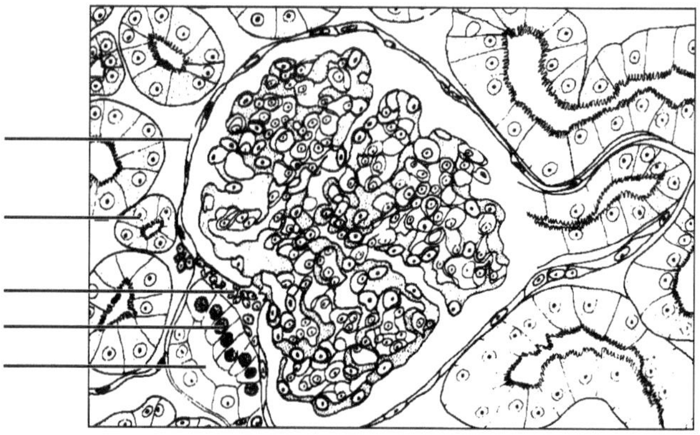

16. Trace the anatomical pathway of a molecule of creatinine (metabolic waste) from the glomerular capsule to the urethra. Note each microscopic and/or gross structure it passes through in its travels. Name the subdivisions of the renal tubule.

Glomerular capsule → ____

____

____ → urethra

17. What is important functionally about the specialized epithelium (transitional epithelium) in the bladder?

____

Urinalysis

MATERIALS

- ☐ Disposable gloves
- ☐ Student urine samples collected at the beginning of the laboratory or "normal" artificial urine provided by the instructor*
- ☐ Numbered "pathological" urine specimens provided by the instructor*
- ☐ Wide-range pH paper
- ☐ Dipsticks: individual (Clinistix, Ketostix, Albustix, Hemastix) or combination (Chemstrip, Combistix, or Multistix)
- ☐ Urinometer
- ☐ Test tubes, test tube rack, and test tube holders
- ☐ 10-cc graduated cylinders
- ☐ Test reagents for sulfates: 10% barium chloride solution, dilute HCl (hydrochloric acid)
- ☐ Hot plate
- ☐ 500-ml beaker
- ☐ Test reagent for phosphates: dilute nitric acid, dilute ammonium molybdate
- ☐ Glass stirring rod
- ☐ Test reagent for chloride: 3.0% silver nitrate solution ($AgNO_3$), freshly prepared
- ☐ Clean microscope slide and coverslip
- ☐ Compound microscope
- ☐ Test reagent for urea: concentrated nitric acid in dropper bottles
- ☐ Test reagent for glucose (Clinitest tablets) and Clinitest color chart
- ☐ Medicine droppers

*Directions for making artificial urine are provided in the Instructor's Guide for this manual.

Text continues on next page

OBJECTIVES

1. To list the physical characteristics of urine, and to indicate the normal pH and specific gravity ranges.
2. To list substances that are normal urinary constituents.
3. To conduct various urinalysis tests and procedures, and to use them to determine the substances present in a urine specimen.
4. To define the following urinary conditions:

calculi	hematuria
glycosuria	hemoglobinuria
albuminuria	pyuria
ketonuria	casts

5. To explain the implications and possible causes of conditions listed in objective 4.

Blood composition depends on three major factors: diet, cellular metabolism, and urinary output. In 24 hours, the kidneys'2 million nephrons filter 150 to 180 liters of blood plasma through their glomeruli into the tubules, where it is selectively processed by tubular reabsorption and secretion. In the same period, urinary output, which contains by-products of metabolism and excess ions, is 1.0 to 1.8 liters. In healthy individuals, the kidneys can maintain blood constancy despite wide variations in diet and metabolic activity. With certain pathological conditions, urine composition often changes dramatically.

Characteristics of Urine

To be valuable as a diagnostic tool, a urinalysis must be done within 30 minutes after the urine is voided or on refrigerated urine. Freshly voided urine is generally clear and pale yellow to amber in color. This normal yellow color is due to *urochrome,* a pigment metabolite arising from the body's destruction of hemoglobin (via bilirubin or bile pigments). As a rule, color variations from pale yellow to deeper amber indicate the relative concentration of solutes to water in the urine. The greater the solute concentration, the deeper the color. Abnormal urine color may be due to certain foods, such as beets, various drugs, bile, or blood.

The odor of freshly voided urine is slightly aromatic, but bacterial action gives it an ammonia-like odor when left standing. Some drugs, vegetables (such as asparagus), and various disease processes (such as diabetes mellitus) alter the characteristic odor of urine. For example, the urine of a person with uncontrolled diabetes mellitus (and elevated levels of ketones) smells fruity or acetone-like.

The pH of urine ranges from 4.5 to 8.0, but its average value, 6.0, is slightly acidic. Diet may markedly influence the pH of the urine. For example, a diet high in protein (meat, eggs, cheese) and whole wheat products increases the acidity of urine. Such foods are called *acid ash foods.* On the other hand, a vegetarian diet *(alkaline ash diet)* increases the alkalinity of the urine.* A bacterial infection of the urinary tract may also result in urine with a high pH.

*The naming of foods as acid or alkaline *ash* derives from the fact that if an acid ash food is burned to ash, the pH of the ash is acidic. The ash of alkaline ash foods is alkaline.

(materials list, continued)

- ☐ Timer (watch or clock with a second hand)
- ☐ Ictotest reagent tablets and test mat
- ☐ Flasks and laboratory buckets containing 10% bleach solution
- ☐ Disposable autoclave bags
- ☐ *Demonstration:* Instructor-prepared specimen of urine sediment set up for microscopic analysis

PEx PhysioEx™ 7.0 Computer Simulation

Specific gravity is the relative weight of a specific volume of liquid compared with an equal volume of distilled water. The specific gravity of distilled water is 1.000, because 1 ml weighs 1 g. Since urine contains dissolved solutes, it weighs more than water, and its customary specific gravity ranges from 1.001 to 1.030. Urine with a specific gravity of 1.001 contains few solutes and is considered very dilute. Dilute urine commonly results when a person drinks excessive amounts of water, uses diuretics, or suffers from diabetes insipidus or chronic renal failure. Conditions that produce urine with a high specific gravity include limited fluid intake, fever, and kidney inflammation, called *pyelonephritis.* If urine becomes excessively concentrated, some of the substances normally held in solution begin to precipitate or crystallize, forming **kidney stones,** or **renal calculi.**

Normal constituents of urine (in order of decreasing concentration) include water; urea;[†] sodium,[‡] potassium, phosphate, and sulfate ions; creatinine;[†] and uric acid.[†] Much smaller but highly variable amounts of calcium, magnesium, and bicarbonate ions are also found in the urine. Abnormally high concentrations of any of these urinary constituents may indicate a pathological condition.

Abnormal Urinary Constituents

Abnormal urinary constituents are substances not normally present in the urine when the body is operating properly. ●

[†]Urea, uric acid, and creatinine are the most important nitrogenous wastes found in urine. Urea is an end product of protein breakdown; uric acid is a metabolite of purine breakdown; and creatinine is associated with muscle metabolism of creatine phosphate.

[‡]Sodium ions appear in relatively high concentration in the urine because of reduced urine volume, not because large amounts are being secreted. Sodium is the major positive ion in the plasma; under normal circumstances, most of it is actively reabsorbed.

Glucose

The presence of glucose in the urine, a condition called **glycosuria,** indicates abnormally high blood sugar levels. Normally, blood sugar levels are maintained between 80 and 100 mg/100 ml of blood. At this level all glucose in the filtrate is reabsorbed by the tubular cells and returned to the blood. Glycosuria may result from carbohydrate intake so excessive that normal physiological and hormonal mechanisms cannot clear it from the blood quickly enough. In such cases, the active transport reabsorption mechanisms of the renal tubules for glucose are exceeded—but only temporarily.

Pathological glycosuria occurs in conditions such as uncontrolled diabetes mellitus, in which the body cells are unable to absorb glucose from the blood because the pancreatic islet cells produce inadequate amounts of the hormone insulin, or there is some abnormality of the insulin receptors. Under such circumstances, the body cells increase their metabolism of fats, and the excess and unusable glucose spills out in the urine.

Albumin

Albuminuria, or the presence of albumin in urine, is an abnormal finding. Albumin is the single most abundant blood protein and is very important in maintaining the osmotic pressure of the blood. Albumin, like other blood proteins, is too large to pass through the glomerular filtration membrane. Thus, albuminuria is generally indicative of abnormally increased permeability of the glomerular membrane. Certain nonpathological conditions, such as excessive exertion, pregnancy, or overabundant protein intake, can temporarily increase the membrane permeability, leading to **physiological albuminuria.** Pathological conditions resulting in albuminuria include events that damage the glomerular membrane, such as kidney trauma due to blows, the ingestion of poisons or heavy metals, bacterial toxins, glomerulonephritis, and hypertension.

Ketone Bodies

Ketone bodies (acetoacetic acid, beta-hydroxybutyric acid, and acetone) normally appear in the urine in very small amounts. **Ketonuria,** the presence of these intermediate products of fat metabolism in excessive amounts, usually indicates that abnormal metabolic processes are occurring. The result may be *acidosis* and its complications. Ketonuria is an expected finding during starvation, or diets very low in carbohydrates, when inadequate food intake forces the body to use its fat stores. Ketonuria coupled with a finding of glycosuria is generally diagnostic for diabetes mellitus.

Red Blood Cells

Hematuria, the appearance of red blood cells, or erythrocytes, in the urine, almost always indicates pathology of the urinary tract, because erythrocytes are too large to pass through the glomerular pores. Possible causes include irritation of the urinary tract organs by calculi (kidney stones), which produces frank bleeding; infection or tumors of the urinary tract; or physical trauma to the urinary organs. In healthy menstruating females, it may reflect accidental contamination of the urine sample with the menstrual flow.

Hemoglobin

Hemoglobinuria, the presence of hemoglobin in the urine, is a result of the fragmentation, or hemolysis, of red blood cells. As a result, hemoglobin is liberated into the plasma and subsequently appears in the kidney filtrate. Hemoglobinuria indicates various pathological conditions including hemolytic anemias, transfusion reactions, burns, poisonous snake bites, or renal disease.

Nitrites

The presence of urinary nitrites might indicate a bacterial infection, particularly *E. coli* or other gram-negative rods. Nitrites are valuable for early detection of bladder infections.

Bile Pigments

Bilirubinuria, the appearance of bilirubin (bile pigments) in urine, is an abnormal finding and usually indicates liver pathology, such as hepatitis, cirrhosis, or bile duct blockage. Bilirubinuria is signaled by a yellow foam that forms when the urine sample is shaken.

Urobilinogen is produced in the intestine from bilirubin and gives feces a brown color. Some urobilinogen is reabsorbed into the blood and either excreted back into the intestine by the liver or excreted by the kidneys in the urine. Complete absence of urobilinogen may indicate renal disease or obstruction of bile flow in the liver. Increased levels may indicate hepatitis A, cirrhosis, or biliary disease.

White Blood Cells

Pyuria is the presence of white blood cells or other pus constituents in the urine. It indicates inflammation of the urinary tract.

Casts

Any complete discussion of the varieties and implications of casts is beyond the scope of this exercise. However, because they always represent a pathological condition of the kidney or urinary tract, they should at least be mentioned. **Casts** are hardened cell fragments, usually cylindrical, which are formed in the distal convoluted tubules and collecting ducts and then flushed out of the urinary tract. Hyaline casts are formed from a mucoprotein secreted by tubule cells. These casts form when the filtrate flow rate is slow, the pH is low, or the salt concentration is high, all conditions which cause protein to denature. Red blood cell casts are typical in glomerulonephritis, as red blood cells leak through the filtration membrane and stick together in the tubules. White blood cell casts form when the kidney is inflamed, which is typically a result of pyelonephritis but sometimes occurs with glomerulonephritis. Degenerated renal tubule cells form granular or waxy casts. Broad waxy casts may indicate end-stage renal disease. Two cast types are shown in Figure 1.

ACTIVITY 1

Analyzing Urine Samples

In this part of the exercise, you will use prepared dipsticks and perform chemical tests to determine the characteristics of normal urine as well as to identify abnormal urinary components. You will investigate two or more urine samples. The first, designated as the *standard urine specimen* in the chart, will be either yours or a "normal" sample provided by your instructor. The second will be an unknown urine specimen provided by your instructor. Make the following determinations on both samples, and record your results by circling the appropriate item or description or by adding data to complete the chart. If you have more than one unknown sample, accurately identify each sample by number.

! *Obtain and wear disposable gloves throughout this laboratory session.* Although the instructor-provided urine samples are actually artificial urine (concocted in the laboratory to resemble real urine), the techniques of safe handling of body fluids should still be observed as part of your learning process. When you have completed the laboratory procedures: (1) dispose of the gloves, used pH paper strips, and dipsticks in the autoclave bag; (2) put used glassware in the bleach-containing laboratory bucket; (3) wash the lab bench down with 10% bleach solution.

Determination of the Physical Characteristics of Urine

1. Determine the color, transparency, and odor of your "normal" sample and one of the numbered pathological samples, and circle the appropriate descriptions in the Urinalysis Results chart.

2. Obtain a roll of wide-range pH paper to determine the pH of each sample. Use a fresh piece of paper for each test, and dip the strip into the urine to be tested two or three times before comparing the color obtained with the chart on the dispenser. Record your results in the chart. (If you will be using one of the combination dipsticks—Chemstrip, Combistix, or Multistix—this pH determination can be done later.)

3. To determine specific gravity, obtain a urinometer cylinder and float. Mix the urine well, and fill the urinometer cylinder about two-thirds full with urine.

4. Examine the urinometer float to determine how to read its markings. In most cases, the scale has numbered lines separated by a series of unnumbered lines. The numbered lines give the reading for the first two decimal places. You must determine the third decimal place by reading the lower edge of the meniscus—the curved surface representing the urine-air junction—on the stem of the float.

5. Carefully lower the urinometer float into the urine. Make sure it is floating freely before attempting to take the reading. Record the specific gravity of both samples in the chart. Do not dispose of this urine if the samples that you have are less than 200 ml in volume because you will need to make several more determinations.

Determination of Inorganic Constituents in Urine

Sulfates Using a 10-cc graduated cylinder, add 5 ml of urine to a test tube, and then add a few drops of dilute hydrochloric acid and 2 ml of 10% barium chloride solution. The appearance of a white precipitate (barium sulfate) indicates the presence of sulfates in the sample. Clean the graduated cylinder and the test tubes well after use. Record your results.

Are sulfates a *normal* constituent of urine? ____________

Phosphates Obtain a hot plate and a 500-ml beaker. To prepare the hot water bath, half fill the beaker with tap water and heat it on the hot plate. Add 5 ml of urine to a test tube, and then add three or four drops of dilute nitric acid and 3 ml of ammonium molybdate. Mix well with a glass stirring rod, and then heat gently in a hot water bath. Formation of a yellow precipitate indicates the presence of phosphates in the sample. Record your results.

Chlorides Place 5 ml of urine in a test tube, and add several drops of silver nitrate ($AgNO_3$). The appearance of a white precipitate (silver chloride) is a positive test for chlorides. Record your results.

Nitrites Use a combination dipstick to test for nitrites. Record your results.

Determination of Organic Constituents in Urine

Individual dipsticks or combination dipsticks (Chemstrip, Combistix, or Multistix) may be used for many of the tests in this section. If combination dipsticks are used, be prepared to take the readings on several factors (pH, protein [albumin], glucose, ketones, blood/hemoglobin, leukocytes, urobilinogen, bilirubin, and nitrites) at the same time. Generally speaking, results for all of these tests may be read *during* the second minute after immersion, but readings taken after 2 minutes have passed should be considered invalid. Pay careful attention to the directions for method and time of immersion and disposal of excess urine from the strip, regardless of the dipstick used. If you are testing your own urine and get an unanticipated result, it is helpful to know that most of the combination dipsticks produce false positive or negative results for certain solutes when the subject is taking vitamin C, aspirin, or certain drugs.

Urea Put two drops of urine on a clean microscope slide and *carefully* add one drop of concentrated nitric acid to the urine. Slowly warm the mixture on a hot plate until it begins to dry at the edges, but do not allow it to boil or to evaporate to dryness. When the slide has cooled, examine the edges of the preparation under low power to identify the rhombic or hexagonal crystals of urea nitrate, which form when urea and nitric acid react chemically. Keep the light low for best contrast. Record your results.

Glucose Use a combination dipstick or obtain a vial of Clinistix, and conduct the dipstick test according to the instructions on the vial. Record your results in the Urinalysis Results chart.

Because the Clinitest reagent is routinely used in clinical agencies for glucose determinations in pediatric patients (children), it is worthwhile to conduct this test as well. Obtain the Clinitest tablets and the associated color chart. You will need a timer (watch or clock with a second hand) for this test. Using a medicine dropper, put 5 drops of urine into a test tube; then rinse the dropper and add 10 drops of water to the tube. Add a Clinitest tablet. Wait 15 seconds and then compare the color obtained to the color chart. Record your results.

Albumin Use a combination dipstick or obtain the Albustix dipsticks, and conduct the determinations as indicated on the vial. Record your results.

Ketones Use a combination dipstick or obtain the Ketostix dipsticks. Conduct the determinations as indicated on the vial. Record your results.

Blood/Hemoglobin Test your urine samples for the presence of hemoglobin by using a Hemastix dipstick or a combination dipstick according to the directions on the vial. Usually a short drying period is required before making the reading, so read the directions carefully. Record your results.

Bilirubin Using a combination dipstick, determine if there is any bilirubin in your urine samples. Record your results.

Also conduct the Ictotest for the presence of bilirubin. Using a medicine dropper, place one drop of urine in the center of one of the special test mats provided with the Ictotest reagent tablets. Place one of the reagent tablets over the drop of urine, and then add two drops of water directly to the tablet. If the mixture turns purple when you add water, bilirubin is present. Record your results.

Leukocytes Use a combination dipstick to test for leukocytes. Record your results.

Urobilinogen Use a combination dipstick to test for urobilinogen. Record your results.

Clean up your area.

Urinalysis Results*

Observation or test	Normal values	Standard urine specimen	Unknown specimen (# ____)
Physical Characteristics			
Color	Pale yellow	Yellow: pale medium dark other ____________	Yellow: pale medium dark other ____________
Transparency	Transparent	Clear Slightly cloudy Cloudy	Clear Slightly cloudy Cloudy
Odor	Characteristic	Describe: ____________	Describe: ____________
pH	4.5–8.0	____________	____________
Specific gravity	1.001–1.030	____________	____________
Inorganic Components			
Sulfates	Present	Present Absent	Present Absent
Phosphates	Present	Present Absent	Present Absent
Chlorides	Present	Present Absent	Present Absent
Nitrites	Absent	Present Absent	Present Absent
Organic Components			
Urea	Present	Present Absent	Present Absent
Glucose Dipstick: ______	Negative	Record results: ____________	Record results: ____________
Clinitest	Negative	____________	____________
Albumin Dipstick: ______	Negative	____________	____________
Ketone bodies Dipstick: ______	Negative	____________	____________
RBCs/hemoglobin Dipstick: ______	Negative	____________	____________
Bilirubin Dipstick: ______	Negative	____________	____________
Ictotest	Negative (no color change)	Negative Positive (purple)	Negative Positive (purple)
Leukocytes	Absent	Present Absent	Present Absent
Urobilinogen	Present	Present Absent	Present Absent

*Circle the appropriate description if provided; otherwise, record the results you observed. Identify dipsticks used.

ACTIVITY 2

Analyzing Urine Sediment Microscopically (Optional)

If desired by your instructor, a microscopic analysis of urine sediment (of "real" urine) can be done. The urine sample to be analyzed microscopically has been centrifuged to spin the more dense urine components to the bottom of a tube, and some of the sediment (mounted on a slide) has been stained with Sedi-stain to make the components more visible.

Go to the demonstration microscope to conduct this study. Using the lowest light source possible, examine the slide under low power to determine if any of the sediments illustrated in Figure 1 can be seen.

Unorganized sediments: Chemical substances that form crystals or precipitate from solution; for example, calcium oxalates, carbonates, and phosphates; uric acid; ammonium ureates; and cholesterol. Also, if one has been taking antibiotics or certain drugs such as sulfa drugs, these may be detectable in the urine in crystalline form. Normal urine contains very small amounts of crystals, but conditions such as urinary retention or urinary tract infection may cause the appearance of much larger amounts (and their possible consolidation into calculi). The high-power lens may be needed to view the various crystals, which tend to be much more minute than the organized (cellular) sediments.

Organized sediments: Include epithelial cells (rarely of any pathological significance), pus cells (white blood cells), red blood cells, and casts. Urine is normally negative for organized sediments, and the presence of the last three categories mentioned, other than trace amounts, always indicates kidney pathology.

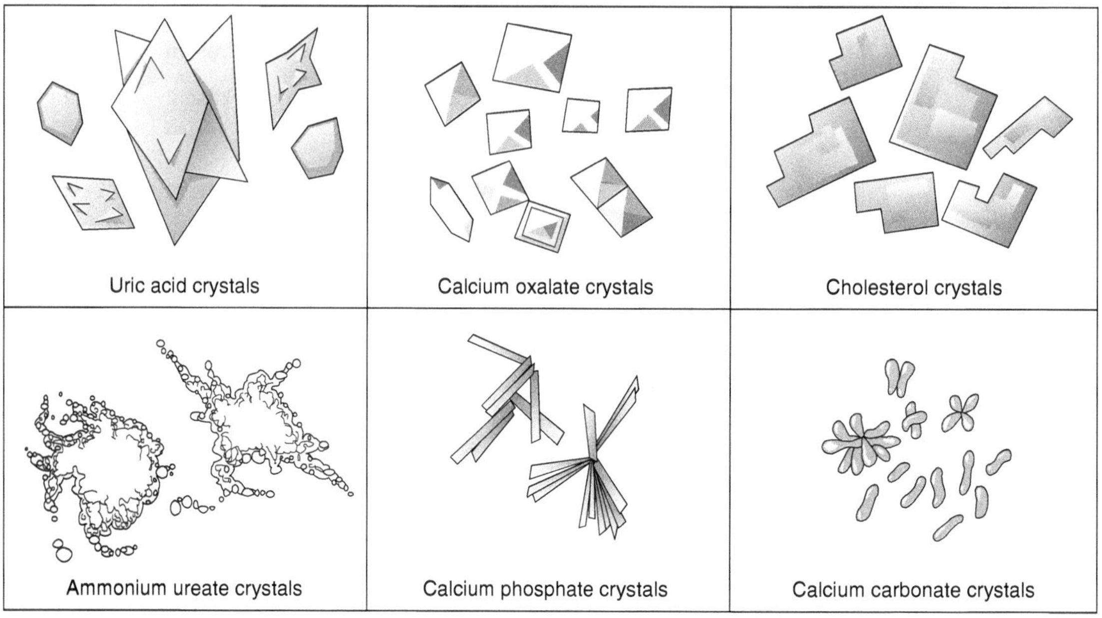
Uric acid crystals
Calcium oxalate crystals
Cholesterol crystals
Ammonium ureate crystals
Calcium phosphate crystals
Calcium carbonate crystals

(a) Unorganized sediments

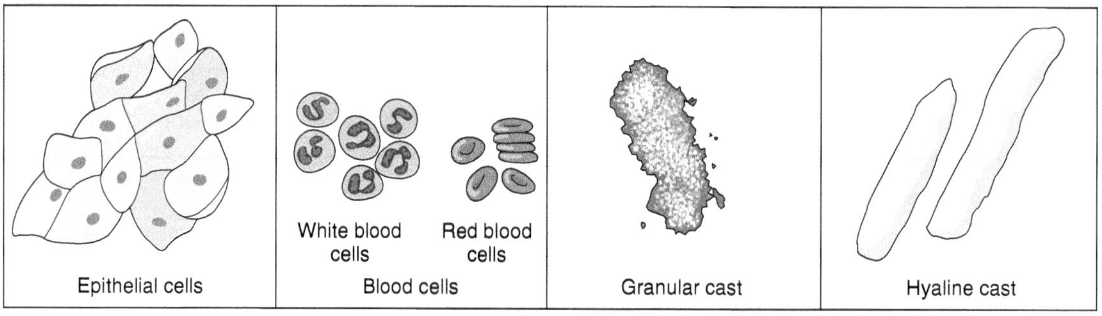
Epithelial cells
White blood cells
Red blood cells
Blood cells
Granular cast
Hyaline cast

(b) Organized sediments

Precision Graphics

FIGURE 1 **Examples of sediments. (a)** Unorganized sediments. **(b)** Organized sediments.

NAME ______________________

LAB TIME/DATE ________________

REVIEW SHEET

Urinalysis

Characteristics of Urine

1. What is the normal volume of urine excreted in a 24-hour period? __________

2. Assuming normal conditions, note whether each of the following substances would be (a) in greater relative concentration in the urine than in the glomerular filtrate, (b) in lesser concentration in the urine than in the glomerular filtrate, or (c) absent from both the urine and the glomerular filtrate.

______ 1. water	______ 6. amino acids	______ 11. uric acid
______ 2. phosphate ions	______ 7. glucose	______ 12. creatinine
______ 3. sulfate ions	______ 8. albumin	______ 13. pus (WBCs)
______ 4. potassium ions	______ 9. red blood cells	______ 14. nitrites
______ 5. sodium ions	______ 10. urea	

3. Explain why urinalysis is a routine part of any good physical examination. ______________________________

____

4. What substance is responsible for the normal yellow color of urine? ______________________________

5. Which has a greater specific gravity: 1 ml of urine or 1 ml of distilled water? ________ Explain your answer. ________

____

6. Explain the relationship between the color, specific gravity, and volume of urine. ______________________________

____

Abnormal Urinary Constituents

7. A microscopic examination of urine may reveal the presence of certain abnormal urinary constituents.

   Name three constituents that might be present if a urinary tract infection exists. ______________________________,

   ______________________________, and ______________________________

8. How does a urinary tract infection influence urine pH? ______________________________

   How does starvation influence urine pH? ______________________________

9. All urine specimens become alkaline and cloudy on standing at room temperature. Explain why. ______________________________

____

10. Several specific terms have been used to indicate the presence of abnormal urine constituents. Identify each of the abnormalities described below by inserting a term from the key at the right that names the condition.

_______________ 1. presence of erythrocytes in the urine

_______________ 2. presence of hemoglobin in the urine

_______________ 3. presence of glucose in the urine

_______________ 4. presence of albumin in the urine

_______________ 5. presence of ketone bodies (acetone and others) in the urine

_______________ 6. presence of pus (white blood cells) in the urine

Key:

a. albuminuria
b. glycosuria
c. hematuria
d. hemoglobinuria
e. ketonuria
f. pyuria

11. What are renal calculi, and what conditions favor their formation? _______________

____

12. Glucose and albumin are both normally absent in the urine, but the reason for their exclusion differs. Explain the reason for the absence of glucose. _______________

Explain the reason for the absence of albumin. _______________

13. The presence of abnormal constituents or conditions in urine may be associated with diseases, disorders, or other causes listed in the key. Select and list all conditions associated with each numbered item.

_______ 1. low specific gravity

_______ 2. high specific gravity

_______ 3. glucose

_______ 4. albumin

_______ 5. blood cells

_______ 6. hemoglobin

_______ 7. bilirubin

_______ 8. ketone bodies

_______ 9. casts

_______ 10. pus

Key:

a. cystitis (inflammation of the bladder)
b. diabetes insipidus
c. diabetes mellitus
d. eating a 5-lb box of sweets for lunch
e. glomerulonephritis
f. gonorrhea
g. hemolytic anemias
h. hepatitis, cirrhosis of the liver
i. kidney stones
j. pregnancy, exertion
k. pylonephritis
l. starvation

14. Name the three major nitrogenous wastes found in the urine. _______________,

_______________, and _______________

15. Explain the difference between organized and unorganized sediments. _______________

____

____

Anatomy of the Digestive System

MATERIALS

- ☐ Dissectible torso model
- ☐ Anatomical chart of the human digestive system
- ☐ Prepared slides of the liver and mixed salivary glands; of longitudinal sections of the gastroesophageal junction and a tooth; and of cross sections of the stomach, duodenum, and ileum
- ☐ Compound microscope
- ☐ Three-dimensional model of a villus (if available)
- ☐ Jaw model or human skull
- ☐ Three-dimensional model of liver lobules (if available)
- ☐ *Human Digestive System* videotape*

AIA This exercise uses the A.D.A.M.® Interactive Anatomy program.

*Available to qualified adopters from Benjamin Cummings.

OBJECTIVES

1. To state the overall function of the digestive system.
2. To identify on an appropriate diagram or torso model the organs comprising the alimentary canal, and to name their subdivisions if any.
3. To name and/or identify the accessory digestive organs.
4. To describe the general functions of the digestive system organs or structures.
5. To describe the general histologic structure of the alimentary canal wall and/or label a cross-sectional diagram of the wall with the following terms: mucosa, submucosa, muscularis externa, and serosa or adventitia.
6. To list and explain the specializations of the structure of the stomach and small intestine that contribute to their functional roles.
7. To list the major enzymes or enzyme groups produced by the salivary glands, stomach, small intestine, and pancreas.
8. To name human deciduous and permanent teeth, and to describe the anatomy of the generalized tooth.
9. To recognize (by microscopic inspection or by viewing an appropriate diagram or photomicrograph) the histologic structure of the following organs:

small intestine	pancreas	stomach
salivary glands	tooth	liver

The **digestive system** provides the body with the nutrients, water, and electrolytes essential for health. The organs of this system ingest, digest, and absorb food and eliminate the undigested remains as feces.

The digestive system consists of a hollow tube extending from the mouth to the anus, into which various accessory organs or glands empty their secretions (Figure 1). Food material within this tube, the *alimentary canal,* is technically outside the body because it has contact only with the cells lining the tract. For ingested food to become available to the body cells, it must first be broken down *physically* (by chewing or churning) and *chemically* (by enzymatic hydrolysis) into its smaller diffusible molecules—a process called **digestion.** The digested end products can then pass through the epithelial cells lining the tract into the blood for distribution to the body cells—a process termed **absorption.** In one sense, the digestive tract can be viewed as a disassembly line, in which food is carried from one stage of its digestive processing to the next by muscular activity, and its nutrients are made available to the cells of the body en route.

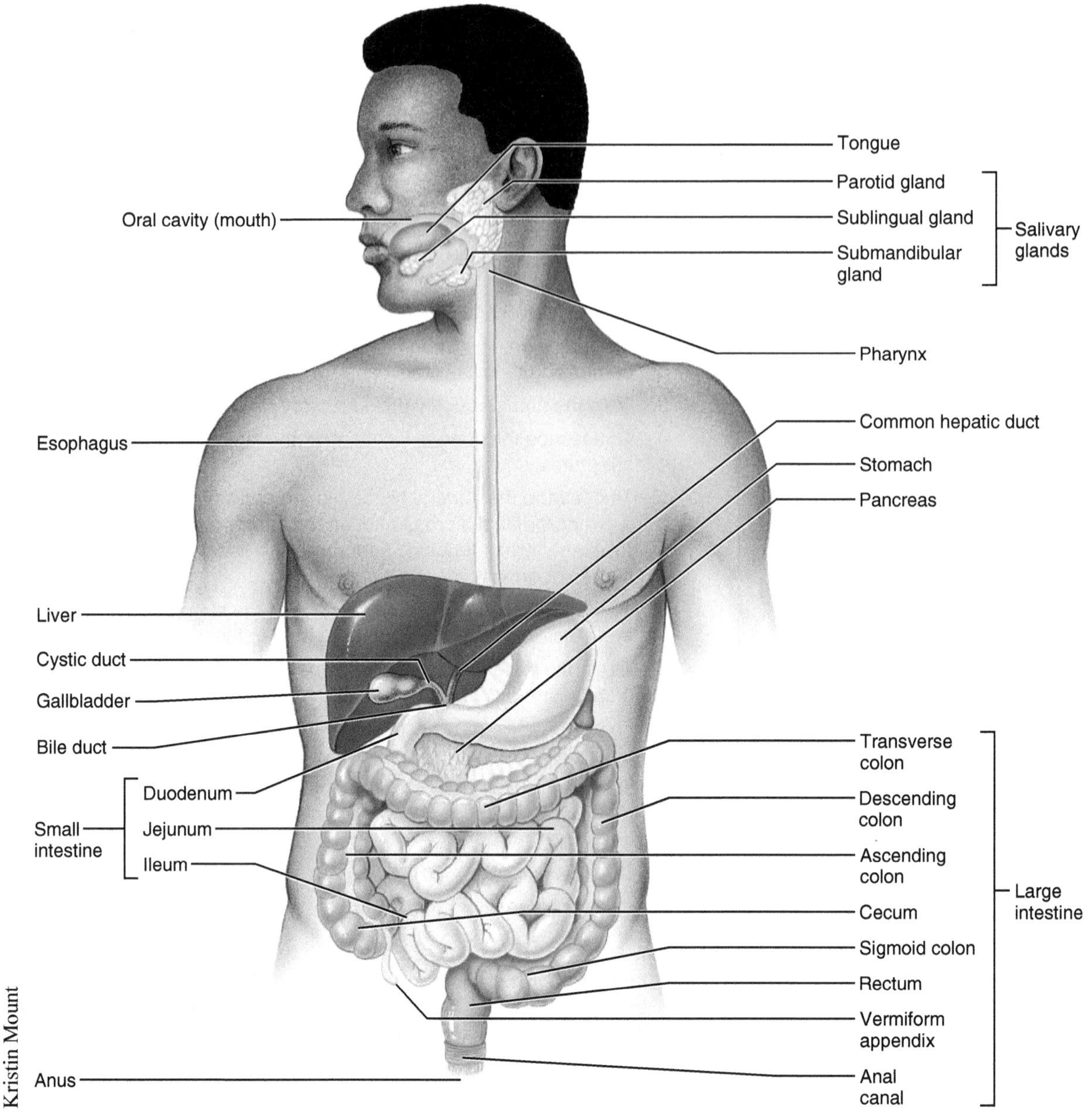

FIGURE 1 **The human digestive system: alimentary tube and accessory organs.** (Liver and gallbladder are reflected superiorly and to the right.)

The organs of the digestive system are traditionally separated into two major groups: the **alimentary canal,** or **gastrointestinal (GI) tract,** and the **accessory digestive organs.** The alimentary canal is approximately 9 meters long in a cadaver but is considerably shorter in a living person due to muscle tone. It consists of the mouth, pharynx, esophagus, stomach, and small and large intestines. The accessory structures include the teeth, which physically break down foods, and the salivary glands, gallbladder, liver, and pancreas, which secrete their products into the alimentary canal. These individual organs are described shortly.

General Histological Plan of the Alimentary Canal

Because the alimentary canal has a shared basic structural plan (particularly from the esophagus to the anus), it makes sense to review that general structure as we begin studying this group of organs. Then our descriptions of individual organs can focus on their specializations for unique functions in the digestive process.

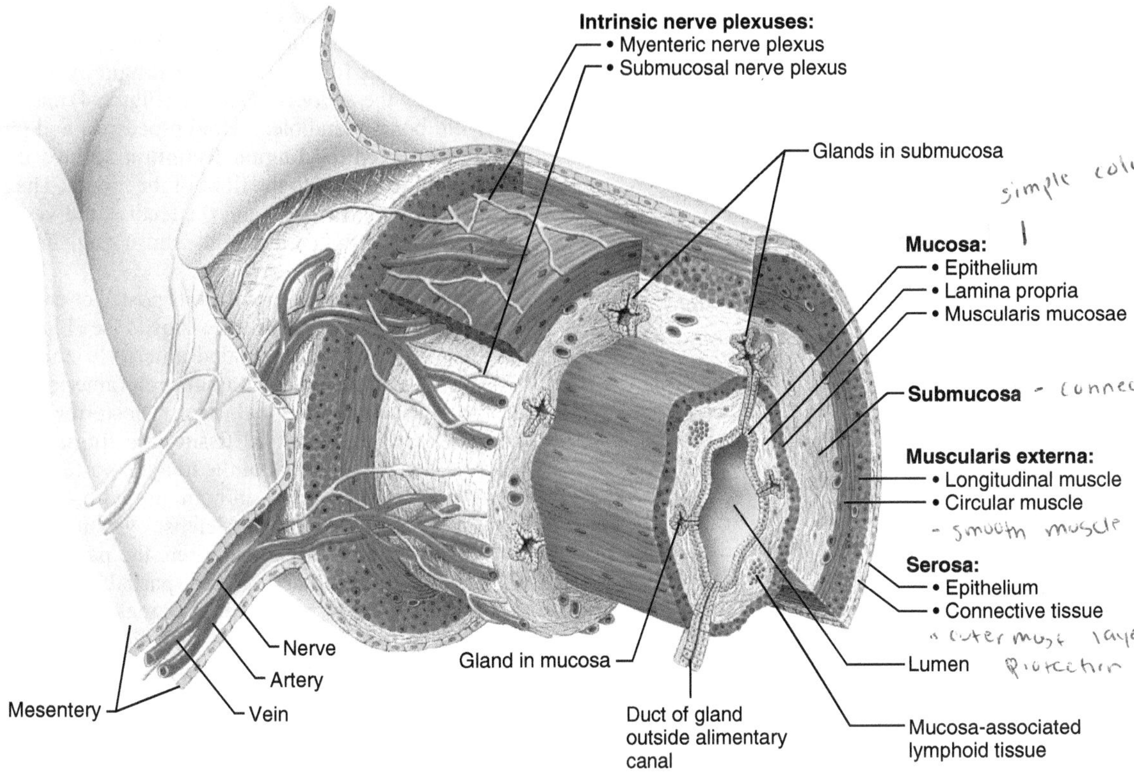
Intrinsic nerve plexuses:
• Myenteric nerve plexus
• Submucosal nerve plexus
Glands in submucosa
Mucosa:
• Epithelium
• Lamina propria
• Muscularis mucosae
Submucosa
Muscularis externa:
• Longitudinal muscle
• Circular muscle
Serosa:
• Epithelium
• Connective tissue
Lumen
Mucosa-associated lymphoid tissue
Duct of gland outside alimentary canal
Gland in mucosa
Nerve
Artery
Vein
Mesentery

Adapted from Seeley, Stephens, and Tate, *Anatomy & Physiology,* 4e, F24.2, New York: WCB/ McGraw-Hill, © McGraw-Hill, 1998

FIGURE 2 **Basic structural pattern of the alimentary canal wall.** (See also Plate 37 in the Histology Atlas.)

Essentially the alimentary canal walls have four basic **tunics** (layers). From the lumen outward, these are the *mucosa,* the *submucosa,* the *muscularis externa,* and either a *serosa* or *adventitia* (Figure 2). Each of these tunics has a predominant tissue type and a specific function in the digestive process.

Mucosa (mucous membrane): The mucosa is the wet epithelial membrane abutting the alimentary canal lumen. It consists of a surface *epithelium* (in most cases, a simple columnar), a *lamina propria* (areolar connective tissue on which the epithelial layer rests), and a *muscularis mucosae* (a scant layer of smooth muscle fibers that enable local movements of the mucosa). The major functions of the mucosa are secretion (of enzymes, mucus, hormones, etc.), absorption of digested foodstuffs, and protection (against bacterial invasion). A particular mucosal region may be involved in one or all three functions.

Submucosa: The submucosa is moderately dense connective tissue containing blood and lymphatic vessels, scattered lymphoid follicles, and nerve fibers. Its intrinsic nerve supply is called the *submucosal plexus.* Its major functions are nutrition and protection.

Muscularis externa: The muscularis externa, also simply called the *muscularis,* typically is a bilayer of smooth muscle, with the inner layer running circularly and the outer layer running longitudinally. Another important intrinsic nerve plexus, the *myenteric plexus,* is associated with this tunic. By controlling the smooth muscle of the muscularis, this plexus is the major regulator of GI motility.

Serosa: The outermost covering of most of the alimentary canal is the serosa, also called the *visceral peritoneum.* It consists of mesothelium associated with a thin layer of areolar connective tissue. In areas *outside* the abdominopelvic cavity, the serosa is replaced by an **adventitia,** a layer of coarse fibrous connective tissue that binds the organ to surrounding tissues. (This is the case with the esophagus.) The serosa reduces friction as the mobile digestive system organs work and slide across one another and the cavity walls. The adventitia anchors and protects the surrounded organ.

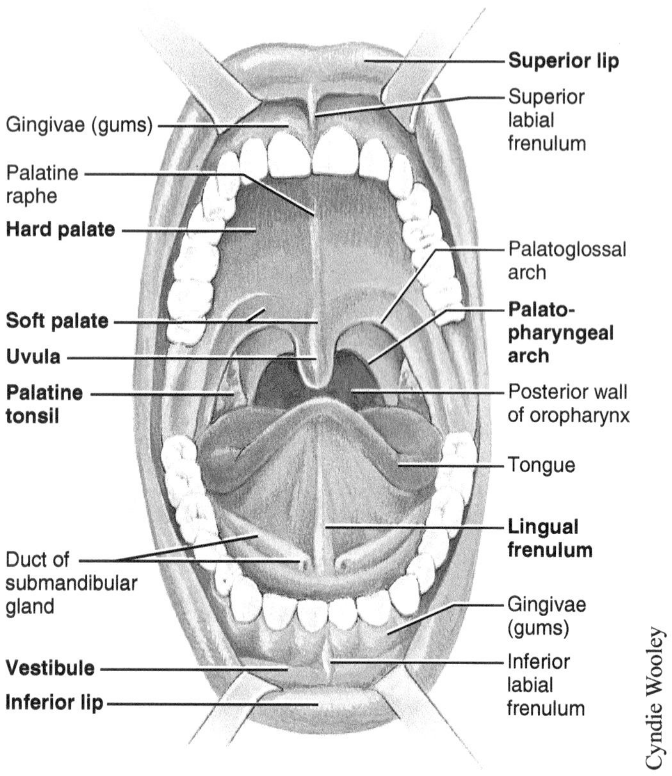
Superior lip
Superior labial frenulum
Gingivae (gums)
Palatine raphe
Hard palate
Palatoglossal arch
Soft palate
Palato-pharyngeal arch
Uvula
Palatine tonsil
Posterior wall of oropharynx
Tongue
Lingual frenulum
Duct of submandibular gland
Gingivae (gums)
Vestibule
Inferior labial frenulum
Inferior lip
Cyndie Wooley

FIGURE 3 Anterior view of the oral cavity.

Organs of the Alimentary Canal

ACTIVITY 1

Identifying Alimentary Canal Organs

The sequential pathway and fate of food as it passes through the alimentary canal organs are described in the next sections. Identify each structure in Figure 1 and on the torso model or anatomical chart of the digestive system as you work.

Oral Cavity or Mouth

Food enters the digestive tract through the **oral cavity,** or **mouth** (Figure 3). Within this mucous membrane–lined cavity are the gums, teeth, tongue, and openings of the ducts of the salivary glands. The **lips (labia)** protect the opening of the chamber anteriorly, the **cheeks** form its lateral walls, and the **palate,** its roof. The anterior portion of the palate is referred to as the **hard palate** because bone (the palatine processes of the maxillae and horizontal plates of the palatine bones) underlies it. The posterior **soft palate** is a fibromuscular structure that is unsupported by bone. The **uvula,** a fingerlike projection of the soft palate, extends inferiorly from its posterior margin. The soft palate rises to close off the oral cavity from the nasal and pharyngeal passages during swallowing. The floor of the oral cavity is occupied by the muscular **tongue,** which is largely supported by the *mylohyoid muscle* (Figure 4) and attaches to the hyoid bone, mandible, styloid processes, and pharynx. A membrane called the **lingual frenulum** secures the inferior midline of the tongue to the floor of the mouth. The space between the lips and cheeks and the teeth is the **vestibule;** the area that lies within the teeth and gums (gingivae) is the **oral cavity** proper.

On each side of the mouth at its posterior end are masses of lymphoid tissue, the **palatine tonsils** (see Figure 3). Each lies in a concave area bounded anteriorly and posteriorly by membranes, the **palatoglossal arch** (anterior membrane) and the **palatopharyngeal arch** (posterior membrane). Another mass of lymphoid tissue, the **lingual tonsil** (see Figure 4), covers the base of the tongue, posterior to the oral cavity proper. The tonsils, in common with other lymphoid tissues, are part of the body's defense system.

Very often in young children, the palatine tonsils become inflamed and enlarge, partially blocking the entrance to the pharynx posteriorly and making swallowing difficult and painful. This condition is called **tonsillitis.** ●

Three pairs of salivary glands duct their secretion, saliva, into the oral cavity. One component of saliva, salivary amylase, begins the digestion of starchy foods within the oral cavity.

As food enters the mouth, it is mixed with saliva and masticated (chewed). The cheeks and lips help hold the food between the teeth during mastication, and the highly mobile tongue manipulates the food during chewing and initiates swallowing. Thus the mechanical and chemical breakdown of food begins before the food has left the oral cavity. The surface of the tongue is covered with papillae, many of which contain taste buds. Taste buds contain taste cells, receptors for taste sensation. So, in addition to its manipulative function, the tongue permits the enjoyment and appreciation of the food ingested.

Pharynx

When the tongue initiates swallowing, the food passes posteriorly into the pharynx, a common passageway for food, fluid, and air (see Figure 4). The pharynx is subdivided anatomically into three parts—the **nasopharynx** (behind the nasal cavity), the **oropharynx** (behind the oral cavity extending from the soft palate to the epiglottis overlying the larynx), and the **laryngopharynx** (extending from the epiglottis to the base of the larynx), which is continuous with the esophagus.

The walls of the pharynx consist largely of two layers of skeletal muscles: an inner layer of longitudinal muscle (the levator muscles) and an outer layer of circular constrictor muscles, which initiate wavelike contractions that propel the food inferiorly into the esophagus. The mucosa of the oropharynx and laryngopharynx, like that of the oral cavity, contains a friction-resistant stratified squamous epithelium.

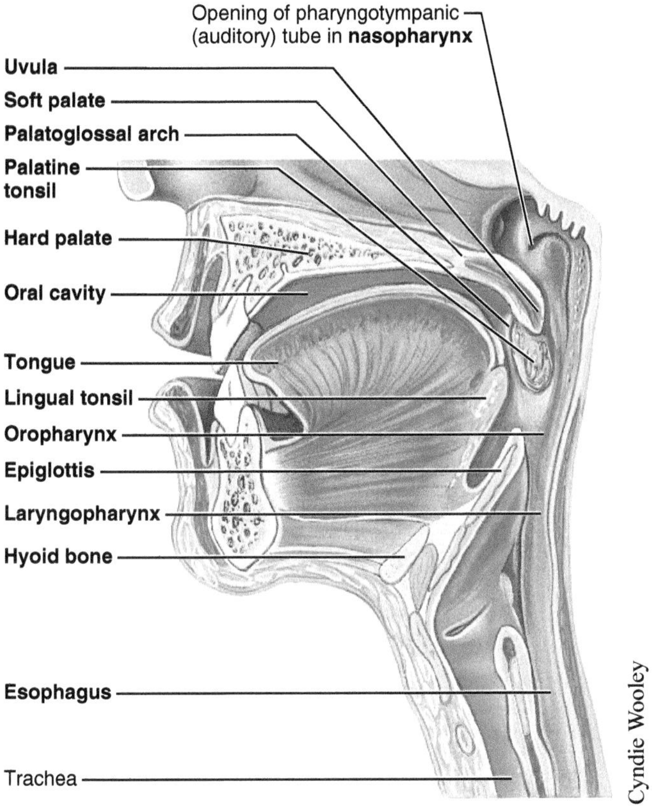

Opening of pharyngotympanic (auditory) tube in nasopharynx
Uvula
Soft palate
Palatoglossal arch
Palatine tonsil
Hard palate
Oral cavity
Tongue
Lingual tonsil
Oropharynx
Epiglottis
Laryngopharynx
Hyoid bone
Esophagus
Trachea
Cyndie Wooley

FIGURE 4 Sagittal view of the head showing oral, nasal, and pharyngeal cavities.

Esophagus

The **esophagus,** or gullet, extends from the pharynx through the diaphragm to the gastroesophageal sphincter in the superior aspect of the stomach. Approximately 25 cm long in humans, it is essentially a food passageway that conducts food to the stomach in a wavelike peristaltic motion. The esophagus has no digestive or absorptive function. The walls at its superior end contain skeletal muscle, which is replaced by smooth muscle in the area nearing the stomach. The **gastroesophageal sphincter,** a slight thickening of the smooth muscle layer at the esophagus-stomach junction, controls food passage into the stomach (see Figure 5). Since the esophagus is located in the thoracic rather than the abdominal cavity, its outermost layer is an *adventitia,* rather than the serosa.

Stomach

The **stomach** (Figures 1 and 5) is on the left side of the abdominal cavity and is hidden by the liver and diaphragm. Different regions of the saclike stomach are the **cardiac region** (the area surrounding the cardiac orifice through which food enters the stomach from the esophagus), the **fundus** (the expanded portion of the stomach, superolateral to the cardiac region), the **body** (midportion of the stomach, inferior to the fundus), and the funnel-shaped **pyloric region** (consisting of the superiormost *pyloric antrum,* the more narrow *pyloric canal,* and the terminal *pylorus,* which is continuous with the small intestine through the **pyloric sphincter**).

The concave medial surface of the stomach is called the **lesser curvature;** its convex lateral surface is the **greater curvature.** Extending from these curvatures are two mesenteries, called *omenta.* The **lesser omentum** extends from the liver to the lesser curvature of the stomach. The **greater omentum,** a saclike mesentery, extends from the greater curvature of the stomach, reflects downward over the abdominal contents to cover them in an apronlike fashion, and then blends with the **mesocolon** attaching the transverse colon to the posterior body wall. Figure 7 illustrates the omenta as well as the other peritoneal attachments of the abdominal organs.

The stomach is a temporary storage region for food as well as a site for mechanical and chemical breakdown of food. It contains a third (innermost) *obliquely* oriented layer of smooth muscle in its muscularis externa that allows it to churn, mix, and pummel the food, physically reducing it to smaller fragments. **Gastric glands** of the mucosa secrete hydrochloric acid (HCl) and hydrolytic enzymes (primarily pepsinogen, the inactive form of *pepsin,* a protein-digesting enzyme), which begin the enzymatic, or chemical, breakdown of protein foods. The *mucosal glands* also secrete a viscous mucus that helps prevent the stomach itself from being digested by the proteolytic enzymes. Most digestive activity occurs in the pyloric region of the stomach. After the food is processed in the stomach, it resembles a creamy mass **(chyme),** which enters the small **intestine through the pyloric sphincter**.

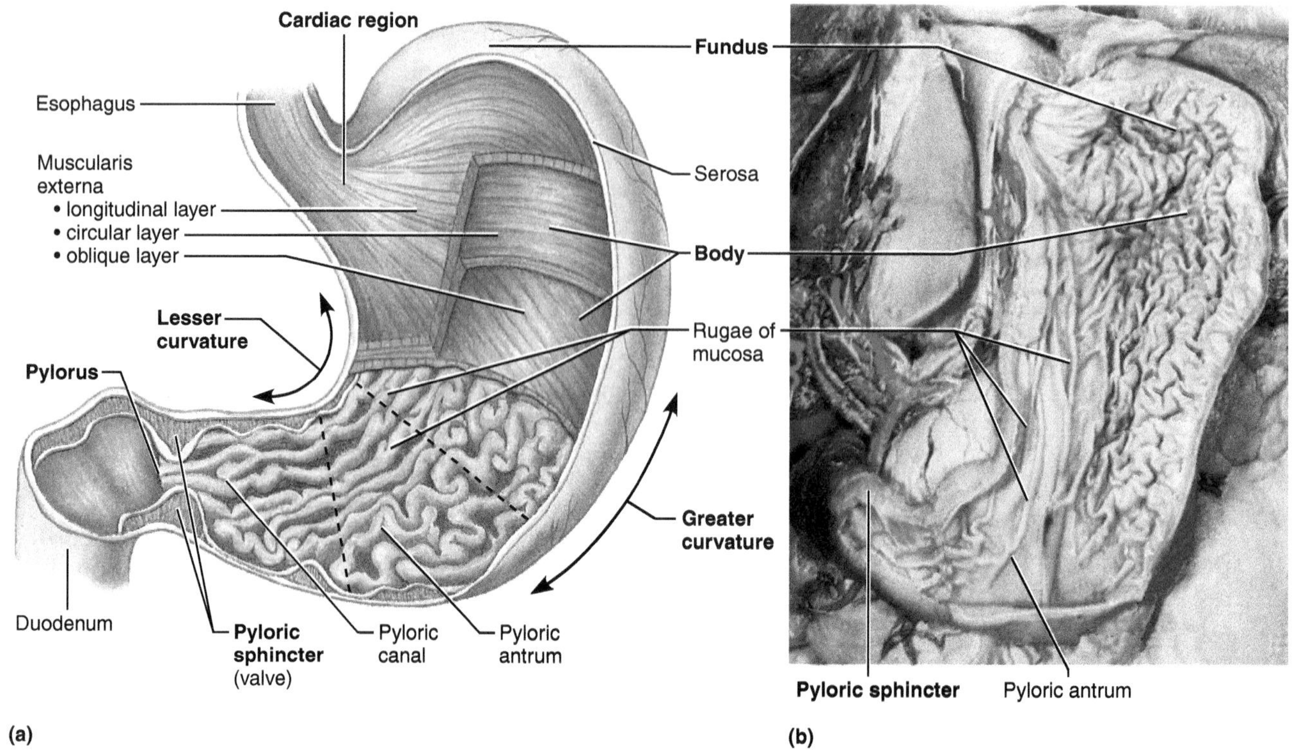
Cardiac region
Esophagus
Muscularis
externa
• longitudinal layer
• circular layer
• oblique layer
Lesser
curvature
Pylorus
Duodenum
Pyloric
sphincter
(valve)
Pyloric
canal
Pyloric
antrum
Fundus
Serosa
Body
Rugae of
mucosa
Greater
curvature
(a)
Pyloric sphincter
Pyloric antrum
(b)

Kristin Otwell

From *Color Atlas of Histology* by Leslie P. Garner and James L. Hiatt, © Williams and Wilkins, 1990

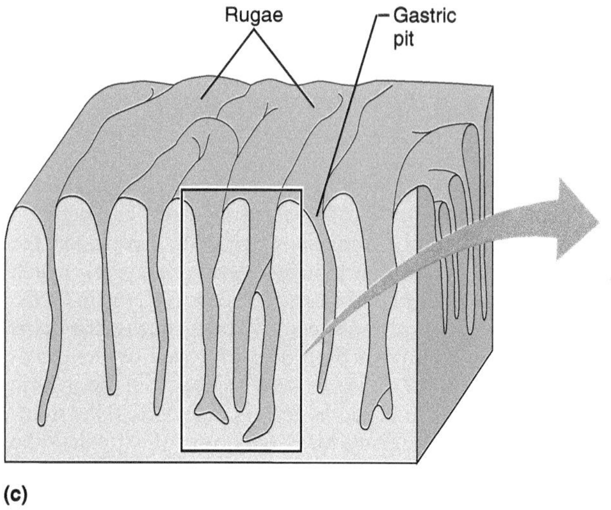
Rugae
Gastric
pit
(c)

Imagineering

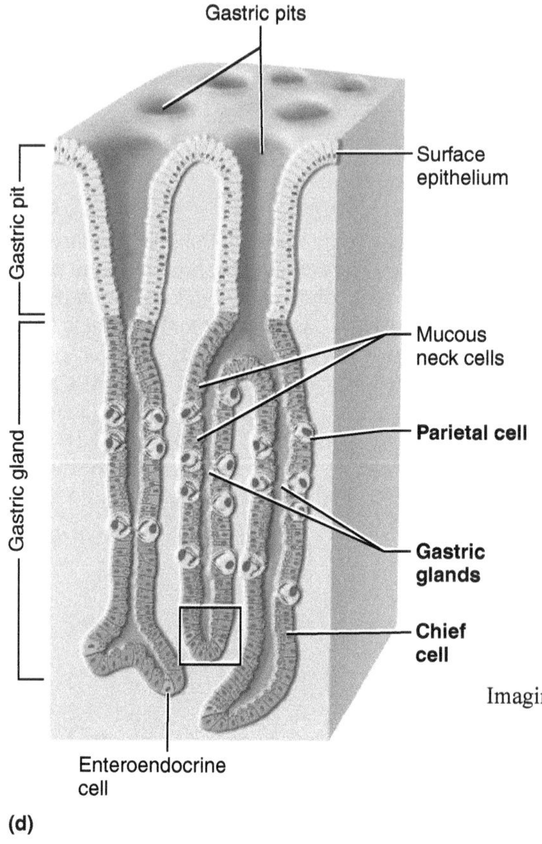
Gastric pits
Surface
epithelium
Gastric pit
Gastric gland
Mucous
neck cells
Parietal cell
Gastric
glands
Chief
cell
Enteroendocrine
cell
(d)

Imagineering

FIGURE 5 Anatomy of the stomach.
(a) Gross internal and external anatomy. **(b)** Photograph of internal aspect of stomach. **(c, d)** Section of the stomach wall showing rugae and gastric pits.

ACTIVITY 2

Studying the Histological Structure of Selected Digestive System Organs

To prepare for the histologic study you will be conducting now and later in the lab, obtain a microscope and the following slides: salivary glands (submandibular or sublingual); liver; cross sections of the duodenum, ileum, and stomach; and longitudinal sections of a tooth and the gastroesophageal junction.

1. **Stomach:** The stomach slide will be viewed first. Refer to Figure 6a as you scan the tissue under low power to locate the muscularis externa; then move to high power to more closely examine this layer. Try to pick out the three smooth muscle layers. How does the extra (oblique) layer of smooth muscle found in the stomach correlate with the stomach's churning movements?

____

____

____

Identify the gastric glands and the gastric pits (see Figures 5 and 6b. If the section is taken from the stomach fundus and is appropriately stained, you can identify, in the gastric glands, the blue-staining **chief (or zymogenic) cells,** which produce pepsinogen, and the red-staining **parietal cells,** which secrete HCl. The enteroendocrine cells that release hormones are indistinguishable. Draw a small section of the stomach wall, and label it appropriately.

2. **Gastroesophageal junction:** Scan the slide under low power to locate the mucosal junction between the end of the esophagus and the beginning of the stomach, the gastroesophageal junction. Compare your observations to Figure 6c. What is the functional importance of the epithelial differences seen in the two organs?

____

____

____

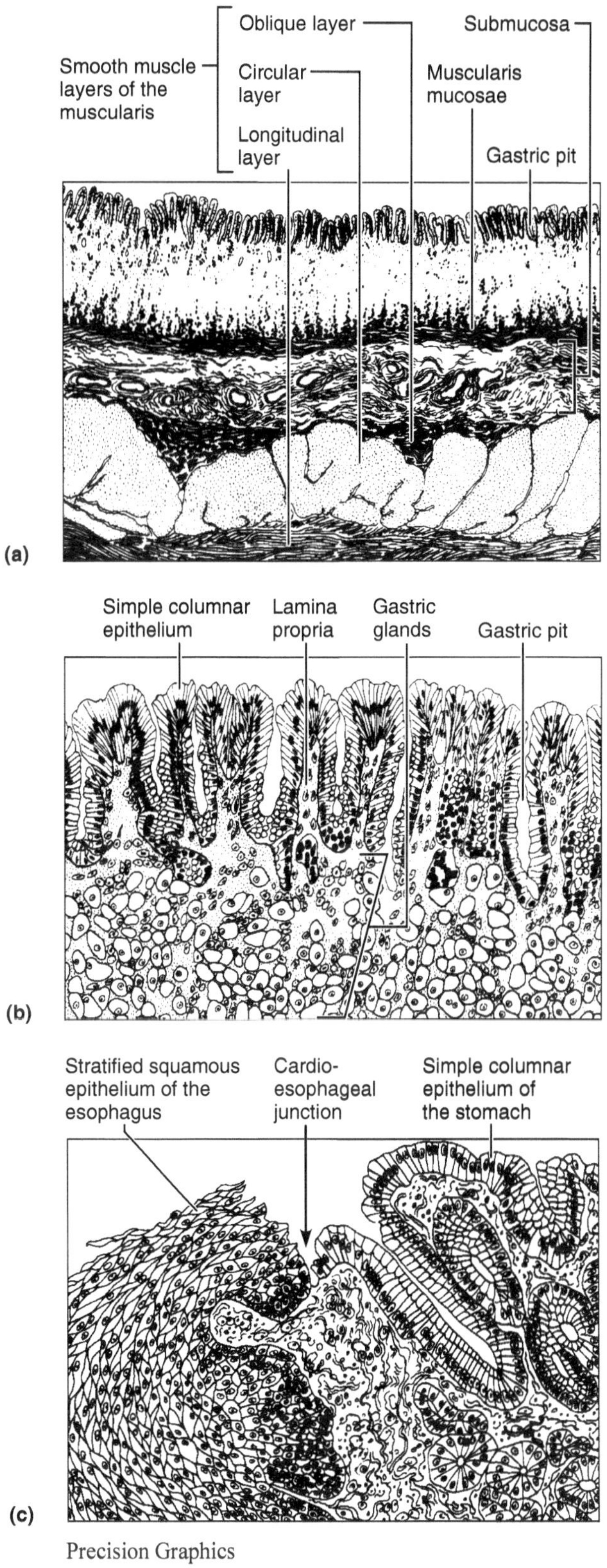

FIGURE 6 Histology of selected regions of the stomach and gastroesophageal junction. (a) Stomach wall. **(b)** Gastric pits and glands. **(c)** Gastroesophageal junction, longitudinal section.

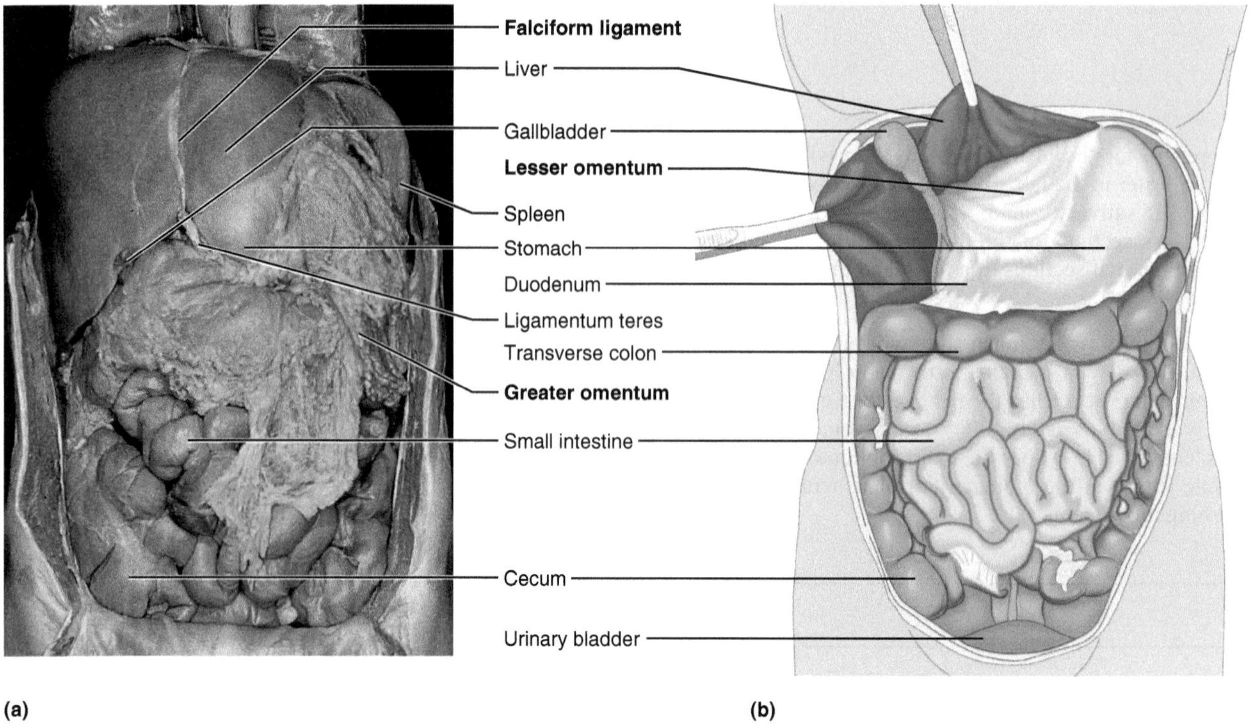
Falciform ligament
Liver
Gallbladder
Lesser omentum
Spleen
Stomach
Duodenum
Ligamentum teres
Transverse colon
Greater omentum
Small intestine
Cecum
Urinary bladder
(a)
(b)

From *A Stereoscopic Atlas of Human Anatomy* by David L. Bassett

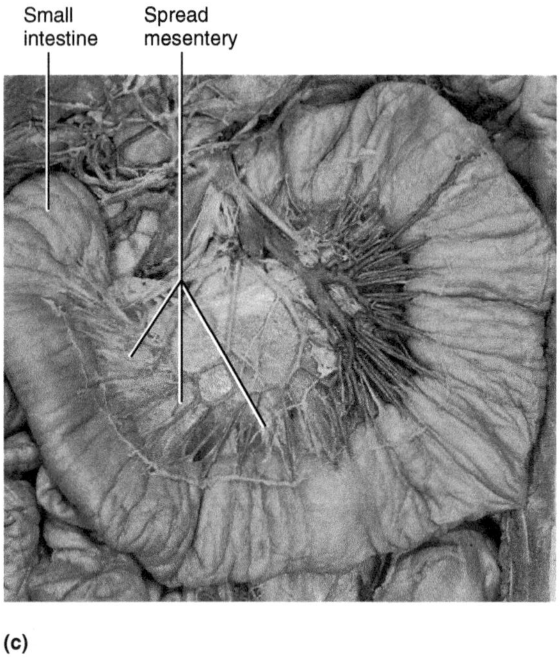
Small intestine
Spread mesentery
(c)

Imagineering

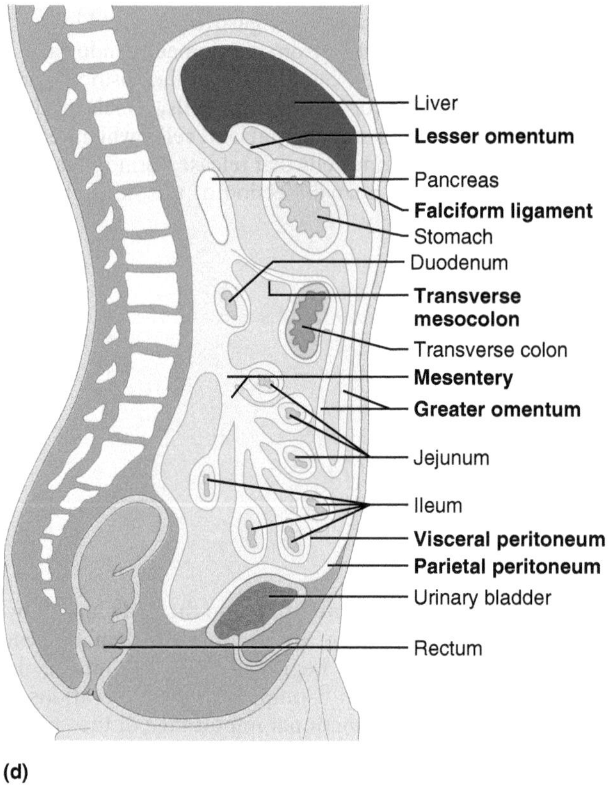
Liver
Lesser omentum
Pancreas
Falciform ligament
Stomach
Duodenum
Transverse mesocolon
Transverse colon
Mesentery
Greater omentum
Jejunum
Ileum
Visceral peritoneum
Parietal peritoneum
Urinary bladder
Rectum
(d)

From *A Stereoscopic Atlas of Human Anatomy* by David L. Bassett

FIGURE 7 **Peritoneal attachments of the abdominal organs.** Superficial anterior views of abdominal cavity: **(a)** photograph with the greater omentum in place and **(b)** diagram showing greater omentum removed and liver and gallbladder reflected superiorly. **(c)** Mesentery of the small intestine. **(d)** Sagittal view of a male torso.

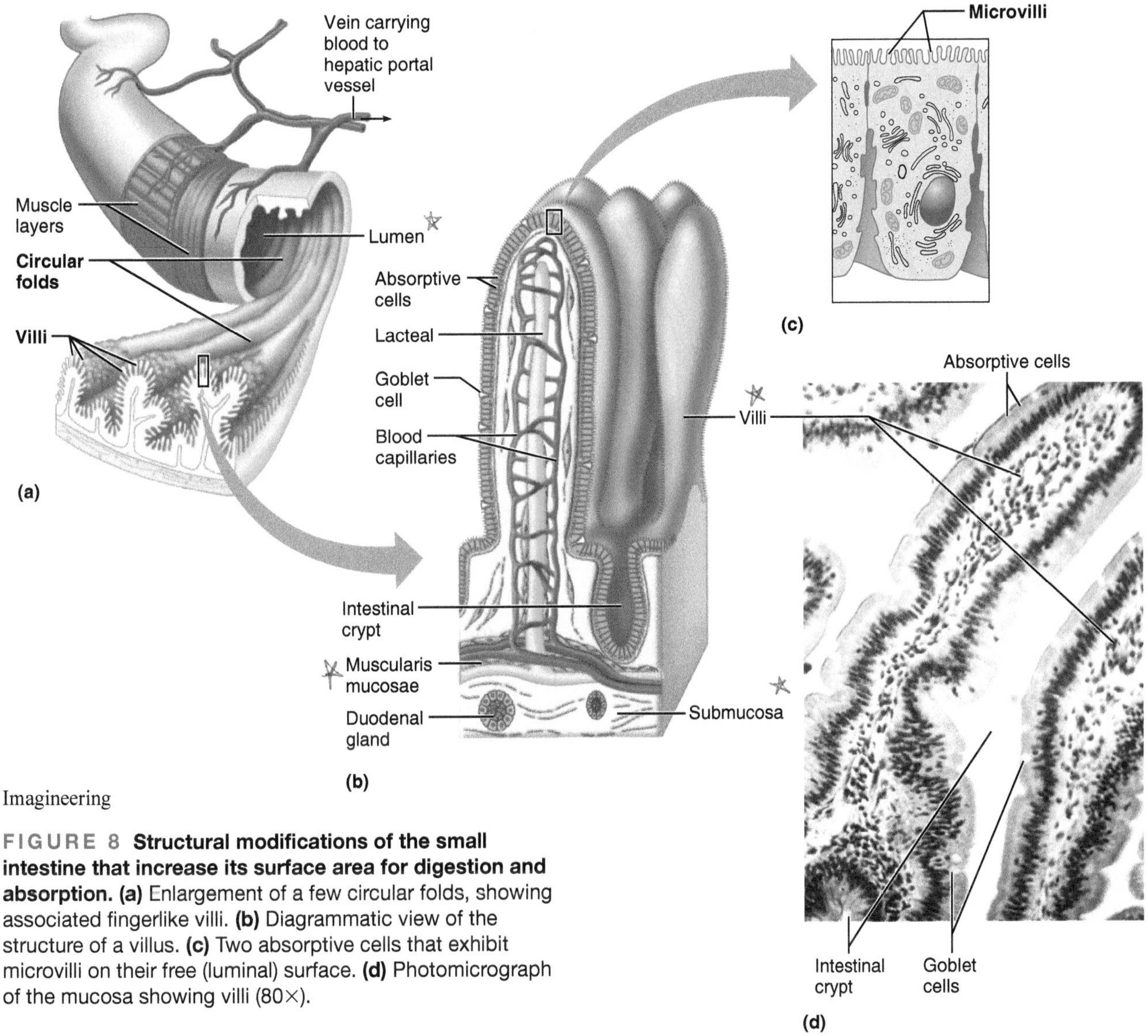
Vein carrying blood to hepatic portal vessel
Muscle layers
Circular folds
Villi
Lumen
(a)
Absorptive cells
Lacteal
Goblet cell
Blood capillaries
Intestinal crypt
Muscularis mucosae
Duodenal gland
Submucosa
Villi
(b)
Microvilli
(c)
Absorptive cells
Villi
Intestinal crypt
Goblet cells
(d)

Imagineering

LUMEN Histology, Loyola University Medical Education Network

FIGURE 8 **Structural modifications of the small intestine that increase its surface area for digestion and absorption. (a)** Enlargement of a few circular folds, showing associated fingerlike villi. **(b)** Diagrammatic view of the structure of a villus. **(c)** Two absorptive cells that exhibit microvilli on their free (luminal) surface. **(d)** Photomicrograph of the mucosa showing villi (80×).

Small Intestine

The **small intestine** is a convoluted tube, 6 to 7 meters (about 20 feet) long in a cadaver but only about 2 m (6 feet) long during life because of its muscle tone. It extends from the pyloric sphincter to the ileocecal valve. The small intestine is suspended by a double layer of peritoneum, the fan-shaped **mesentery,** from the posterior abdominal wall (see Figure 7), and it lies, framed laterally and superiorly by the large intestine, in the abdominal cavity. The small intestine has three subdivisions (see Figure 1): (1) the **duodenum** extends from the pyloric sphincter for about 25 cm (10 inches) and curves around the head of the pancreas; most of the duodenum lies in a retroperitoneal position. (2) The **jejunum,** continuous with the duodenum, extends for 2.5 m (about 8 feet). Most of the jejunum occupies the umbilical region of the abdominal cavity. (3) The **ileum,** the terminal portion of the small intestine, is about 3.6 m (12 feet) long and joins the large intestine at the **ileocecal valve.** It is located inferiorly and somewhat to the right in the abdominal cavity, but its major portion lies in the hypogastric region.

Brush border enzymes, hydrolytic enzymes bound to the microvilli of the columnar epithelial cells, and, more importantly, enzymes produced by the pancreas and ducted into the duodenum via the **pancreatic duct** complete the enzymatic digestion process in the small intestine. Bile (formed in the liver) also enters the duodenum via the **bile duct** in the same area. At the duodenum, the ducts join to form the bulblike **hepatopancreatic ampulla** and empty their products into the duodenal lumen through the **major duodenal papilla,** an orifice controlled by a muscular valve called the **hepatopancreatic sphincter (sphincter of Oddi).**

Nearly all nutrient absorption occurs in the small intestine, where three structural modifications that increase the mucosa absorptive area appear—the microvilli, villi, and circular folds (Figure 8). **Microvilli** are minute projections of

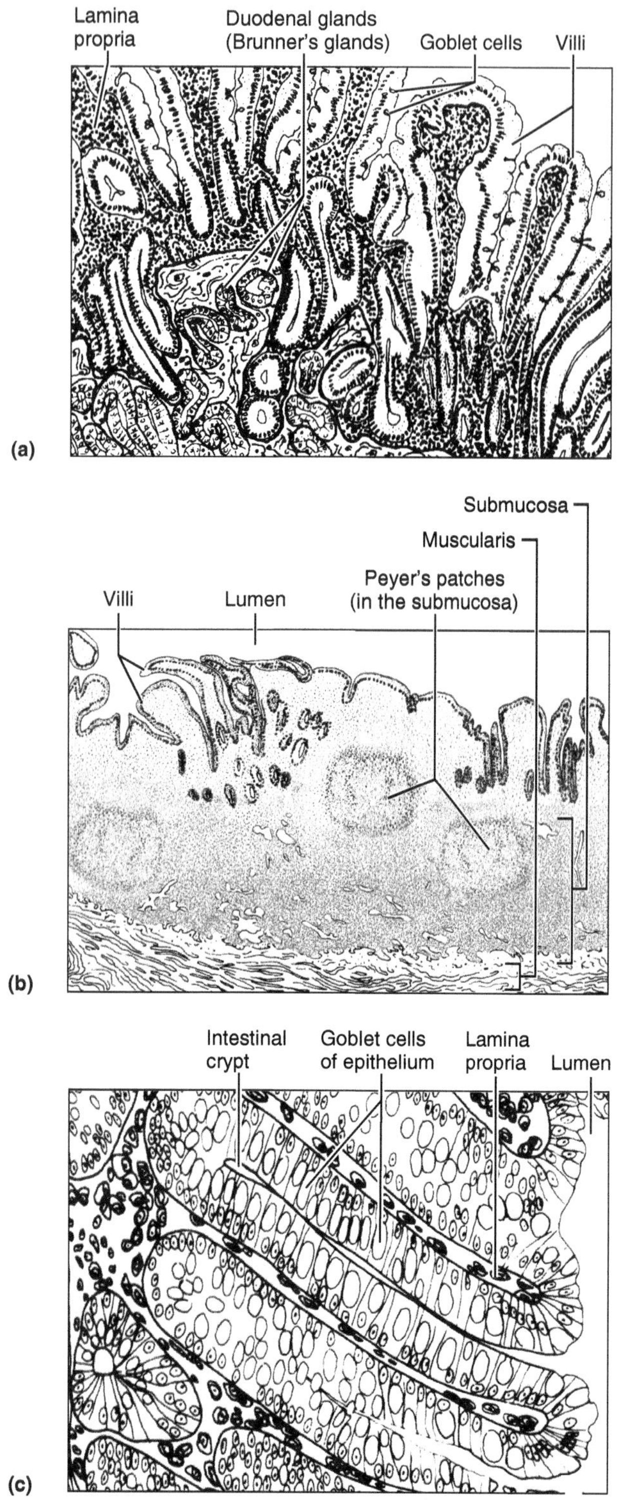
Lamina propria
Duodenal glands (Brunner's glands)
Goblet cells
Villi
(a)
Submucosa
Muscularis
Peyer's patches (in the submucosa)
Villi
Lumen
(b)
Intestinal crypt
Goblet cells of epithelium
Lamina propria
Lumen
(c)

FIGURE 9 Histology of selected regions of the small and large intestines. Cross-sectional views. **(a)** Duodenum of the small intestine. **(b)** Ileum of the small intestine. **(c)** Large intestine.

the surface plasma membrane of the columnar epithelial lining cells of the mucosa. **Villi** are the fingerlike projections of the mucosa tunic that give it a velvety appearance and texture. The **circular folds (plicae circulares)** are deep, permanent folds of the mucosa and submucosa layers that force chyme to spiral through the intestine, mixing it and slowing its progress. These structural modifications, which increase the surface area, decrease in frequency and elaboration toward the end of the small intestine. Any residue remaining undigested and unabsorbed at the terminus of the small intestine enters the large intestine through the ileocecal valve. In contrast, the amount of lymphoid tissue in the submucosa of the small intestine (especially the aggregated lymphoid follicles called **Peyer's patches,** Figure 9b) increases along the length of the small intestine and is very apparent in the ileum. This reflects the fact that the remaining undigested food residue contains large numbers of bacteria that must be prevented from entering the bloodstream.

ACTIVITY 3

Observing the Histological Structure of the Small Intestine

1. **Duodenum:** Secure the slide of the duodenum (cross section) to the microscope stage. Observe the tissue under low power to identify the four basic tunics of the intestinal wall—that is, the **mucosa** (the lining and its three sublayers), the **submucosa** (areolar connective tissue layer deep to the mucosa), the **muscularis externa** (composed of circular and longitudinal smooth muscle layers), and the **serosa** (the outermost layer, also called the *visceral peritoneum*). Consult Figure 9a to help you identify the scattered mucus-producing **duodenal glands** (Brunner's glands) in the submucosa.

What type of epithelium do you see here? ______________

____

Examine the large leaflike *villi,* which increase the surface area for absorption. Notice the scattered mucus-producing goblet cells in the epithelium of the villi. Note also the **intestinal crypts** (crypts of Lieberkühn, see also Figure 8), invaginated areas of the mucosa between the villi containing the cells that produce intestinal juice, a watery mucus-containing mixture that serves as a carrier fluid for absorption of nutrients from the chyme. Sketch and label a small section of the duodenal wall, showing all layers and villi.

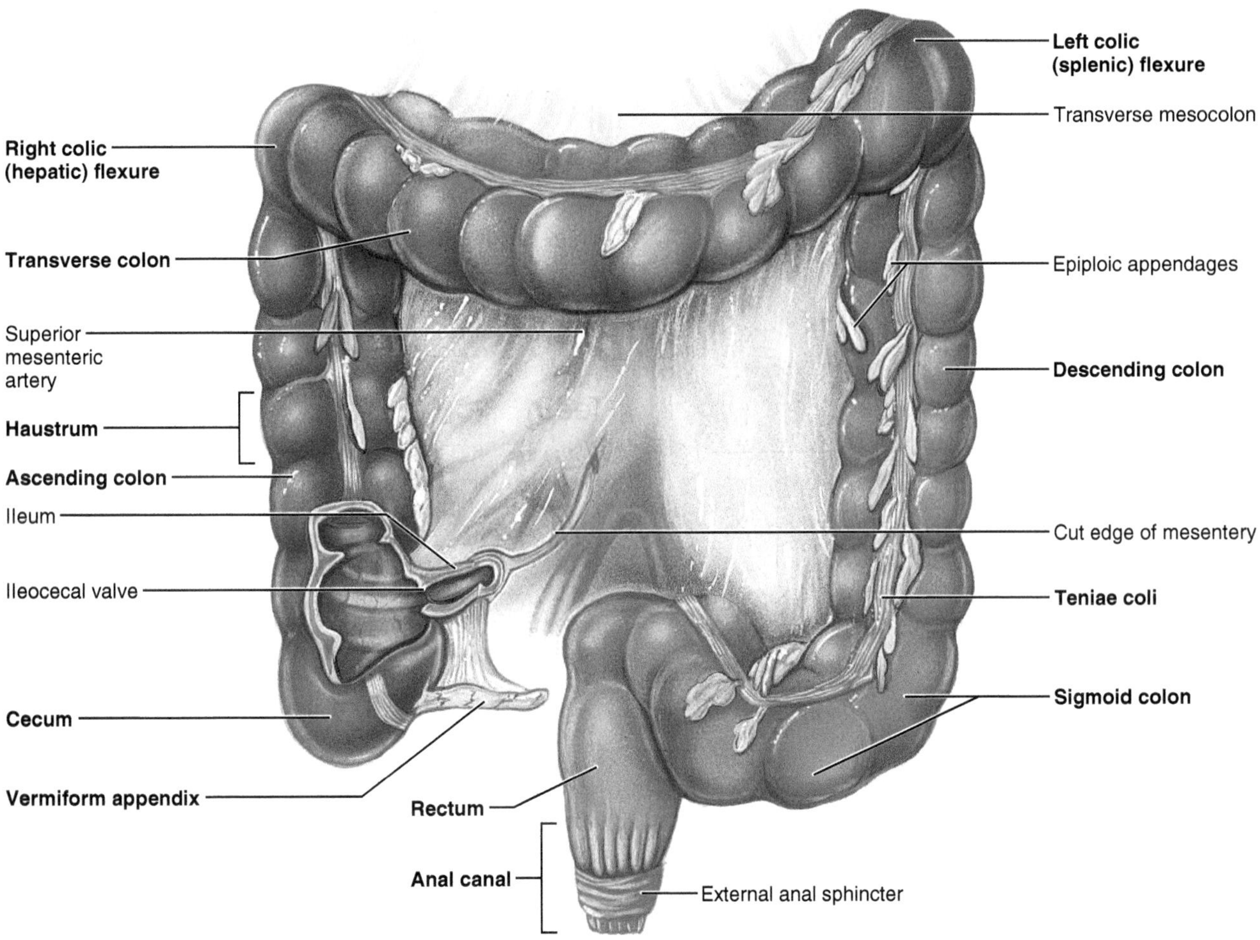
Left colic
(splenic) flexure
Transverse mesocolon
Right colic
(hepatic) flexure
Transverse colon
Epiploic appendages
Superior
mesenteric
artery
Descending colon
Haustrum
Ascending colon
Ileum
Cut edge of mesentery
Ileocecal valve
Teniae coli
Cecum
Sigmoid colon
Vermiform appendix
Rectum
Anal canal
External anal sphincter
Karl Miyajima

FIGURE 10 The large intestine. (Section of the cecum removed to show the ileocecal valve.)

2. **Ileum:** The structure of the ileum resembles that of the duodenum, except that the villi are less elaborate (most of the absorption has occurred by the time the ileum is reached). Secure a slide of the ileum to the microscope stage for viewing. Observe the villi, and identify the four layers of the wall and the large, generally spherical Peyer's patches (Figure 9b). What tissue composes Peyer's patches?

____

3. If a villus model is available, identify the following cells or regions before continuing: absorptive epithelium, goblet cells, lamina propria, slips of the muscularis mucosae, capillary bed, and lacteal. If possible, also identify the intestinal crypts.

Large Intestine

The **large intestine** (Figure 10) is about 1.5 m (5 feet) long and extends from the ileocecal valve to the anus. It encircles the small intestine on three sides and consists of the following subdivisions: **cecum, vermiform appendix, colon, rectum,** and **anal canal.**

The blind tubelike appendix, which hangs from the cecum, is a trouble spot in the large intestine. Since it is generally twisted, it provides an ideal location for bacteria to accumulate and multiply. Inflammation of the appendix, or appendicitis, is the result. ●

The colon is divided into several distinct regions. The **ascending colon** travels up the right side of the abdominal cavity and makes a right-angle turn at the **right colic (hepatic) flexure** to cross the abdominal cavity as the **transverse colon.** It then turns at the **left colic (splenic) flexure** and continues down the left side of the abdominal cavity as the **descending colon,** where it takes an S-shaped course as the **sigmoid colon.** The sigmoid colon, rectum, and the anal canal lie in the pelvis anterior to the sacrum and thus are not considered abdominal cavity structures. Except for the transverse and sigmoid colons, which are secured to the dorsal body wall by mesocolons (see Figure 7), the colon is retroperitoneal.

The anal canal terminates in the **anus,** the opening to the exterior of the body. The anus, which has an external sphincter of skeletal muscle (the voluntary sphincter) and an internal sphincter of smooth muscle (the involuntary sphincter), is normally closed except during defecation when the undigested remains of the food and bacteria are eliminated from the body as feces.

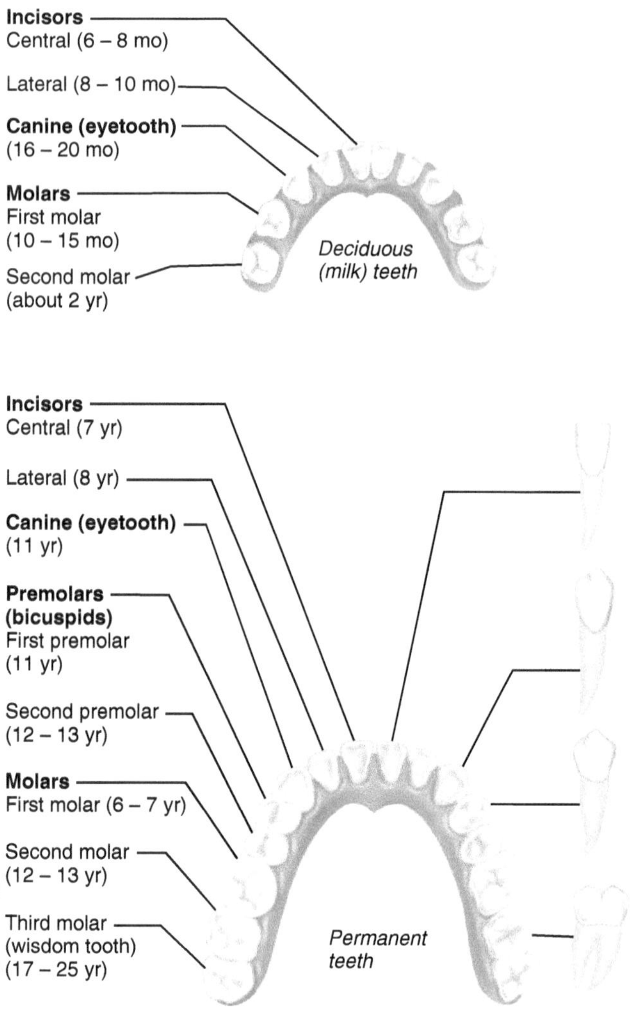
Incisors
Central (6 – 8 mo)
Lateral (8 – 10 mo)
Canine (eyetooth)
(16 – 20 mo)
Molars
First molar
(10 – 15 mo)
Second molar
(about 2 yr)
Deciduous
(milk) teeth
Incisors
Central (7 yr)
Lateral (8 yr)
Canine (eyetooth)
(11 yr)
Premolars
(bicuspids)
First premolar
(11 yr)
Second premolar
(12 – 13 yr)
Molars
First molar (6 – 7 yr)
Second molar
(12 – 13 yr)
Third molar
(wisdom tooth)
(17 – 25 yr)
Permanent
teeth

Imagineering

FIGURE 11 Human deciduous teeth and permanent teeth. (Approximate time of teeth eruption shown in parentheses.)

In the large intestine, the longitudinal muscle layer of the muscularis externa is reduced to three longitudinal muscle bands called the **teniae coli.** Since these bands are shorter than the rest of the wall of the large intestine, they cause the wall to pucker into small pocketlike sacs called **haustra.** Fat-filled pouches of visceral peritoneum, called *epiploic appendages,* hang from the colon's surface.

The major function of the large intestine is to consolidate and propel the unusable fecal matter toward the anus and eliminate it from the body. While it does that chore, it (1) provides a site for the manufacture, by intestinal bacteria, of some vitamins (B and K), which it then absorbs into the bloodstream; and (2) reclaims most of the remaining water from undigested food, thus conserving body water.

Watery stools, or **diarrhea,** result from any condition that rushes undigested food residue through the large intestine before it has had sufficient time to absorb the water (as in irritation of the colon by bacteria). Conversely, when food residue remains in the large intestine for extended periods (as with atonic colon or failure of the defecation reflex), excessive water is absorbed and the stool becomes hard and difficult to pass **(constipation).** ●

ACTIVITY 4

Examining the Histological Structure of the Large Intestine

Examine Figure 9c to compare the histology of the large intestine to that of the small intestine just studied. ■

Accessory Digestive Organs

Teeth

By the age of 21, two sets of teeth have developed (Figure 11). The initial set, called the **deciduous** (or **milk**) **teeth,** normally appears between the ages of 6 months and 2½ years. The first of these to erupt are the lower central incisors. The child begins to shed the deciduous teeth around the age of 6, and a second set of teeth, the **permanent teeth,** gradually replaces them. As the deeper permanent teeth progressively enlarge and develop, the roots of the deciduous teeth are resorbed, leading to their final shedding. During years 6 to 12, the child has mixed dentition—both permanent and deciduous teeth. Generally, by the age of 12, all of the deciduous teeth have been shed, or exfoliated.

Teeth are classified as **incisors, canines** *(eye teeth),* **premolars** *(bicuspids),* and **molars.** Teeth names reflect differences in relative structure and function. The incisors are chisel-shaped and exert a shearing action used in biting. Canines are cone-shaped or fanglike, the latter description being much more applicable to the canines of animals whose teeth are used for the tearing of food. Incisors, canines, and premolars typically have single roots, though the first upper premolars may have two. The lower molars have two roots but the upper molars usually have three. The premolars have two *cusps* (grinding surfaces); the molars have broad crowns with rounded cusps specialized for the fine grinding of food.

Dentition is described by means of a **dental formula,** which designates the numbers, types, and position of the teeth in one side of the jaw. (Because tooth arrangement is bilaterally symmetrical, it is only necessary to designate one side of the jaw.) The complete dental formula for the deciduous teeth from the medial aspect of each jaw and proceeding posteriorly is as follows:

$$\frac{\text{Upper teeth: 2 incisors, 1 canine, 0 premolars, 2 molars}}{\text{Lower teeth: 2 incisors, 1 canine, 0 premolars, 2 molars}} \times 2$$

This formula is generally abbreviated to read as follows:

$$\frac{2,1,0,2}{2,1,0,2} \times 2 = 20 \text{ (number of deciduous teeth)}$$

The 32 permanent teeth are then described by the following dental formula:

$$\frac{2,1,2,3}{2,1,2,3} \times 2 = 32 \text{ (number of permanent teeth)}$$

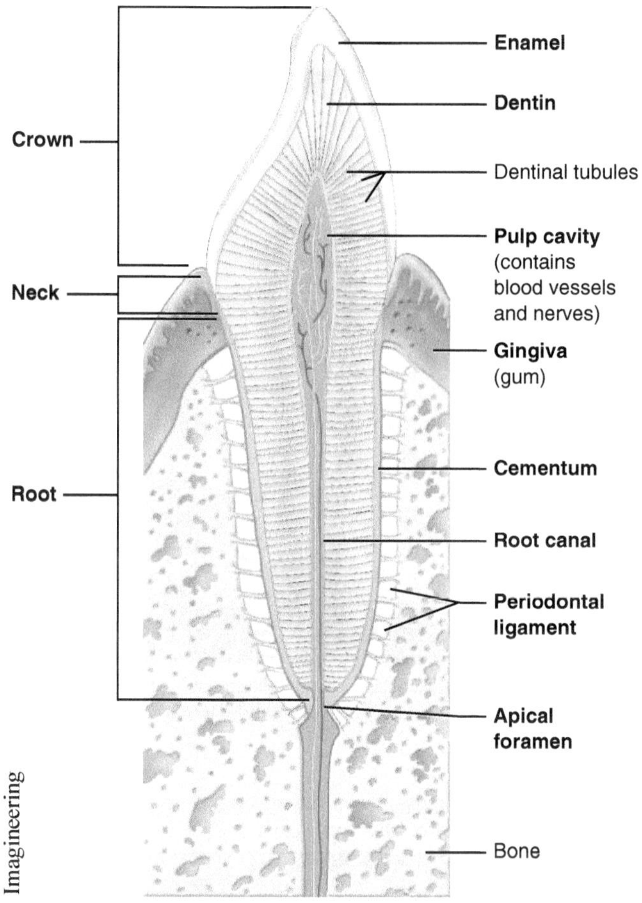

Crown
Neck
Root
Enamel
Dentin
Dentinal tubules
Pulp cavity (contains blood vessels and nerves)
Gingiva (gum)
Cementum
Root canal
Periodontal ligament
Apical foramen
Bone
Imagineering

FIGURE 12 Longitudinal section of human canine tooth within its bony alveolus.

Although 32 is designated as the normal number of permanent teeth, not everyone develops a full complement. In many people, the third molars, commonly called *wisdom teeth,* never erupt.

ACTIVITY 5

Identifying Types of Teeth

Identify the four types of teeth (incisors, canines, premolars, and molars) on the jaw model or human skull.

A tooth consists of two major regions, the **crown** and the **root.** A longitudinal section made through a tooth shows the following basic anatomical plan (Figure 12). The crown is the superior portion of the tooth. The portion of the crown visible above the **gingiva,** or **gum,** is referred to as the *clinical crown.* The entire area covered by **enamel** is called the *anatomical crown.* Enamel is the hardest substance in the body and is fairly brittle. It consists of 95% to 97% inorganic calcium salts and thus is heavily mineralized. The crevice between the end of the anatomical crown and the upper margin of the gingiva is referred to as the *gingival sulcus* and its apical border is the *gingival margin.*

That portion of the tooth embedded in the alveolar portion of the jaw is the root, and the root and crown are connected by a slight constriction, the **neck.** The outermost surface of the root is covered by **cementum,** which is similar to bone in composition and less brittle than enamel. The cementum attaches the tooth to the **periodontal ligament,** which holds the tooth in the alveolar socket and exerts a cushioning effect. **Dentin,** which composes the bulk of the tooth, is the bonelike material medial to the enamel and cementum.

The **pulp cavity** occupies the central portion of the tooth. **Pulp,** connective tissue liberally supplied with blood vessels, nerves, and lymphatics, occupies this cavity and provides for tooth sensation and supplies nutrients to the tooth tissues. **Odontoblasts,** specialized cells that reside in the outer margins of the pulp cavity, produce the dentin. The pulp cavity extends into distal portions of the root and becomes the **root canal.** An opening at the root apex, the **apical foramen,** provides a route of entry into the tooth for blood vessels, nerves, and other structures from the tissues beneath.

ACTIVITY 6

Studying Microscopic Tooth Anatomy

Observe a slide of a longitudinal section of a tooth, and compare your observations with the structures detailed in Figure 12. Identify as many of these structures as possible.

Salivary Glands

Three pairs of major **salivary glands** (see Figure 1) empty their secretions into the oral cavity.

Parotid glands: Large glands located anterior to the ear and ducting into the mouth over the second upper molar through the parotid duct.

Submandibular glands: Located along the medial aspect of the mandibular body in the floor of the mouth, and ducting under the tongue to the base of the lingual frenulum.

Sublingual glands: Small glands located most anteriorly in the floor of the mouth and emptying under the tongue via several small ducts.

Food in the mouth and mechanical pressure (even chewing rubber bands or wax) stimulate the salivary glands to secrete saliva. Saliva consists primarily of *mucin* (a viscous glycoprotein), which moistens the food and helps to bind it together into a mass called a **bolus,** and a clear serous fluid containing the enzyme *salivary amylase.* Salivary amylase begins the digestion of starch (a large polysaccharide), breaking it down into disaccharides, or double sugars, and glucose. Parotid gland secretion is mainly serous; the submandibular is a mixed gland that produces both mucin and serous components; and the sublingual gland produces mostly mucin.

ACTIVITY 7

Examining Salivary Gland Tissue

Examine salivary gland tissue under low power and then high power to become familiar with the appearance of a glandular tissue. Notice the clustered arrangement of the cells around

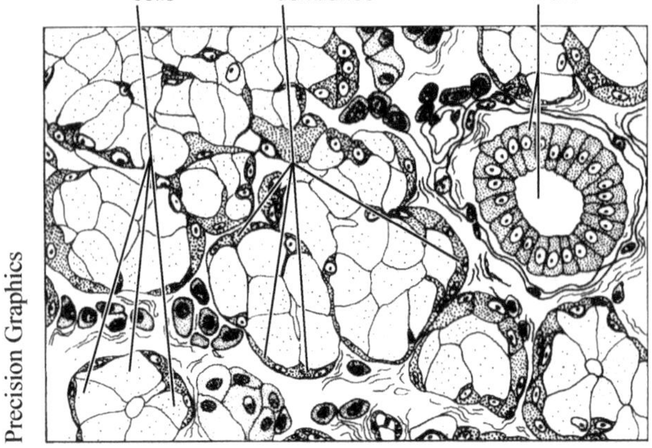
Mucous cells
Serous demilunes
Duct
Precision Graphics

FIGURE 13 **Histology of a mixed salivary gland.**

their ducts. The cells are basically triangular, with their pointed ends facing the duct orifice. If possible, differentiate between mucus-producing cells, which look hollow or have a clear cytoplasm, and serous cells, which produce the clear, enzyme-containing fluid and have granules in their cytoplasm. The serous cells often form *demilunes* (caps) around the more central mucous cells. Figure 13 may be helpful in this task. In the space below, draw your version of a small portion of the salivary gland tissue and label it appropriately.

Liver and Gallbladder

The **liver** (see Figure 1), the largest gland in the body, is located inferior to the diaphragm, more to the right than the left side of the body. As noted earlier, it hides the stomach from view in a superficial observation of abdominal contents. The human liver has four lobes and is suspended from the diaphragm and anterior abdominal wall by the **falciform ligament** (see Figure 14).

The liver is one of the body's most important organs, and it performs many metabolic roles. However, its digestive function is to produce bile, which leaves the liver through the **common hepatic duct** and then enters the duodenum through the **bile duct.** Bile has no enzymatic action but emulsifies fats (breaks up large fat particles into smaller ones), thus creating a larger surface area for more efficient lipase activity. Without bile, very little fat digestion or absorption occurs.

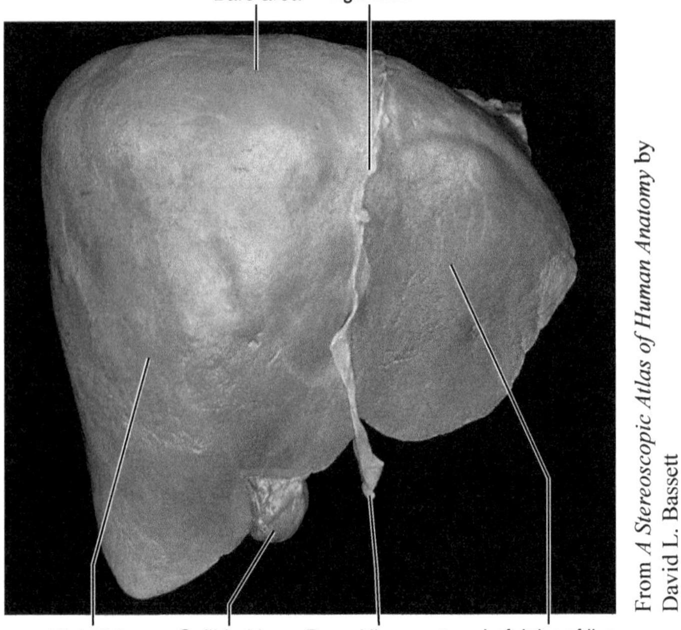
Bare area
Falciform ligament
Right lobe of liver
Gallbladder
Round ligament (ligamentum teres)
Left lobe of liver
From *A Stereoscopic Atlas of Human Anatomy* by David L. Bassett

(a)

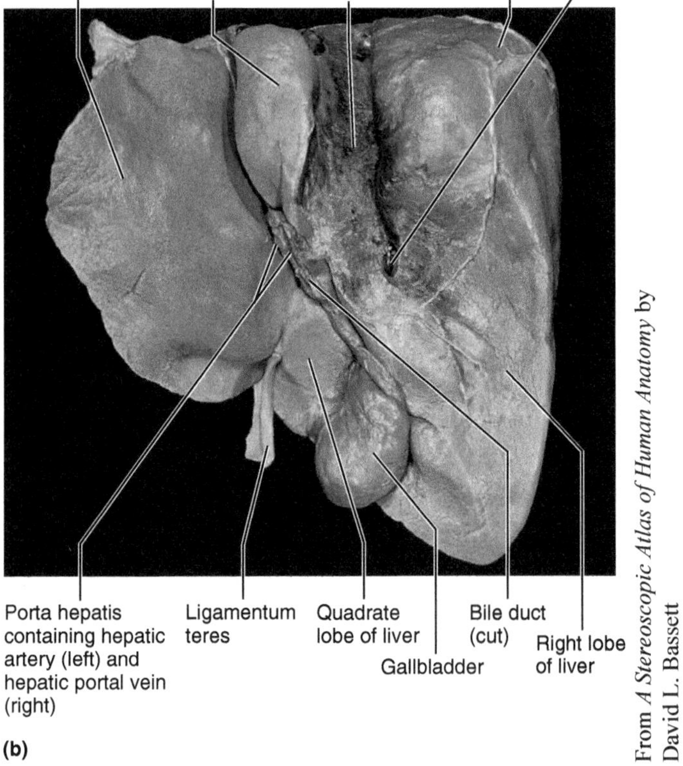
Left lobe of liver
Caudate lobe of liver
Sulcus for inferior vena cava
Bare area
Hepatic vein (cut)
Porta hepatis containing hepatic artery (left) and hepatic portal vein (right)
Ligamentum teres
Quadrate lobe of liver
Gallbladder
Bile duct (cut)
Right lobe of liver
From *A Stereoscopic Atlas of Human Anatomy* by David L. Bassett

(b)

FIGURE 14 **Gross anatomy of the human liver.** **(a)** Anterior view. **(b)** Posteroinferior aspect. The four liver lobes are separated by a group of fissures in this view.

When digestive activity is not occurring in the digestive tract, bile backs up into the **cystic duct** and enters the **gallbladder,** a small, green sac on the inferior surface of the liver. It is stored there until needed for the digestive process. While in the gallbladder, bile is concentrated by the removal of water and some ions. When fat-rich food enters the duodenum, a hormonal stimulus causes the gallbladder to contract, releasing the stored bile and making it available to the duodenum.

If the common hepatic or bile duct is blocked (for example, by wedged gallstones), bile is prevented from entering the small intestine, accumulates, and eventually backs up into the liver. This exerts pressure on the liver cells, and bile begins to enter the bloodstream. As the bile circulates through the body, the tissues become yellow, or jaundiced.

Blockage of the ducts is just one cause of jaundice. More often it results from actual liver problems such as **hepatitis** (an inflammation of the liver) or **cirrhosis,** a condition in which the liver is severely damaged and becomes hard and fibrous. Cirrhosis is almost guaranteed in those who drink excessive alcohol for many years. ●

As demonstrated by its highly organized anatomy, the liver (Figure 15) is very important in the initial processing of the nutrient-rich blood draining the digestive organs. Its structural and functional units are called **lobules.** Each lobule is a basically cylindrical structure consisting of cordlike arrays of **hepatocytes** or *liver cells,* which radiate outward from a central vein running upward in the longitudinal axis of the lobule. At each of the six corners of the lobule is a **portal triad** (portal tract), so named because three basic structures are always present there: a *portal arteriole* (a branch of the *hepatic artery,* the functional blood supply of the liver), a *portal venule* (a branch of the *hepatic portal vein* carrying nutrient-rich blood from the digestive viscera), and a *bile duct.* Between the liver cells are blood-filled spaces, or **sinusoids,** through which blood from the hepatic portal vein and hepatic artery percolates. Special phagocytic cells, **Kupffer cells,** line the sinusoids and remove debris such as bacteria from the blood as it flows past, while the hepatocytes pick up oxygen and nutrients. Much of the glucose transported to the liver from the digestive system is stored as glycogen in the liver for later use, and amino acids are taken from the blood by the liver cells and utilized to make plasma proteins. The sinusoids empty into the central vein, and the blood ultimately drains from the liver via the *hepatic vein.*

Bile is continuously being made by the hepatocytes. It flows through tiny canals, the **bile canaliculi,** which run between adjacent cells toward the bile duct branches in the triad regions, where the bile eventually leaves the liver. Notice that the directions of blood and bile flow in the liver lobule are exactly opposite.

ACTIVITY 8

Examining the Histology of the Liver

Examine a slide of liver tissue and identify as many as possible of the structural features illustrated in Figure 15. Also examine a three-dimensional model of liver lobules if this is available. Reproduce a small pie-shaped section of a liver lobule in the space below. Label the hepatocytes, the Kupffer cells, sinusoids, a portal triad, and a central vein. ■

Pancreas

The **pancreas** is a soft, triangular gland that extends horizontally across the posterior abdominal wall from the spleen to the duodenum (see Figure 1). Like the duodenum, it is a retroperitoneal organ (see Figure 7). The pancreas has both an endocrine function (it produces the hormones insulin and glucagon) and an exocrine (enzyme-producing) function. It produces a whole spectrum of hydrolytic enzymes, which it secretes in an alkaline fluid into the duodenum through the pancreatic duct. Pancreatic juice is very alkaline. Its high concentration of bicarbonate ion (HCO_3^-) neutralizes the acidic chyme entering the duodenum from the stomach, enabling the pancreatic and intestinal enzymes to operate at their optimal pH. (Optimal pH for digestive activity to occur in the stomach is very acidic and results from the presence of HCl; that for the small intestine is slightly alkaline.)

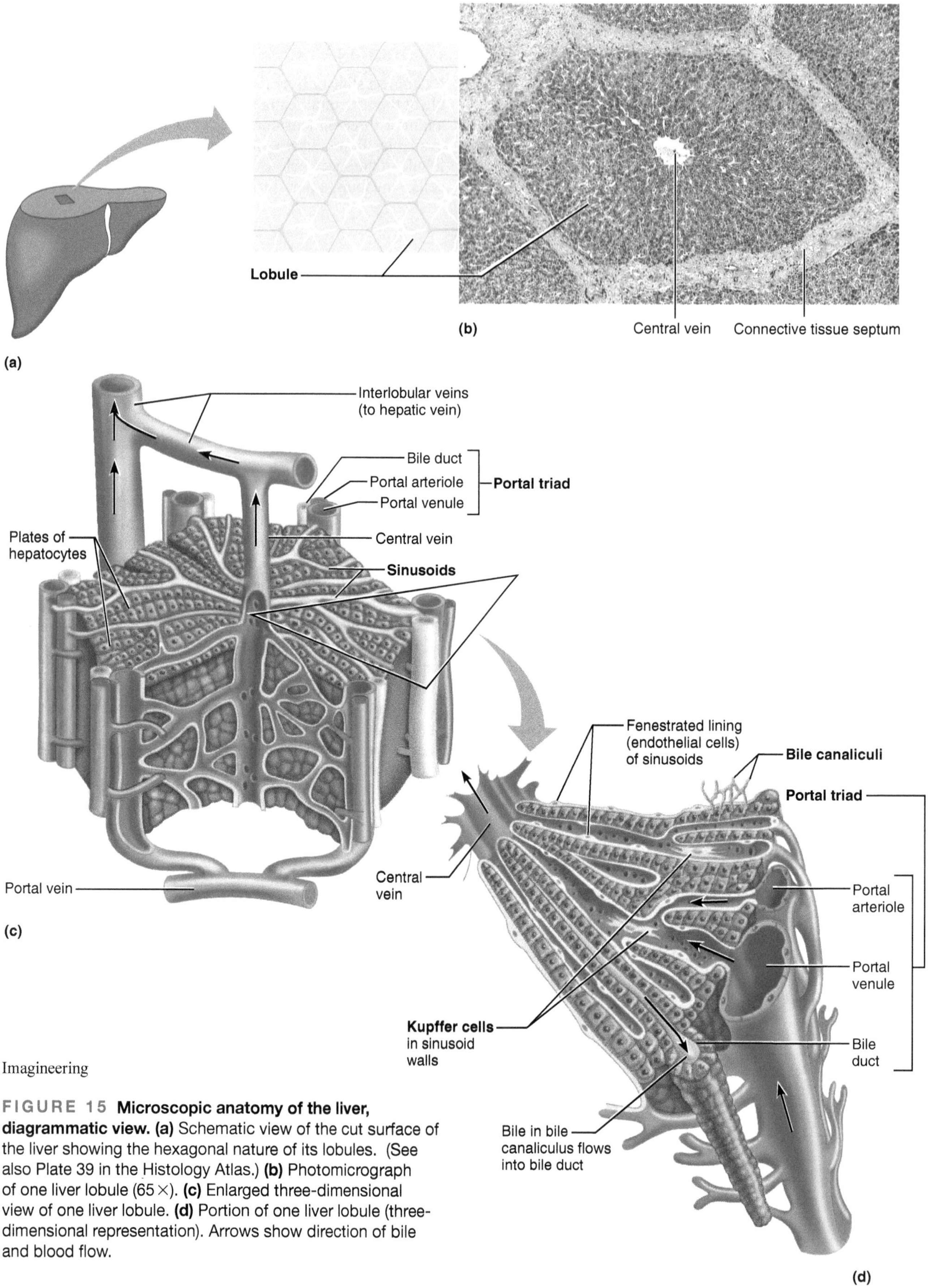

Lobule
(a)
(b)
Central vein
Connective tissue septum
Interlobular veins
(to hepatic vein)
Bile duct
Portal arteriole
Portal venule
Portal triad
Central vein
Plates of
hepatocytes
Sinusoids
Portal vein
(c)
Fenestrated lining
(endothelial cells)
of sinusoids
Bile canaliculi
Portal triad
Central
vein
Portal
arteriole
Portal
venule
Kupffer cells
in sinusoid
walls
Bile
duct
Bile in bile
canaliculus flows
into bile duct
(d)

From *A Stereoscopic Atlas of Human Anatomy* by David L. Bassett

Imagineering

FIGURE 15 **Microscopic anatomy of the liver, diagrammatic view. (a)** Schematic view of the cut surface of the liver showing the hexagonal nature of its lobules. (See also Plate 39 in the Histology Atlas.) **(b)** Photomicrograph of one liver lobule (65×). **(c)** Enlarged three-dimensional view of one liver lobule. **(d)** Portion of one liver lobule (three-dimensional representation). Arrows show direction of bile and blood flow.

NAME ____________________

LAB TIME/DATE ____________________

REVIEW SHEET

Anatomy of the Digestive System

General Histological Plan of the Alimentary Canal

1. The general anatomical features of the alimentary canal are listed below. Fill in the table to complete the information.

Wall layer	Subdivisions of the layer (if applicable)	Major functions
mucosa		
submucosa		
muscularis externa		
serosa or adventitia		

Organs of the Alimentary Canal

2. The tubelike digestive system canal that extends from the mouth to the anus is known as the ____________________ canal or the ____________________ tract.

3. How is the muscularis externa of the stomach modified? ____________________

   How does this modification relate to the function of the stomach? ____________________

4. What transition in epithelial type exists at the gastroesophageal junction? ____________________

   How do the epithelia of these two organs relate to their specific functions? ____________________

5. Differentiate between the colon and the large intestine. ____________________

6. Match the items in column B with the descriptive statements in column A.

Column A

_______ 1. structure that suspends the small intestine from the posterior body wall

_______ 2. fingerlike extensions of the intestinal mucosa that increase the surface area for absorption

_______ 3. large collections of lymphoid tissue found in the submucosa of the small intestine

_______ 4. deep folds of the mucosa and submucosa that extend completely or partially around the circumference of the small intestine

_______, _______ 5. regions that break down foodstuffs mechanically

_______ 6. mobile organ that manipulates food in the mouth and initiates swallowing

_______ 7. conduit for both air and food

_______, _______, _______ 8. three structures continuous with and representing modifications of the peritoneum

_______ 9. the "gullet"; no digestive/absorptive function

_______ 10. folds of the gastric mucosa

_______ 11. sacculations of the large intestine

_______ 12. projections of the plasma membrane of a mucosal epithelial cell

_______ 13. valve at the junction of the small and large intestines

_______ 14. primary region of food and water absorption

_______ 15. membrane securing the tongue to the floor of the mouth

_______ 16. absorbs water and forms feces

_______ 17. area between the teeth and lips/cheeks

_______ 18. wormlike sac that outpockets from the cecum

_______ 19. initiates protein digestion

_______ 20. structure attached to the lesser curvature of the stomach

_______ 21. organ distal to the stomach

_______ 22. valve controlling food movement from the stomach into the duodenum

_______ 23. posterosuperior boundary of the oral cavity

_______ 24. location of the hepatopancreatic sphincter through which pancreatic secretions and bile pass

_______ 25. serous lining of the abdominal cavity wall

_______ 26. principal site for the synthesis of vitamin K by microorganisms

_______ 27. region containing two sphincters through which feces are expelled from the body

_______ 28. bone-supported anterosuperior boundary of the oral cavity

Column B

a. anus
b. appendix
c. circular folds
d. esophagus
e. frenulum
f. greater omentum
g. hard palate
h. haustra
i. ileocecal valve
j. large intestine
k. lesser omentum
l. mesentery
m. microvilli
n. oral cavity
o. parietal peritoneum
p. Peyer's patches
q. pharynx
r. pyloric valve
s. rugae
t. small intestine
u. soft palate
v. stomach
w. tongue
x. vestibule
y. villi
z. visceral peritoneum

7. Correctly identify all organs depicted in the diagram below.

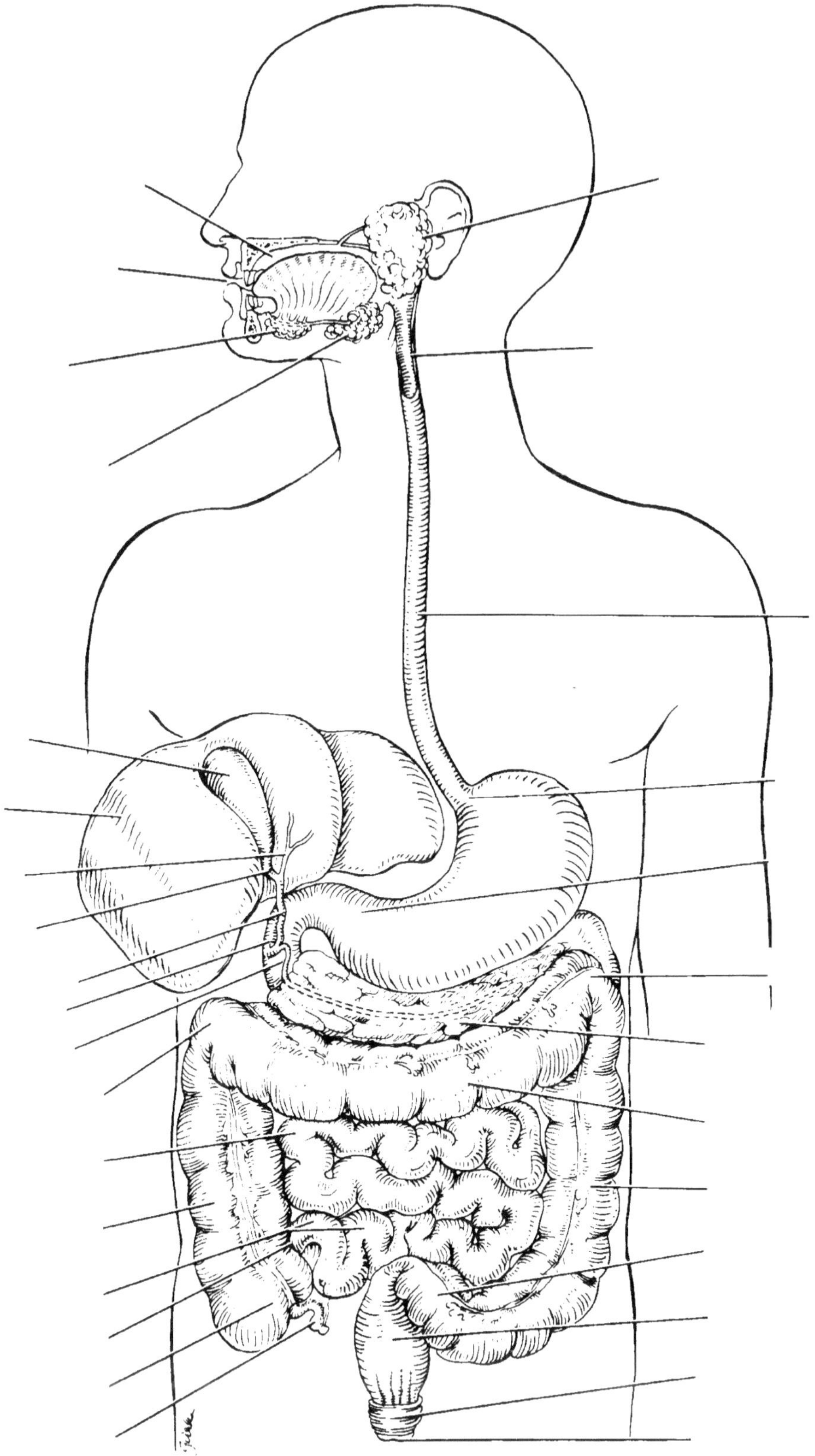

8. You have studied the histological structure of a number of organs in this laboratory. Three of these are diagrammed below. Identify and correctly label each.

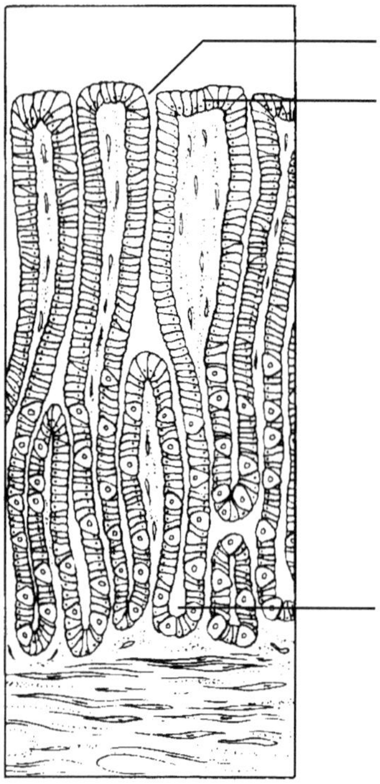

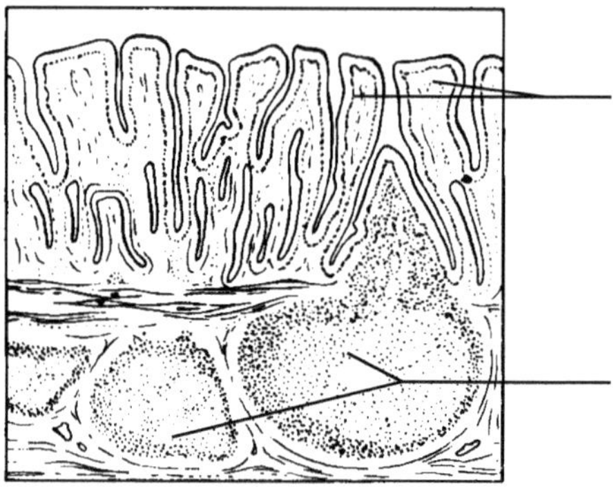

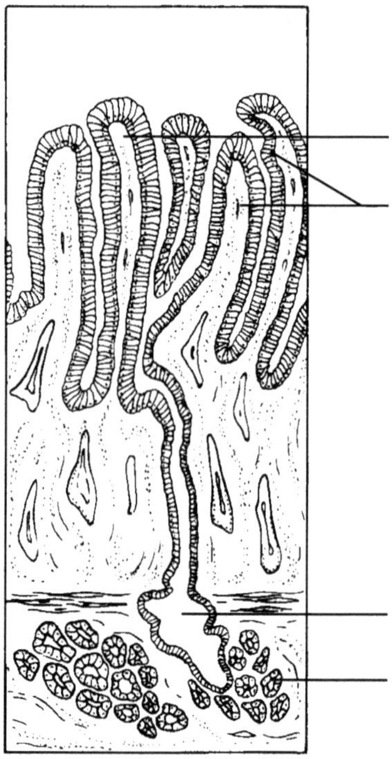

Accessory Digestive Organs

9. Correctly label all structures provided with leader lines in the diagram of a molar below. (Note: Some of the terms in the key for question 10 may be helpful in this task.)

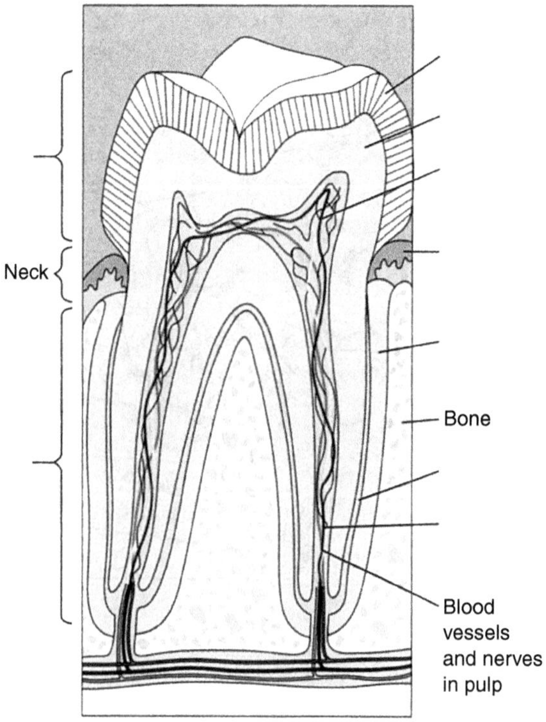
Neck
Bone
Blood vessels and nerves in pulp

10. Use the key to identify each tooth area described below.

_______ 1. visible portion of the tooth in situ

_______ 2. material covering the tooth root

_______ 3. hardest substance in the body

_______ 4. attaches the tooth to bone and surrounding alveolar structures

_______ 5. portion of the tooth embedded in bone

_______ 6. forms the major portion of tooth structure; similar to bone

_______ 7. produces the dentin

_______ 8. site of blood vessels, nerves, and lymphatics

_______ 9. entire portion of the tooth covered with enamel

Key:
a. anatomical crown
b. cementum
c. clinical crown
d. dentin
e. enamel
f. gingiva
g. odontoblast
h. periodontal ligament
i. pulp
j. root

11. In the human, the number of deciduous teeth is _______; the number of permanent teeth is _______________.

12. The dental formula for permanent teeth is $\frac{2,1,2,3}{2,1,2,3} \times 2$

Explain what this means. ____

____

What is the dental formula for the deciduous teeth? _______________ × _______________ = _______________

13. What teeth are the "wisdom teeth"? ____

14. Various types of glands form a part of the alimentary tube wall or duct their secretions into it. Match the glands listed in column B with the function/locations described in column A.

Column A

_______ 1. produce(s) mucus; found in the submucosa of the small intestine

_______ 2. produce(s) a product containing amylase that begins starch breakdown in the mouth

_______ 3. produce(s) a whole spectrum of enzymes and an alkaline fluid that is secreted into the duodenum

_______ 4. produce(s) bile that it secretes into the duodenum via the bile duct

_______ 5. produce(s) HCl and pepsinogen

_______ 6. found in the mucosa of the small intestine; produce(s) intestinal juice

Column B

a. duodenal glands
b. gastric glands
c. intestinal crypts
d. liver
e. pancreas
f. salivary glands

15. Which of the salivary glands produces a secretion that is mainly serous? _______________________________

16. What is the role of the gallbladder? ______________________________

17. Name three structures always found in the portal triad regions of the liver. ______________________________,

______________________________ and ______________________________

18. Where would you expect to find the Kupffer cells of the liver? ______________________________

What is their function? ______________________________

19. Why is the liver so dark red in the living animal? ______________________________

____

20. The pancreas has two major populations of secretory cells—those in the islets and the acinar cells. Which population serves the digestive process? ______________________________

* know small intestine slide *

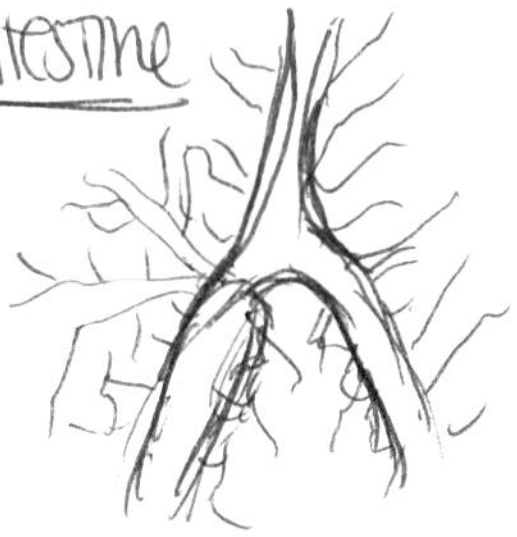

digestion starts in mouth - mechanical

- salivary alpha amalase - digests sugar *

pyloric sphincter - from stomach to duodenum

^lower esophageal sphincter - stops stomach acid from going ↑

*

stomach chemically digests proteins (HCl activates pepsinogen to pepsin)

pancreas secretes digestive juices

→ breakes down DNA, carbs

gall bladder - stores bile made by liver

↳ mechanically breaks down fat *

lipase - chemically digests fat *

small intestine - duodenum, jejunum, ileum

Bile - mech dig fat

saliva / pancreas — ~~Amylase - breaks down sugar~~

Trypsin - " " protein

/

Stomach

sm intestine

PROTEIN DIGESTION

Setting up the experiment

GROUP 1

1. Select three test tubes and label as A, B, or C.
2. To each of the three test tubes, add the following solutions:

Test Tube A	Test Tube B	Test Tube C
5 drops trypsin (pH 2)	5 drops BAPNA	5 drops trypsin (pH 2)
+	+	+
5 drops water	5 drops water	5 drops BAPNA

3. Carefully place all three test tubes in the rack submerged in the heated water bath (37°C).

GROUP 2

1. Select three test tubes and label as A, B, or C.
2. To each of the three test tubes, add the following solutions:

Test Tube A	Test Tube B	Test Tube C
5 drops trypsin (pH 7)	5 drops BAPNA	5 drops trypsin (pH 7)
+	+	+
5 drops water	5 drops water	5 drops BAPNA

3. Carefully place all three test tubes in the rack submerged in the heated water bath (37°C).

Interpreting your results

Appearance of a yellow color indicates a positive reaction (protein digestion occurred). Here's why:

- Trypsin is a protease, i.e., an enzyme that breaks down proteins by cutting peptide bonds. Peptide bonds hold the component parts (= amino acids) of the protein together.
- Trypsin requires a neutral pH (pH of 7) and temperature (37°C) for optimal activity.
- BAPNA is a synthetic protein bound to a yellow dye molecule via a peptide bond.
- So, under these optimal conditions, trypsin successfully breaks down BAPNA. This results in the release of the dye molecule from BAPNA and the appearance of the yellow color!

FAT (LIPID) DIGESTION

Setting up the experiment

1. Select three test tubes and label as A, B, or C.
2. To each of the three test tubes, add the following solutions:

Test Tube A	Test Tube B	Test Tube C

10 drops water	10 drops water	10 drops water
+	+	+
2 drops oil	2 drops oil	2 drops oil
	+	+
	10 drops bile	10 drops bile
		+
		5 drops lipase

3. Cover each test tube with a square of Parafilm and shake the tube thoroughly.
4. Examine what happens to the size of the oil droplets and the consistency of the mixture.

Interpreting the results

- Oil is hydrophobic and forms large droplets when put in water.
- The presence of bile emulsifies the oil and makes the oil droplets more water soluble thus smaller.
- Once the fats are emulsified, lipases act on the small oil droplets and break them down into their component parts (fatty acids, monoglycerides, and diglycerides), so now the solution appears to be a more homogenous cloudy mixture.

CARBOHYDRATE DIGESTION

Setting up the experiment

1. Select three test tubes and label as A, B, or C.
2. To each of the three test tubes, add the following solutions:

Test Tube A	Test Tube B	Test Tube C
10 drops starch	10 drops amylase	10 drops starch
+	+	+
10 drops water	10 drops water	10 drops amylase

3. Gently shake each test tube.
4. Immediately place one drop of the solution in Tube A in one well of the ceramic test plate. Add one drop of iodine to this well. Note the color. Do the same for Tubes B and C.

5. *Repeat these steps at 10-minute intervals for up to 30 minutes, so your test plate should be arranged as follows:*

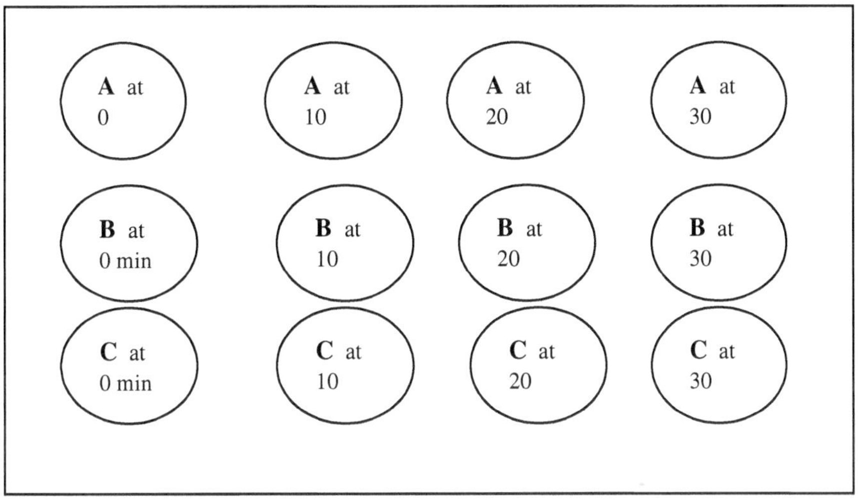

Interpreting the results

- *Iodine reacts to starch and indicates a dark blue color when starch is present.*
- *If starch is not present, the solution will appear to be a more yellowish color.*
- *Amylase is a carbohydrase, an enzyme that breaks down starch into maltose (a disaccharide).*
- *The extent to which amylase breaks down the starch increases with time. As more and more starch is broken down by amylase, the less blue/more yellow the test solutions become.*

Chemical and Physical Processes of Digestion: Wet Lab

MATERIALS

Part I: Enzyme Action

General Supply Area

- ☐ Hot plates
- ☐ 250-ml beakers
- ☐ Boiling chips
- ☐ Test tubes and test tube rack
- ☐ Wax markers
- ☐ Water bath set at 37°C (if not available, incubate at room temperature and double the time)
- ☐ Ice water bath
- ☐ Chart on chalkboard for recording class results

Activity 1: Starch Digestion

- ☐ Dropper bottle of distilled water
- ☐ Dropper bottles of the following:
  - 1% alpha-amylase solution*
  - 1% boiled starch solution, freshly prepared†
  - 1% maltose solution
  - Lugol's iodine solution (IKI)
  - Benedict's solution
- ☐ Spot plate

Activity 2: Protein Digestion

- ☐ Dropper bottles of 1% trypsin and 0.01% BAPNA solution

*The alpha-amylase must be a low-maltose preparation for good results.

†Prepare by adding 1 g starch to 100 ml distilled water; boil and cool; add a pinch of salt (NaCl). Prepare fresh daily.

Text continues on next page

OBJECTIVES

1. To list the digestive system enzymes involved in the digestion of proteins, fats, and carbohydrates; to state their site of origin; and to summarize the environmental conditions promoting their optimal functioning.
2. To recognize the variation between different types of enzyme assays.
3. To name the end products of protein, fat, and carbohydrate digestion.
4. To perform the appropriate chemical tests to determine if digestion of a particular foodstuff has occurred.
5. To cite the function(s) of bile in the digestive process.
6. To discuss the possible role of temperature and pH in the regulation of enzyme activity.
7. To define *enzyme, catalyst, control, substrate,* and *hydrolase.*
8. To explain why swallowing is both a voluntary and a reflex activity.
9. To discuss the role of the tongue, larynx, and gastroesophageal sphincter in swallowing.
10. To compare and contrast segmentation and peristalsis as mechanisms of propulsion.

Because nutrients can be absorbed only when broken down to their monomers, food digestion is a prerequisite to food absorption. You may have already studied mechanisms of passive and active absorption. Before proceeding, review that material.

Chemical Digestion of Foodstuffs: Enzymatic Action

Enzymes are large protein molecules produced by body cells. They are biological **catalysts,** meaning they increase the rate of a chemical reaction without themselves becoming part of the product. The digestive enzymes are hydrolytic enzymes, or **hydrolases.** Their **substrates,** or the molecules on which they act, are organic food molecules which they break down by adding water to the molecular bonds, thus cleaving the bonds between the subunits or monomers.

The various hydrolytic enzymes are highly specific in their action. Each enzyme hydrolyzes only one or a small group of substrate molecules, and specific environmental conditions are necessary for it to function optimally. Since digestive enzymes actually function outside the body cells in the digestive tract, their hydrolytic activity can also be studied in a test tube. Such an in vitro study provides a convenient laboratory environment for investigating the effect of such variations on enzymatic activity.

(materials list, continued)

Activity 3: Bile Action and Fat Digestion

- ☐ Dropper bottles of 1% pancreatin solution, litmus cream (fresh cream to which powdered litmus is added to achieve a deep blue color), 0.1 *N* HCl, and vegetable oil
- ☐ Bile salts (sodium taurocholate)
- ☐ Parafilm (small squares to cover the test tubes)

Part II: Physical Processes

Activity 5: Observing Digestion

- ☐ Water pitcher
- ☐ Paper cups
- ☐ Stethoscope
- ☐ Alcohol swab
- ☐ Disposable autoclave bag
- ☐ Watch, clock, or timer

Activity 6: Videotape

- ☐ *The Human Digestive System Video*
- ☐ Television and VCR for independent viewing of videocassette by student

PEx PhysioEx™ 7.0 Computer Simulation

‡Available from Ward's Biology.

Figure 1 is a flowchart of the progressive digestion of carbohydrates, proteins, fats, and nucleic acids. It indicates specific enzymes involved, their site of formation, and their site of action. Acquaint yourself with the flowchart before beginning this experiment, and refer to it as necessary during the laboratory session.

General Instructions for Activities 1–3

Work in groups of four, with each group taking responsibility for setting up and conducting one of the following experiments. In each of the digestive procedures being studied (starch, protein, and fat digestion) and in the amylase assay, you are directed to boil the contents of one or more test tubes. To do this, obtain a 250-ml beaker, boiling chips, and a hot plate from the general supply area. Place a few boiling chips into the beaker and add about 125 ml of water, and bring to a boil. Place the test tube for each specimen in the water for the number of minutes specified in the directions. You will also be using a 37°C and an ice water bath for parts of these experiments. You will need to use your time very efficiently in order to set up and perform each test properly.

Upon completion of the experiments, each group should communicate its results to the rest of the class by recording them in a chart on the chalkboard. All members of the class should observe the **controls** (the specimens or standards against which experimental samples are compared) as well as the positive and negative examples of all experimental results. Additionally, all members of the class should be able to explain the tests used and the results observed and anticipated for each experiment. Note that water baths and hot plates are at the general supply area.

ACTIVITY 1

Assessing Starch Digestion by Salivary Amylase

1. From the general supply area, obtain a test tube rack, 10 test tubes, and a wax marking pencil. From the Activity 1 supply area, obtain a dropper bottle of distilled water and dropper bottles of maltose, amylase, and starch solutions.

2. In this experiment you will investigate the hydrolysis of starch to maltose by **salivary amylase** (the enzyme produced by the salivary glands and secreted into the mouth), so you will need to be able to identify the presence of starch and maltose to determine to what extent the enzymatic activity has occurred. Thus controls must be prepared to provide a known standard against which comparisons can be made. Starch decreases and sugar increases as digestion occurs, according to the following formula:

$$\text{Starch} + \text{water} \xrightarrow{\text{Amylase}} \text{maltose}$$

Two students should prepare the controls (tubes 1A to 3A) while the other two prepare the experimental samples (tubes 4A and 5A).

- Mark each tube with a wax pencil and load the tubes as indicated in the Salivary Amylase chart, using 3 drops (gtt) of each indicated substance.
- Place all tubes in a rack in the 37°C water bath for approximately 1 hour. Shake the rack gently from time to time to keep the contents evenly mixed.
- At the end of the hour, perform the amylase assay described below.
- While these tubes are incubating, proceed to Physical Processes: Mechanisms of Food Propulsion and Mixing. Be sure to monitor the time so as to complete this activity as needed.

Amylase Assay

1. After one hour, obtain a spot plate and dropper bottles of Lugol's solution (for the IKI, or iodine, test) and Benedict's solution from the Activity 1 supply area. Set up your boiling water bath using a hot plate, boiling chips, and a 250-ml beaker obtained from the general supply area.

2. While the water is heating, mark five depressions of the spot plate 1A–5A (*A* for amylase) for sample identification.

3. Pour about a drop of the sample from each of the tubes 1A–5A into the appropriately numbered spot. Into each sample droplet, place a drop of Lugol's IKI solution. A blue-black color indicates the presence of starch and is referred to as a **positive starch test.** If starch is not present, the mixture will not turn blue, which is referred to as a **negative starch test.** Record your results (+ for positive, − for negative) in the chart on page 600 and on the chalkboard.

4. Into the remaining mixture in each tube, place 3 drops of Benedict's solution. Put each tube into the beaker of boiling water for about 5 minutes. If a green-to-orange precipitate forms, maltose is present; this is a **positive sugar test.** A **negative sugar test** is indicated by no color change. Record your

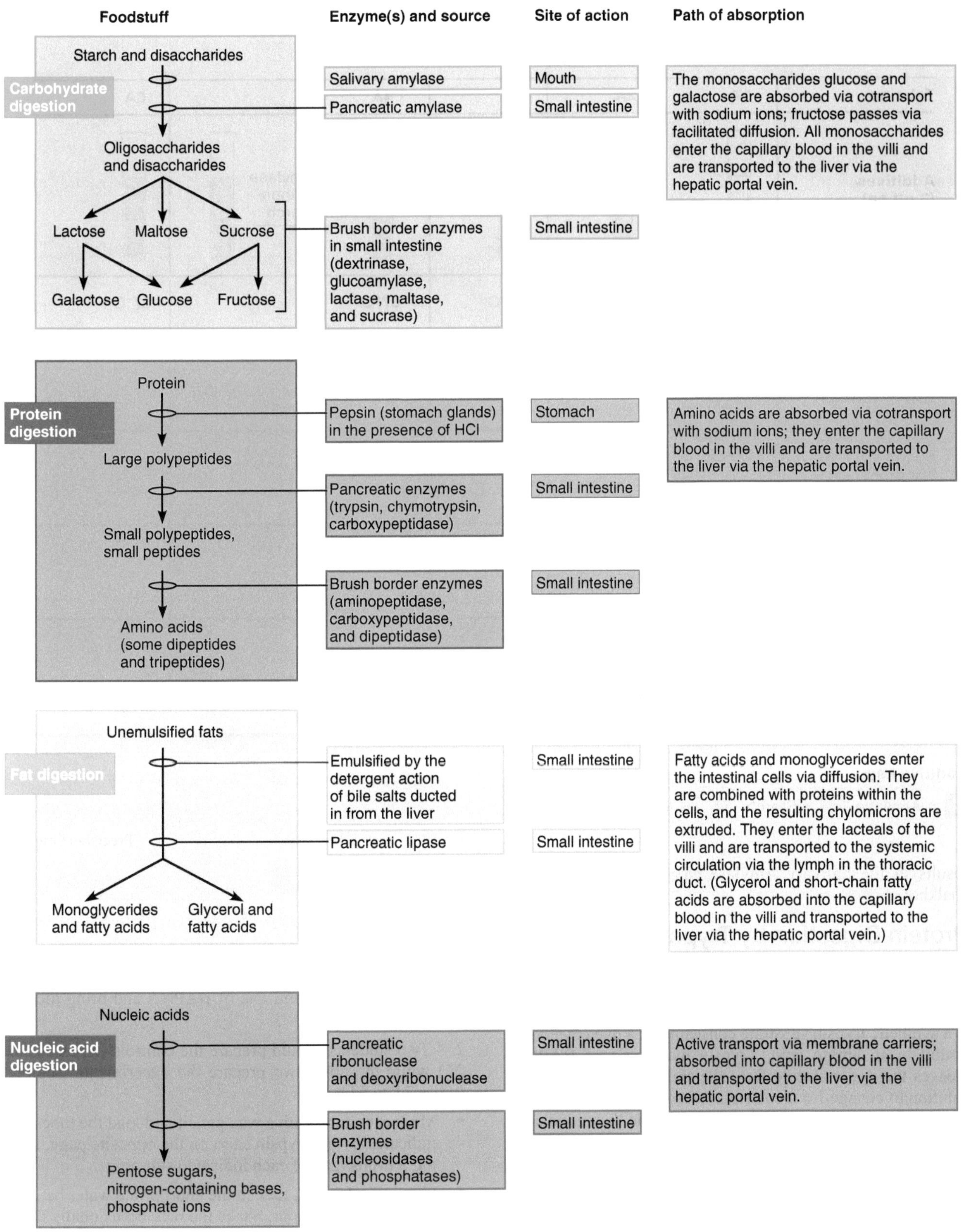

Imagineering

FIGURE 1 Flowchart of digestion and absorption of foodstuffs.

Salivary Amylase Digestion of Starch

Tube no.	1A	2A	3A	4A	5A
Additives (3 gtt ea)				 Boil amylase 4 min, then add starch → 	
Incubation condition	37°C	37°C	37°C	37°C	37°C
IKI test (color change)					
Positive (+) or negative (−) result					
Benedict's test (color change)					
Positive (+) or negative (−) result					

Additive key:

= Amylase = Starch = Maltose = Water

Precision Graphics

results in the Salivary Amylase chart above and on the chalkboard.

Protein Digestion by Trypsin

Trypsin, an enzyme produced by the pancreas, hydrolyzes proteins to small fragments (proteoses, peptones, and peptides). BAPNA (*N*-alpha-benzoyl-L-arginine-*p*-nitroanilide) is a synthetic trypsin substrate consisting of a dye covalently bound to an amino acid. Trypsin hydrolysis of BAPNA cleaves the dye molecule from the amino acid, causing the solution to change from colorless to bright yellow. Since the covalent bond between the dye molecule and the amino acid is the same as the peptide bonds that link amino acids together, the appearance of a yellow color indicates the presence and activity of an enzyme that is capable of peptide bond hydrolysis. The color change from clear to yellow is direct evidence of hydrolysis, so additional tests are not required when determining trypsin activity using BAPNA.

ACTIVITY 2

Assessing Protein Digestion by Trypsin

1. From the general supply area, obtain five test tubes and a test tube rack, and from the Activity 2 supply area get a dropper bottle of trypsin and one of BAPNA and bring them to your bench.

2. Two students should prepare the controls (tubes 1T and 2T) while the other two prepare the experimental samples (tubes 3T to 5T).

- Mark each tube with a wax pencil and load the tubes as indicated in the Trypsin chart on the opposite page, using 3 drops (gtt) of each indicated substance.
- Place all tubes in a rack in the appropriate water bath for approximately 1 hour. Shake the rack occasionally to keep the contents well mixed.

Trypsin Digestion of Protein

Tube no.	1T	2T	3T	4T	5T
Additives (3 gtt ea)	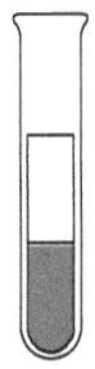	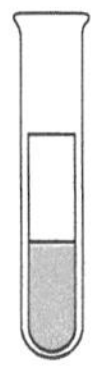	 Boil trypsin 4 min, then add BAPNA. → 	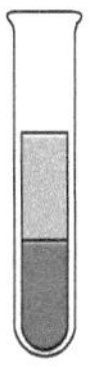	
Incubation condition	37°C	37°C	37°C	37°C	0°C
Color change					
Positive (+) or negative (−) result					

Additive key:

= Trypsin = BAPNA = Water

Precision Graphics

- At the end of the hour, examine the tubes for the results of the trypsin assay (detailed below).
- While these tubes are incubating, proceed to Physical Processes: Mechanisms of Food Propulsion and Mixing.

Trypsin Assay

Since BAPNA is a synthetic colorigenic (color-producing) substrate, the presence of yellow color indicates a **positive hydrolysis test;** the dye molecule has been cleaved from the amino acid. If the sample mixture remains clear, a **negative hydrolysis test** has occurred.

Record the results in the Trypsin chart and on the chalkboard.

Pancreatic Lipase Digestion of Fats and the Action of Bile

The treatment that fats and oils go through during digestion in the small intestine is a bit more complicated than that of carbohydrates or proteins—pretreatment with bile to physically emulsify the fats is required. Hence, two sets of reactions occur.

First:

$$\text{Fats/oils} \xrightarrow[\text{(emulsification)}]{\text{Bile}} \text{minute fat/oil droplets}$$

Then:

$$\text{Fat/oil droplets} \xrightarrow[\text{(digestion)}]{\text{Lipase}} \text{monoglycerides and fatty acids}$$

The term **pancreatin** describes the enzymatic product of the pancreas, which includes enzymes that digest proteins, carbohydrates, nucleic acids, and fats. It is used here to investigate the properties of **pancreatic lipase,** which hydrolyzes fats and oils to their component monoglycerides and two fatty acids (and occasionally to glycerol and three fatty acids).

The fact that some of the end products of fat digestion (fatty acids) are organic acids that decrease the pH provides an easy way to recognize that digestion is ongoing or completed. You will be using a pH indicator called *litmus blue* to follow these changes; it changes from blue to pink as the test tube contents become acid.

ACTIVITY 3

Demonstrating the Emulsification Action of Bile and Assessing Fat Digestion by Lipase

1. From the general supply area, obtain nine test tubes and a test tube rack, plus one dropper bottle of each of the solutions in the Activity 3 supply area.

2. Although *bile,* a secretory product of the liver, is not an enzyme, it is important to fat digestion because of its emulsifying action (the physical breakdown of larger particles into smaller ones) on fats. Emulsified fats provide a larger surface area for enzymatic activity. To demonstrate the action of bile on fats, prepare two test tubes and mark them 1E and 2E (*E* for emulsified fats).

Pancreatic Lipase Digestion of Fats

Tube no.	1L	2L	3L	4L	5L	4B	5B
Additives (5 gtt ea)	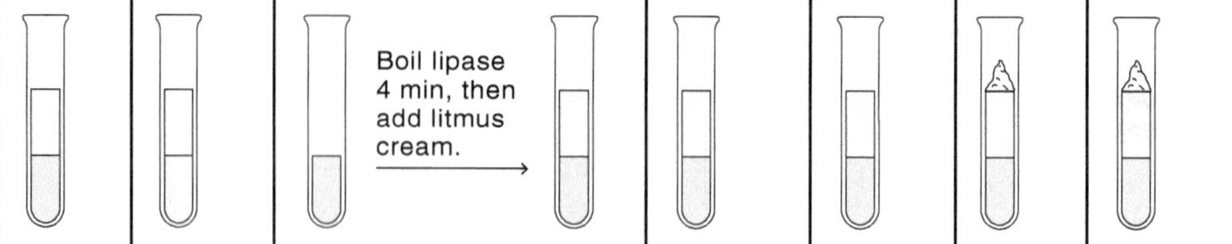Boil lipase 4 min, then add litmus cream.						
Incubation condition	37°C	37°C	37°C	37°C	0°C	37°C	0°C
Color change							
Positive (+) or negative (−) result							

Additive key:

= Lipase = Litmus cream = Water = Pinch bile salts

Precision Graphics

- To tube 1E, add 10 drops of water and 2 drops of vegetable oil.
- To tube 2E, add 10 drops of water, 2 drops of vegetable oil, and a pinch of bile salts.
- Cover each tube with a small square of Parafilm, shake vigorously, and allow the tubes to stand at room temperature.

After 10 to 15 minutes, observe both tubes. If emulsification has not occurred, the oil will be floating on the surface of the water. If emulsification has occurred, the fat droplets will be suspended throughout the water, forming an emulsion.

In which tube has emulsification occurred? ____________

3. Two students should prepare the controls (1L and 2L, *L* for lipase), while the other two students in the group set up the experimental samples (3L to 5L, 4B, and 5B, where *B* is for bile) as illustrated in the Pancreatic Lipase chart above.

- Mark each tube with a wax pencil and load the tubes using 5 drops (gtt) of each indicated solution.
- Place a pinch of bile salts in tubes 4B and 5B.
- Cover each tube with a small square of Parafilm, and shake to mix the contents of the tube.
- Remove the Parafilm, and place all tubes in a rack in the appropriate water bath for approximately 1 hour. Shake the test tube rack from time to time to keep the contents well mixed.
- At the end of the hour, perform the lipase assay (below).
- While these tubes are incubating proceed to Physical Processes: Mechanisms of Food Propulsion and Mixing. Be sure to monitor the time so as to complete this activity when needed.

Lipase Assay

The basis of this assay is a pH change that is detected by a litmus powder indicator. Alkaline or neutral solutions containing litmus are blue but will turn reddish in the presence of acid. Since fats are digested to fatty acids (organic acids) during hydrolysis, they lower the pH of the sample they are in. Litmus cream (fresh cream providing the fat substrate to which litmus powder was added) will turn from blue to pink if the solution is acid. Because the effect of hydrolysis is directly seen, additional assay reagents are not necessary.

1. To prepare a color control, add 0.1 *N* HCl drop by drop to tubes 1L and 2L (covering the tubes with a square of Parafilm after each addition and shaking to mix) until the cream turns pink.

2. Record the color of the tubes in the Pancreatic Lipase chart above and on the chalkboard.

ACTIVITY 4

Reporting Results and Conclusions

1. Share your results with the class as directed in the General Instructions.

2. Suggest additional experiments, and carry out experiments if time permits.

3. Prepare a lab report for the experiments on digestion.

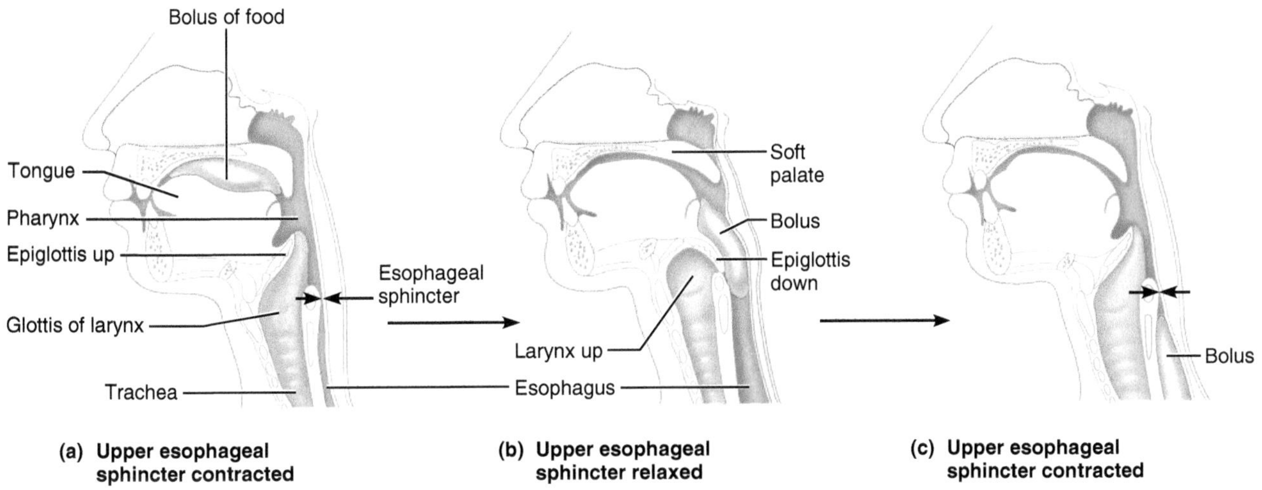

FIGURE 2 **Swallowing.** The process of swallowing consists of voluntary (buccal) and involuntary (pharyngeal-esophageal) phases. **(a)** During the buccal phase, the tongue pushes the food bolus posteriorly and against the soft palate. The soft palate rises to close off the nasal passages as the bolus enters the pharynx where the involuntary phase of swallowing begins. **(b)** The larynx rises so that the epiglottis covers its opening, preventing food from entering the lower respiratory passages. Relaxation of the upper esophageal sphincter allows food to enter the esophagus. **(c)** Peristalsis of the pharyngeal constrictor muscles forces the food through the esophagus to the stomach. The upper esophageal sphincter contracts again as the larynx and epiglottis return to their former positions.

Physical Processes: Mechanisms of Food Propulsion and Mixing

Although enzyme activity is a very important part of the overall digestion process, foods must also be processed physically (by churning and chewing) and moved by mechanical means along the tract if digestion and absorption are to be completed. Just about any time organs exhibit mobility, muscles are involved, and movements of and in the gastrointestinal tract are no exception. Although we tend to think only of smooth muscles when visceral activities are involved, both skeletal and smooth muscles are involved in digestion. This fact is amply demonstrated by the simple activities that follow.

Deglutition (Swallowing)

Swallowing, or **deglutition,** which is largely the result of skeletal muscle activity, occurs in two phases: *buccal* (mouth) and *pharyngeal-esophageal.* The initial phase—the buccal (Figure 2a)—is voluntarily controlled and initiated by the tongue. Once begun, the process continues involuntarily in the pharynx and esophagus, through peristalsis, resulting in the delivery of the swallowed contents to the stomach (Figure 2b and c).

ACTIVITY 5

Observing Movements and Sounds of Digestion

1. Obtain a pitcher of water, a stethoscope, a paper cup, an alcohol swab, and an autoclave bag in preparation for making the following observations.

2. While swallowing a mouthful of water, consciously note the movement of your tongue during the process. Record your observations.

____

____

____

3. Repeat the swallowing process while your laboratory partner watches the externally visible movements of your larynx. (This movement is more obvious in a male, since males have a larger Adam's apple.) Record your observations.

____

What do these movements accomplish? ________________

____

____

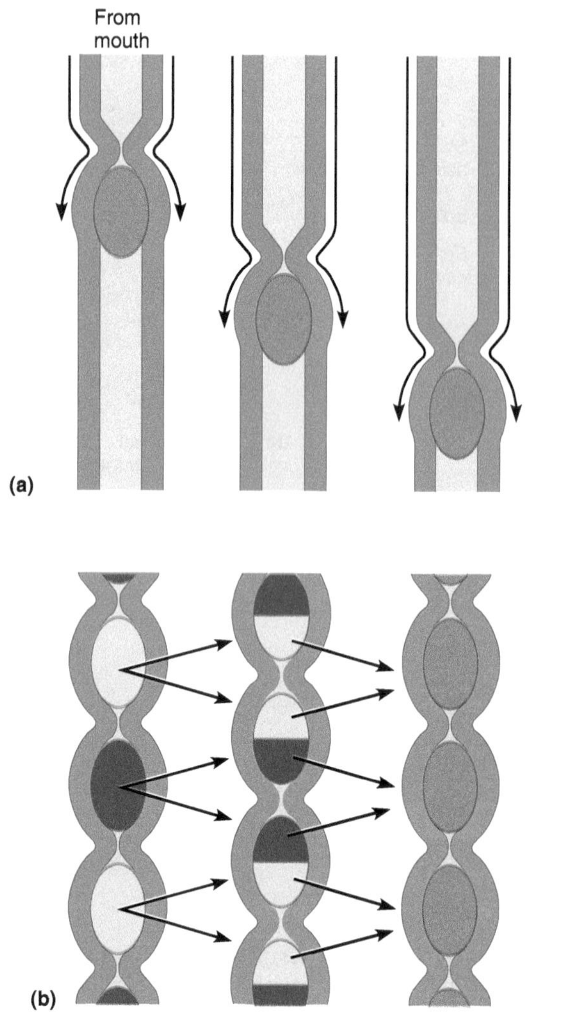

Imagineering

FIGURE 3 Peristaltic and segmental movements of the digestive tract. (a) Peristalsis: neighboring segments of the intestine alternately contract and relax, moving food along the tract. **(b)** Segmentation: single segments of intestine alternately contract and relax. Because inactive segments exist between active segments, food mixing occurs to a greater degree than food movement. Peristalsis is superimposed on segmentation during digestion.

4. Before donning the stethoscope, your lab partner should clean the earpieces with an alcohol swab. Then, he or she should place the diaphragm of the stethoscope over your abdominal wall, approximately 2.5 cm (1 inch) below the xiphoid process and slightly to the left, to listen for sounds as you again take two or three swallows of water. There should be two audible sounds—one when the water splashes against the gastroesophageal sphincter and the second when the peristaltic wave of the esophagus arrives at the sphincter and the sphincter opens, allowing water to gurgle into the stomach. Determine, as accurately as possible, the time interval between these two sounds and record it below.

Interval between arrival of water at the sphincter and the opening of the sphincter: _______ sec

This interval gives a fair indication of the time it takes for the peristaltic wave to travel down the 25 cm (10 inches) of the esophagus. (Actually the time interval is slightly less than it seems, because pressure causes the sphincter to relax before the peristaltic wave reaches it.)

! Dispose of the used paper cup in the autoclave bag. ■

Segmentation and Peristalsis

Although several types of movements occur in the digestive tract organs, peristalsis and segmentation are most important as mixing and propulsive mechanisms (Figure 3).

Peristaltic movements are the major means of propelling food through most of the digestive viscera. Essentially they are waves of contraction followed by waves of relaxation that squeeze foodstuffs through the alimentary canal, and they are superimposed on segmental movements.

Segmental movements are local constrictions of the organ wall that occur rhythmically. They serve mainly to mix the foodstuffs with digestive juices and to increase the rate of absorption by continually moving different portions of the chyme over adjacent regions of the intestinal wall. However, segmentation is also an important means of food propulsion in the small intestine, and slow segmenting movements called haustral contractions are frequently seen in the large intestine.

ACTIVITY 6

Viewing Segmental and Peristaltic Movements

If a videotape showing some of the propulsive movements is available, go to a viewing station to view it before leaving the laboratory. ■

NAME ______________________

LAB TIME/DATE ______________________

REVIEW SHEET

Chemical and Physical Processes of Digestion: Wet Lab

Chemical Digestion of Foodstuffs: Enzymatic Action

1. Match the following definitions with the proper choices from the key.

Key: a. catalyst b. control c. enzyme d. substrate

______________ 1. increases the rate of a chemical reaction without becoming part of the product

______________ 2. provides a standard of comparison for test results

______________ 3. biologic catalyst; protein in nature

______________ 4. substance on which a catalyst works

2. List the three characteristics of enzymes. ______________________

____

____

3. The enzymes of the digestive system are classified as hydrolases. What does this mean?

____

____

4. Fill in the following chart about the various digestive system enzymes encountered in this exercise.

Enzyme	Organ producing it	Site of action	Substrate(s)	Optimal pH
Salivary amylase				
Trypsin				
Lipase (pancreatic)				

5. Name the end products of digestion for the following types of foods.

proteins: ______________________ carbohydrates: ______________________

fats: ______________________ and ______________________

6. You used several indicators or tests in the laboratory to determine the presence or absence of certain substances. Choose the correct test or indicator from the key to correspond to the condition described below.

Key: a. Lugol's iodine (IKI) b. Benedict's solution c. litmus d. BAPNA

_______ 1. used to test for protein hydrolysis, which was indicated by a yellow color

_______ 2. used to test for the presence of starch, which was indicated by a blue-black color

_______ 3. used to test for the presence of fatty acids, which was evidenced by a color change from blue to pink

_______ 4. used to test for the presence of reducing sugars (maltose, sucrose, glucose) as indicated by a blue to green or orange color change

7. What conclusions can you draw when an experimental sample gives both a positive starch test and a positive maltose test after incubation? _______

Why was 37°C the optimal incubation temperature? _______

Why did very little, if any, starch digestion occur in test tube 4A? _______

____

If starch was incubated with amylase at 0°C, would you expect to see any starch digestion? _______

Why or why not? _______

____

Assume you have made the statement to a group of your peers that amylase is capable of starch hydrolysis to maltose. If you had not done control tube 1A, what objection to your statement could be raised? _______

____

What if you had not done tube 2A? _______

8. In the exercise concerning trypsin function, why was an enzyme assay like Benedict's or Lugol's IKI (which test for the presence of a reaction product) not necessary? _______

Why was tube 1T necessary? _______

Why was tube 2T necessary? _______

Trypsin is a protease similar to pepsin, the protein-digesting enzyme in the stomach. Would trypsin work well in the stomach? _______ Why? _______

9. In the procedure concerning pancreatic lipase digestion of fats and the action of bile salts, how did the appearance of tubes 1E and 2E differ? _______

____

Explain the reason for the difference. _______

____

Why did the litmus indicator change from blue to pink during fat hydrolysis? ______________________

____

Why is bile not considered an enzyme? ______________________

How did the tubes containing bile compare with those not containing bile? ______________________

What role does bile play in fat digestion? ______________________

____

10. The three-dimensional structure of a functional protein is altered by intense heat or nonphysiological pH even though peptide bonds may not break. Such inactivation is called denaturation, and denatured enzymes are nonfunctional. Explain why.

____

____

What specific experimental conditions resulted in denatured enzymes? ______________________

____

11. Pancreatic and intestinal enzymes operate optimally at a pH that is slightly alkaline, yet the chyme entering the duodenum from the stomach is very acid. How is the proper pH for the functioning of the pancreatic-intestinal enzymes ensured?

____

____

12. Assume you have been chewing a piece of bread for 5 or 6 minutes. How would you expect its taste to change during this interval? ______________________

Why? ______________________

13. Note the mechanism of absorption (passive or active transport) of the following food breakdown products, and indicate by a check mark (✓) whether the absorption would result in their movement into the blood capillaries or the lymph capillaries (lacteals).

Substance	Mechanism of absorption	Blood	Lymph
Monosaccharides			
Fatty acids and glycerol			
Amino acids			
Water			
Na^{+}, Cl^{-}, Ca^{2+}			

14. People on a strict diet to lose weight begin to metabolize stored fats at an accelerated rate. How does this condition affect blood pH? ______________________

15. Using a flowchart, trace the pathway of a ham sandwich (ham = protein and fat; bread = starch) from the mouth to the site of absorption of its breakdown products, noting where digestion occurs and what specific enzymes are involved.

16. Some of the digestive organs have groups of secretory cells that liberate hormones (parahormones) into the blood. These exert an effect on the digestive process by acting on other cells or structures and causing them to release digestive enzymes, expel bile, or increase the mobility of the digestive tract. For each hormone below, note the organ producing the hormone and its effects on the digestive process. Include the target organs affected.

Hormone	Produced by	Target organ(s) and effects
Secretin		
Gastrin		
Cholecystokinin		

Physical Processes: Mechanisms of Food Propulsion and Mixing

17. Complete the following statements.

Swallowing, or __1__, occurs in two phases—the __2__ and __3__. One of these phases, the __4__ phase, is voluntary. During the voluntary phase, the __5__ is used to push the food into the back of the throat. During swallowing, the __6__ rises to ensure that its passageway is covered by the epiglottis so that the ingested substances don't enter the respiratory passageways. It is possible to swallow water while standing on your head because the water is carried along the esophagus involuntarily by the process of __7__. The pressure exerted by the foodstuffs on the __8__ sphincter causes it to open, allowing the foodstuffs to enter the stomach.

The two major types of propulsive movements that occur in the small intestine are __9__ and __10__. One of these movements, the __11__, acts to continually mix the foods and to increase the absorption rate by moving different parts of the chyme mass over the intestinal mucosa, but it has less of a role in moving foods along the digestive tract.

1. ____________________
2. ____________________
3. ____________________
4. ____________________
5. ____________________
6. ____________________
7. ____________________
8. ____________________
9. ____________________
10. ____________________
11. ____________________

Chemical and Physical Processes of Digestion: Computer Simulation

OBJECTIVES

1. To list the digestive system enzymes involved in the digestion of proteins, fats, and carbohydrates; to state their site of origin; and to summarize the environmental conditions promoting their optimal functioning.
2. To recognize the variation between different types of enzyme assays.
3. To name the end products of digestion of proteins, fats, and carbohydrates.
4. To perform the appropriate chemical tests to determine if digestion of a particular food has occurred.
5. To cite the function(s) of bile in the digestive process.
6. To discuss the possible role of temperature and pH in the regulation of enzyme activity.
7. To define *enzyme, catalyst, hydrolase, substrate,* and *control.*
8. To explain why swallowing is both a voluntary and a reflex activity.
9. To discuss the role of the tongue, larynx, and gastroesophageal sphincter in swallowing.
10. To compare and contrast segmentation and peristalsis as mechanisms of propulsion.

The digestive system is a physiological marvel, composed of finely orchestrated chemical and physical activities. The food we ingest must be broken down into smaller subunits for us to absorb the nutrients we need, and digestion involves a complex sequence of mechanical and chemical processes designed to achieve this goal as efficiently as possible. As food passes through the gastrointestinal tract, it is progressively broken down by the mechanical action of smooth muscle and the chemical action of enzymes until most nutrients have been extracted and absorbed into the blood.

Chemical Digestion of Foodstuffs: Enzymatic Action

Nutrients can only be absorbed when broken down into their monomer form, so food digestion is a prerequisite to food absorption.

Enzymes are large protein molecules produced by body cells. They are biological **catalysts** that increase the rate of a chemical reaction without becoming part of the product. The digestive enzymes are hydrolytic enzymes, or **hydrolases,** which break down organic food molecules, or **substrates,** by adding water to the molecular bonds, thus cleaving the bonds between the subunits or monomers.

A hydrolytic enzyme is highly specific in its action. Each enzyme hydrolyzes one or, at most, a small group of substrate molecules, and specific environmental conditions are necessary for an enzyme to function optimally. For example, in extreme environments such as high temperature, an enzyme can unravel or denature due to the effect that temperature has on the three-dimensional structure of the protein.

Because digestive enzymes actually function outside the body cells in the digestive tract lumen, their hydrolytic activity can also be studied in a test tube.

See Figure 1b for an overview of chemical digestion sites in the body. Such in vitro studies provide a convenient laboratory environment for investigating the effect of various factors on enzymatic activity.

Carbohydrate Digestion

In this experiment you will investigate the hydrolysis of starch to maltose by salivary amylase, the enzyme produced by the salivary glands and secreted into the mouth. For you to be able to detect whether or not enzymatic action has occurred, you need to be able to identify the presence of these substances to determine to what extent hydrolysis has occurred. Thus, **controls** must be prepared to provide a known standard against which comparisons can be made. The controls will vary for each experiment and will be discussed in each enzyme section in this exercise.

Starch decreases and sugar increases as digestion proceeds according to the following equation:

$$\text{Starch} + \text{water} \xrightarrow{\text{amylase}} \text{X maltose}$$

Because the chemical changes that occur as starch is digested to maltose cannot be seen by the naked eye, you need to conduct an *enzyme assay,* the chemical method of detecting the presence of digested substances. You will perform two enzyme assays on each sample. The IKI assay detects the presence of starch and the Benedict's assay tests for the presence of reducing sugars, such as glucose or maltose, which are the digestion products of starch. Normally a caramel-colored solution, IKI turns blue-black in the presence of starch. Benedict's reagent is a bright blue solution that changes to green to orange to reddish-brown with increasing amounts of maltose. It is important to understand that enzyme assays only indicate the presence or absence of substances. It is up to you to analyze the results of the experiments to decide if enzymatic hydrolysis has occurred.

Choose **Exercise 39B: Chemical and Physical Processes of Digestion** from the drop-down menu and click **GO.** Then click **Amylase.** The opening screen will appear in a few seconds (Figure 1). To familiarize yourself with the equipment, choose **Balloons On/Off** from the **Help** menu. This feature allows you to scroll around the screen and view equipment labels. You can turn off this feature by returning to the **Help**

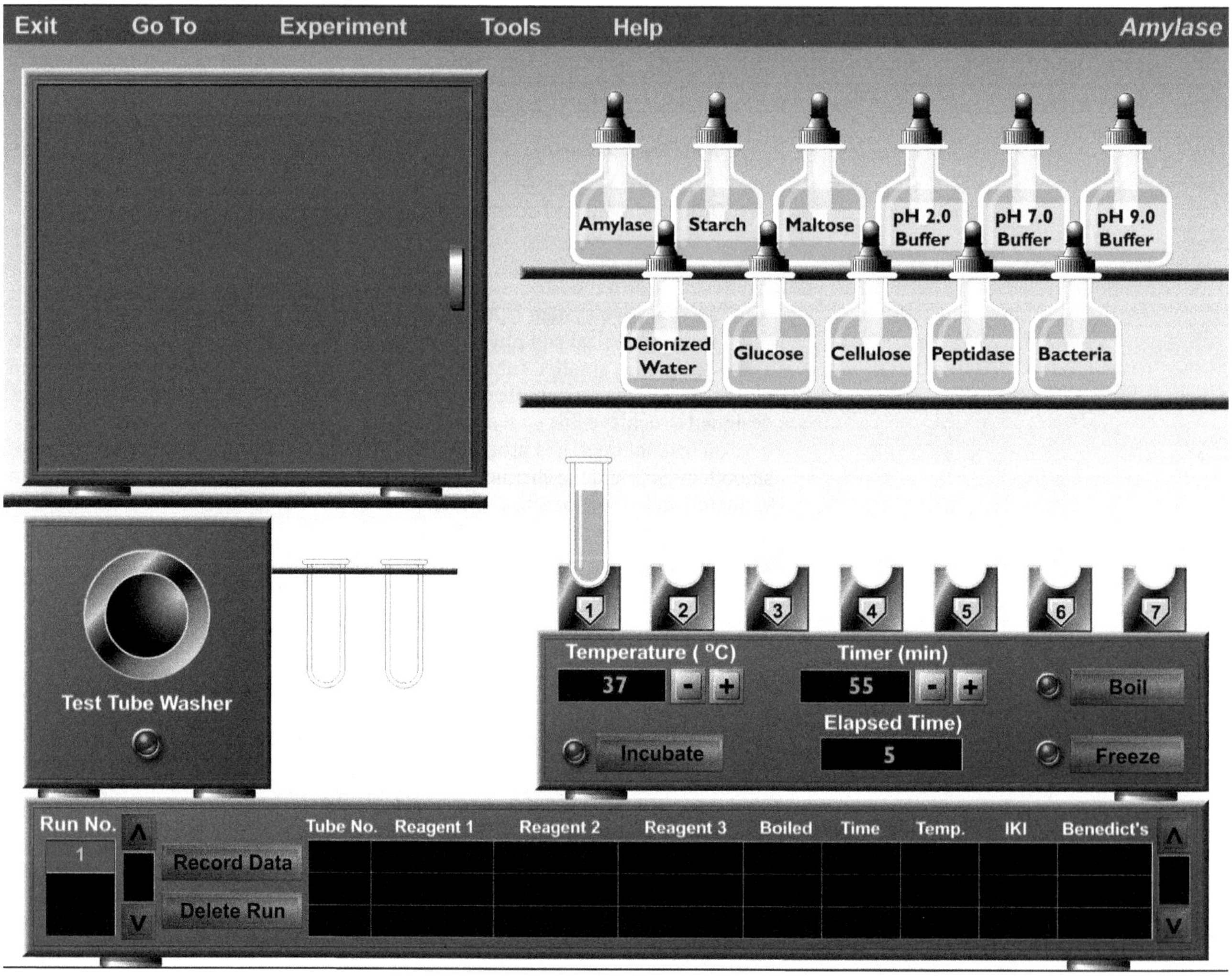

(a)

FIGURE 1 **Chemical digestion.** (**a**) Opening screen of the Amylase experiment.

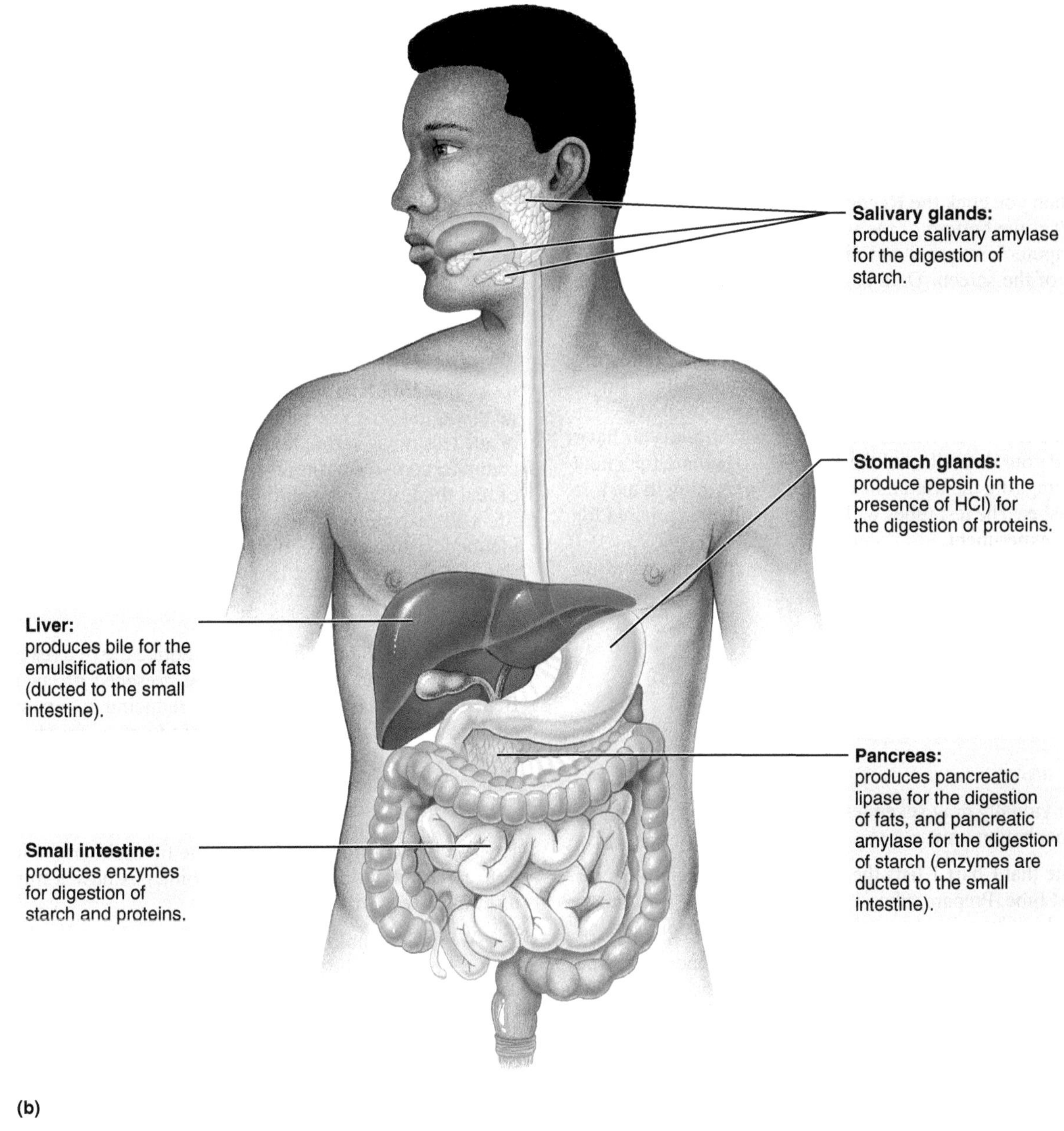
Salivary glands:
produce salivary amylase for the digestion of starch.
Stomach glands:
produce pepsin (in the presence of HCl) for the digestion of proteins.
Liver:
produces bile for the emulsification of fats (ducted to the small intestine).
Pancreas:
produces pancreatic lipase for the digestion of fats, and pancreatic amylase for the digestion of starch (enzymes are ducted to the small intestine).
Small intestine:
produces enzymes for digestion of starch and proteins.
(b)

FIGURE 1 *(Continued)* **Chemical digestion.** (**b**) A few sites of chemical digestion and the organs that produce the enzymes of chemical digestion.

menu and selecting **Balloons On/Off**. The *solutions shelf* in the upper right part of the screen contains the substances to be used in the experiment. The *incubation unit* beneath the solutions shelf contains a rack of test tube holders and the apparatus needed to run the experiments. Test tubes from the *test tube washer* on the left part of the screen are loaded into the rack in the incubation unit by clicking and holding the mouse button on the first tube, and then releasing (dragging-and-dropping) it into any position in the rack. The substances in the dropper bottles on the solutions shelf are dispensed by dragging-and-dropping the dropper cap to a position over any test tube in the rack and then releasing it. During each dispensing event, five drops of solution drip into the test tube; then the dropper cap automatically returns to its position in the bottle.

Each test tube holder in the incubation unit not only supports but also allows you to boil the contents of a single test tube. Clicking the numbered button at the base of a test tube holder causes that single tube to descend into the incubation unit. To boil the contents of all tubes inside the incubation unit, click **Boil.** After they have been boiled, the tubes automatically rise. You can adjust the incubation temperature for the experiment by clicking the (+) or (−) buttons next to the Temperature window. Set the incubation time by clicking the **(+)** or **(−)** buttons next to the Timer window. Clicking the **Incubate** button starts the timer and causes the entire rack of tube holders to descend into the incubation unit where the tubes will be incubated at the temperature and the time indicated. While incubating, the tubes are automatically agitated to ensure that their contents are well mixed. During the experiment, elapsed time is displayed in the Elapsed Time window.

The cabinet doors in the *assay cabinet* above the test tube washer are closed at the beginning of the experiment, but they automatically open when the set time for incubation has elapsed. The assay cabinet contains the reagents and glassware needed to assay your experimental samples.

When you click the **Record Data** button in the *data control unit* at the bottom of the screen, your data is recorded in the computer's memory and displayed in the data grid at the bottom of the screen. Data displayed in the grid include the tube number, the three substances (additives) dispensed into each tube, whether or not a sample was boiled, the time and incubation temperature, and (+) or (−) marks indicating enzyme assay results. If you are not satisfied with a single run, you can click **Delete Run** to erase an experiment.

Once an experimental run is completed and you have recorded your data, discard the test tubes to prepare for a new run by dragging the used tubes to the large opening in the test tube washer. The test tubes will automatically be prepared for the next experiment.

The enzymes used in this simulation and their secreting organs are summarized in Figure 1b.

ACTIVITY 1

Assessing Starch Digestion by Salivary Amylase

Incubation

1. Individually drag seven test tubes to the test tube holders in the incubation unit.

2. Note that Chart 1 lists the substances and conditions for each test tube. Prepare tubes 1 through 7 with the substances indicated in Chart 1 below using the following approach.

- Click and hold the mouse button on the dropper cap of the desired substance on the solutions shelf.
- While still holding the mouse button down, drag the dropper cap to the top of the desired test tube.
- Release the mouse button to dispense the substance. The dropper cap automatically returns to its bottle.

3. When all tubes are prepared, click the number **(1)** under the first test tube. The tube will descend into the incubation unit. All other tubes should remain in the raised position.

4. Click **Boil** to boil tube 1. After boiling for a few moments, the tube will automatically rise.

5. Now adjust the incubation temperature to 37°C and the timer to 60 min (compressed time) by clicking the (+) or (−) buttons.

6. Click **Incubate** to start the run. The incubation unit will gently agitate the test tube rack, evenly mixing the contents of all test tubes throughout the incubation. Notice that the computer compresses the 60-minute time period into 60 seconds of real time, so what would be a 60-minute incubation in real life will take only 60 seconds in the simulation. When the incubation time elapses, the test tube rack will automatically rise, and the doors to the assay cabinet will open.

Assays

After the assay cabinet doors open, notice the two reagents in the assay cabinet. IKI tests for the presence of starch and Benedict's detects the presence of reducing sugars such as glucose or maltose, the digestion products of starch. Below the reagents are seven small assay tubes into which you will dispense a small amount of test solution from the incubated samples in the incubation unit, plus a drop of IKI.

1. Click and hold the mouse on the first tube in the incubation unit. Notice that the mouse pointer is now a miniature test tube tilted to the left.

2. While still holding the mouse button down, move the mouse pointer to the first small assay tube on the left side of

CHART 1 Salivary Amylase Digestion of Starch

Tube no.	1	2	3	4	5	6	7
Additives	Amylase Starch pH 7.0 buffer	Amylase Starch pH 7.0 buffer	Amylase D.I. water pH 7.0 buffer	D.I. water Starch pH 7.0 buffer	D.I. water Maltose pH 7.0 buffer	Amylase Starch pH 2.0 buffer	Amylase Starch pH 9.0 buffer
Incubation condition	Boil first, then incubate at 37°C for 60 minutes	37°C	37°C	37°C	37°C	37°C	37°C
IKI test							
Benedict's test							

Note: D.I. water = deionized water

the assay cabinet. Release the mouse button. Watch the first test tube automatically decant approximately half of its contents into the first assay tube on the left.

3. Repeat steps 1 and 2 for the remaining tubes in the incubation unit, moving to a fresh assay tube each time.

4. Next, click and hold the mouse on the IKI dropper cap and drag it to the first assay tube. Release the mouse button to dispense a drop of IKI into the first assay tube on the left. You will see IKI drip into the tube, which may cause a color change in the solution. A blue-black color indicates a **positive starch test.** If starch is not present, the mixture will look like diluted IKI, a **negative starch test.** Intermediate starch amounts result in a pale gray color. The dropper will automatically move across and dispense IKI to the remaining tubes.

5. Record your results (+ for positive, − for negative) in Chart 1.

6. Dispense Benedict's reagent into the remaining mixture in each tube in the incubation unit by dragging-and-dropping the Benedict's dropper cap to the first tube. Repeat this for the remaining test tubes on top of the incubator.

7. After Benedict's reagent has been delivered to each tube in the incubation unit, click **Boil.** The entire tube rack will descend into the incubation unit and automatically boil the tube contents for a few moments.

8. When the rack of tubes rises, inspect the tubes for color change. A green-to-reddish color indicates that a reducing sugar is present; this is a **positive sugar test.** An orange-colored sample contains more sugar than a green sample. A reddish-brown color indicates even more sugar. A negative sugar test is indicated by no color change from the original bright blue. Record your results in Chart 1. Use a (+) for a green sample, a (++) for a reddish-brown sample, and a (−) for a blue sample.

9. Click **Record Data** to display your results in the grid and retain your data in the computer's memory for later analysis. To repeat the experiment, drag all test tubes to the test tube washer and start again.

10. Answer the following questions, referring to the chart (or the data grid in the simulation) as necessary. Hint: Closely examine the IKI and Benedict's results for each tube.

What do tubes 2, 6, and 7 reveal about pH and amylase activity? Hint: What variable was changed in the procedure?

____

____

Which pH buffer allowed the highest amylase activity?

____

Which tube indicates that the amylase was not contaminated with maltose? ______________________

Which tubes indicate that the deionized water did not contain contaminating starch or maltose? ______________

If we left out control tubes 3, 4, or 5, what objections could be raised to the statement: "Amylase digests starch to maltose"? (Hint: Think about the purity of the chemical solutions.)

____

____

Would the amylase present in saliva be active in the stomach? Explain your answer.

____

____

What effect does boiling have on enzyme activity?

____

____

ACTIVITY 2

Assessing Cellulose Digestion

If any test tubes are still in the incubator, click and drag them to the test tube washer before beginning this activity. In this activity, we will test to see whether amylase digests *cellulose.*

Incubation

1. Individually drag seven test tubes to the test tube holders in the incubation unit.

2. Prepare tubes 1 through 7 with the substances indicated in Chart 2 on the next page using the following approach:

- Click and hold the mouse button on the dropper cap of the desired substance on the solutions shelf.
- While holding the mouse button down, drag the dropper cap to the top of the desired test tube.
- Release the mouse button to dispense the substance. The dropper cap automatically returns to its bottle.

3. When all tubes are prepared, click the number **(1)** under the first test tube. The tube will descend into the incubation unit.

4. Click **Freeze.** The tube's contents will be subjected to a temperature of −25°C. The tube will then automatically rise, with the contents of the tube frozen.

5. Adjust the incubation temperature to 37°C and the timer to 60 minutes by clicking the appropriate (+) or (−) buttons.

6. Click **Incubate** to start the run. The incubation unit will gently agitate the tubes as they incubate to thoroughly mix the tubes' contents. At the end of the incubation period, the tubes will ascend to their original positions on top of the incubator, and the doors to the assay cabinet will open.

Assays

When the assay cabinet opens, notice the two reagents in the cabinet. They are the same ones as in the previous activity: IKI will test for the presence of starch, and Benedict's solution will test for the presence of maltose. IKI turns blue-black in the presence of cellulose as well as starch. On the floor of the cabinet are seven small tubes that you will use to test the results of your experiment. The procedure will be identical to the one from the previous activity:

1. Click and hold the mouse on the first tube in the incubation unit. Notice that the mouse pointer is now a miniature test tube tilted to the left.

2. While still holding the mouse button down, move the mouse pointer to the first small assay tube on the left side of the assay cabinet. Release the mouse button.

3. Repeat steps 1 and 2 for the remaining tubes in the incubation unit, moving to a fresh assay tube each time.

4. Next, click and hold the mouse on the IKI dropper cap, and drag it to the first assay tube. Release the mouse button to dispense a drop of IKI into the first assay tube on the left. You will see IKI drip into the tube, which may cause a color change in the solution. A blue-black color indicates the presence of starch. If there is only a small amount of starch, you may see a pale gray color. If starch is not present, the mixture will look like diluted IKI. The dropper will automatically move across and dispense IKI to the remaining tubes.

5. Note the color of each tube. Record your results in Chart 2.

6. Dispense Benedict's reagent into the remaining mixture in each tube in the incubation unit by dragging-and-dropping the Benedict's dropper cap to the first tube. Repeat this for the remaining test tubes on top of the incubator.

7. After Benedict's reagent has been delivered to each tube in the incubation unit, click **Boil.** The entire tube rack will descend into the incubation unit and automatically boil the tube contents for a few moments.

8. When the rack of tubes rises, inspect the tubes for color change. A green to reddish color indicates that a reducing sugar is present for a positive sugar test. An orange sample indicates more sugar than the green color, and a reddish-brown indicates the highest amounts of sugar. If there has been no color change from the original blue, no sugar is present in the tube. Record your results in Chart 2. Use a (+) for a green sample, a (++) for a reddish-brown sample, and a (−) for a blue sample.

9. Click **Record Data** to display your results in the grid and retain your data in the computer's memory for later analysis. To repeat the experiment, drag all test tubes to the test tube washer and start again.

10. Answer the following questions, referring to the chart.

Which tubes showed that starch or cellulose was still present?

____

Which tubes tested positive for the presence of reducing sugars?

____

What was the effect of freezing tube 1?

____

How does the effect of freezing differ from the effect of boiling?

____

____

CHART 2 **Enzyme Digestion of Starch and Cellulose**

Tube no.	1	2	3	4	5	6	7
Additives	Amylase Starch pH 7.0 buffer	Amylase Starch pH 7.0 buffer	Amylase Glucose pH 7.0 buffer	Amylase Cellulose pH 7.0 buffer	Amylase Cellulose D.I. water	Peptidase Starch pH 7.0 buffer	Bacteria Cellulose pH 7.0 buffer
Incubation condition	Freeze first, then incubate at 37°C for 60 minutes	37°C 60 min	37°C 60 min	37°C 60 min	37°C 60 min	37°C 60 min	37°C 60 min
IKI test							
Benedict's test							

Note: D.I. water = deionized water

Does amylase use cellulose as a substrate? Hint: Look at the results for tube 4.

____

____

What effect did the addition of bacteria have on the digestion of cellulose?

____

____

What was the effect of the different enzyme, peptidase, used in tube 6? Explain your answer, based on what you know about the substrate of peptidase.

____

____

11. Click **Tools** → **Print Data** to print your recorded data.

Protein Digestion by Pepsin

The chief cells of the stomach glands produce pepsin, a protein-digesting enzyme. Pepsin hydrolyzes proteins to small fragments (polypeptides and a few free amino acids). In this experiment, you will use BAPNA, a synthetic "protein" that is transparent and colorless when in solution. However, if an active, protein-digesting enzyme such as pepsin is present, the solution will become yellow. You can use this characteristic to detect pepsin activity: the solution turns yellow if the enzyme digests the BAPNA substrate; it remains colorless if pepsin is not active or not present. One advantage of using a synthetic substrate is that you do not need any additional indicator reagents to see enzyme activity.

Choose **Pepsin** from the **Experiment** menu. The opening screen will appear in a few seconds (Figure 2). The solutions shelf, test tube washer, and incubation equipment are the same as in the amylase experiment; only the solutions have changed.

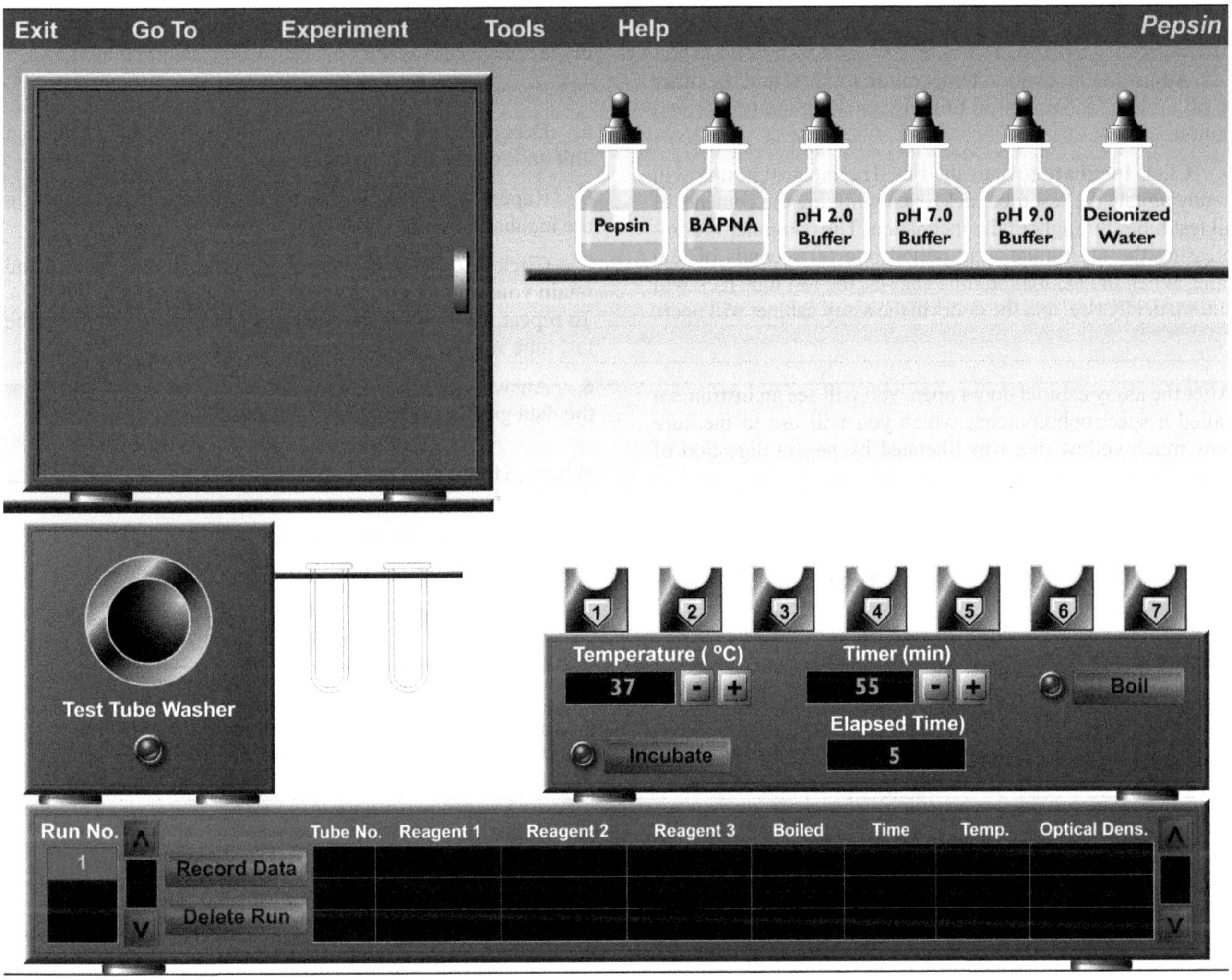

FIGURE 2 Opening screen of the Pepsin Experiment.

Data displayed in the grid include the tube number, the three substances dispensed into each tube, a (+) or (−) mark indicating whether or not a sample was boiled, the time and temperature of the incubation, and the optical density measurement indicating enzyme assay results.

ACTIVITY 3

Assessing Protein Digestion by Pepsin

Pepsin Incubation

1. Individually drag six test tubes to the test tube holders in the incubation unit.
2. Prepare the tubes with the substances indicated in Chart 3 below using the following method.
   - Click and hold the mouse button on the dropper cap of the desired substance and drag the dropper cap to the top of the desired test tube.
   - Release the mouse button to dispense the substance.
3. Once all tubes are prepared, click the number **(1)** under the first test tube. The tube will descend into the incubation unit. All other tubes should remain in the raised position.
4. Click **Boil** to boil tube 1. After boiling for a few moments, the tube will automatically rise.
5. Adjust the incubation temperature to 37°C and the timer to 60 minutes (compressed time) by clicking the (+) or (−) button.
6. Click **Incubate** to start the run. The incubation unit will gently agitate the test tube rack, evenly mixing the contents of all test tubes throughout the incubation. The computer is compressing the 60-minute time period into 60 seconds of real time. When the incubation time elapses, the test tube rack will automatically rise, and the doors to the assay cabinet will open.

Pepsin Assay

After the assay cabinet doors open, you will see an instrument called a spectrophotometer, which you will use to measure how much yellow dye was liberated by pepsin digestion of BAPNA. When a test tube is dragged to the holder in the spectrophotometer and the **Analyze** button is clicked, the instrument will shine a light through a specimen to measure the amount of light absorbed by the sample within the tube. The measure of the amount of light absorbed by the solution is known as its *optical density.* A colorless solution does not absorb light, whereas a colored solution has a relatively high light absorbance. For example, a colorless solution has an optical density of 0.0. A colored solution, however, absorbs some of the light emitted by the spectrophotometer, resulting in an optical density reading greater than zero.

In this experiment a yellow-colored solution is a direct indication of the amount of BAPNA digested by pepsin. Although you can visually estimate the yellow color produced by pepsin digestion of BAPNA, the spectrophotometer precisely measures how much BAPNA digestion occurred in the experiment.

1. Click and hold the mouse on the first tube in the incubation unit and drag it to the holder in the spectrophotometer.
2. Release the mouse button to drop the tube into the holder.
3. Click **Analyze.** You will see light shining through the solution in the test tube as the spectrophotometer measures its optical density. The optical density of the sample will be displayed in the optical density window below the Analyze button.
4. Record the optical density in Chart 3.
5. Drag the tube to its original position in the incubation unit and release the mouse button.
6. Repeat steps 1 through 5 for the remaining test tubes in the incubation unit.
7. Click **Record Data** to display your results in the grid and retain your data in the computer's memory for later analysis. To repeat the experiment, you must drag all test tubes to the test tube washer and start again.
8. Answer the following questions, referring to Chart 3 (or the data grid in the simulation) as necessary.

Which pH provided the highest pepsin activity? __________

CHART 3 **Pepsin Digestion of Protein**

Tube no.	1	2	3	4	5	6
Additives	Pepsin BAPNA pH 2.0 buffer	Pepsin BAPNA pH 2.0 buffer	Pepsin D.I. water pH 2.0 buffer	D.I. water BAPNA pH 2.0 buffer	Pepsin BAPNA pH 7.0 buffer	Pepsin BAPNA pH 9.0 buffer
Incubation condition	Boil first, then incubate at 37°C for 60 minutes	37°C 60 min	37°C 60 min	37°C 60 min	37°C 60 min	37°C 60 min
Optical density	>					

Note: D.I. water = deionized water

Would pepsin be active in the mouth? Explain your answer.

____

____

How did the results of tube 1 compare with those of tube 2?

____

Tubes 1 and 2 contained the same substances. Explain why their optical density measurements were different.

____

____

Did the pepsin or deionized water contain any contaminating digested BAPNA? Which tubes confirm this?

____

____

What do you think would happen if you reduced the incubation time to 30 minutes? Use the simulation to help you answer this question if you are not sure.

____

____

What do you think would happen if you decreased the temperature of incubation to 10°C? Use the simulation to help you answer this question if you are not sure.

____

____

9. Click **Tools** → **Print Data** to print your recorded data.

Fat Digestion by Pancreatic Lipase and the Action of Bile

The treatment that fats and oils undergo during digestion in the small intestine is a bit more complicated than that of carbohydrates or proteins. Fats and oils require pretreatment with bile to physically emulsify the fats. As a result, two sets of reactions must occur. First:

$$\text{Fats/oils} \xrightarrow[\text{(emulsification)}]{\text{bile}} \text{minute fat/oil droplets}$$

Then:

$$\text{Fat/oil droplets} \xrightarrow{\text{lipase}} \text{monoglycerides and fatty acids}$$

Lipase hydrolyzes fats and oils to their component monoglycerides and two fatty acids. Occasionally lipase hydrolyzes fats and oils to glycerol and three fatty acids.

The fact that some of the end products of fat digestion (fatty acids) are organic acids that decrease the pH provides an easy way to recognize that digestion is ongoing or completed. You will be using a pH meter in the assay cabinet to record the drop in pH as the test tube contents become acid.

Choose **Lipase** from the **Experiment** menu. The opening screen will appear in a few seconds (Figure 3). The solutions shelf, test tube washer, and incubation equipment are the same as in the previous two experiments; only the solutions have changed.

Data displayed in the grid include the tube number, the four reagents dispensed into each tube, a (+) or (−) mark indicating whether or not a sample was boiled, the time and temperature of the incubation, and the pH measurement indicating enzyme assay results.

ACTIVITY 4

Assessing Fat Digestion by Pancreatic Lipase and the Action of Bile

Lipase Incubation

1. Individually drag 6 test tubes to the test tube holders in the incubation unit.

2. Prepare the tubes with the solutions indicated in Chart 4 by using the following method.

- Click and hold the mouse button on the dropper cap of the desired substance.
- While holding the mouse button down, drag the dropper cap to the top of the desired test tube.
- Release the mouse button to dispense the substance.

3. Adjust the incubation temperature to 37°C and the timer to 60 minutes (compressed time) by clicking the (+) or (−) button.

4. Click **Incubate** to start the run. The incubation unit will gently agitate the test tube rack, evenly mixing the contents of all test tubes throughout the incubation. The computer is compressing the 60-minute time period into 60 seconds of real time. When the incubation time elapses, the test tube rack automatically rises, and the doors to the assay cabinet open.

Lipase Assay

After the assay cabinet doors open, you will see a pH meter that you will use to measure the relative acidity of your test solutions. When a test tube is dragged to the holder in the pH meter and the Measure pH button is clicked, a probe will descend into the sample, take a pH reading, and then retract. The pH of the sample will be displayed in the pH window below the Measure pH button. A solution containing fatty acids liberated from fat by the action of lipase will exhibit a lower pH than one without fatty acids.

1. Click and hold the mouse on the first tube in the incubation unit, and drag it to the holder in the pH meter. Release the mouse button to drop the tube into the holder.

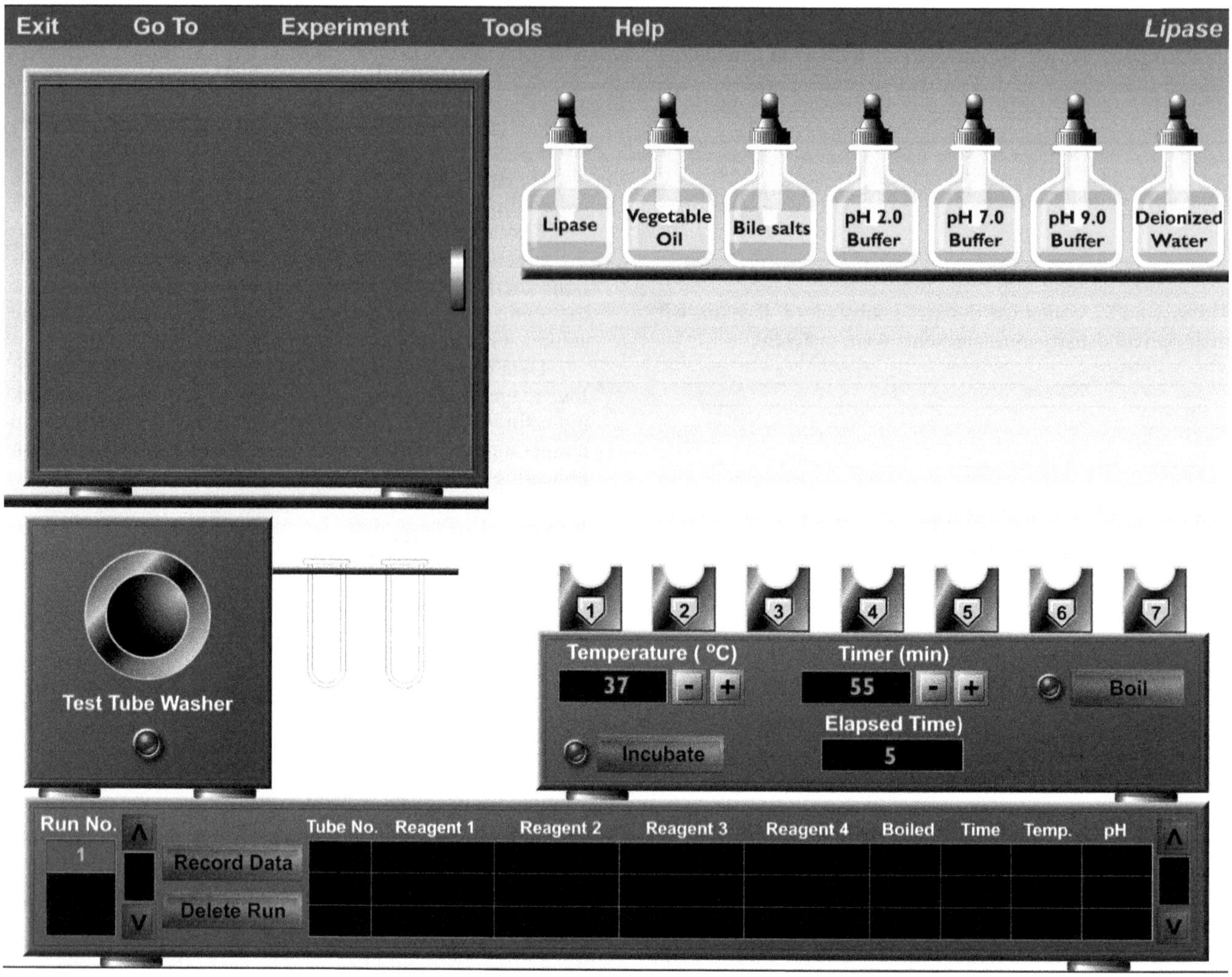

FIGURE 3 **Opening screen of the Lipase experiment.**

2. Click **Measure pH.**
3. In Chart 4, record the pH displayed in the pH window.
4. Drag the test tube in the pH meter to its original position in the incubation unit, and release the mouse button.
5. Repeat steps 1 through 4 for the remaining test tubes in the incubation unit.
6. Click **Record Data** to display your results in the grid and retain your data in the computer's memory for later analysis. To repeat the experiment, you must drag all test tubes to the test tube washer and begin again.
7. Answer the following questions, referring to chart 4 (or the data grid in the simulation) as necessary.

Explain the difference in activity between tubes 1 and 2.

____

____

Can we determine if fat hydrolysis has occurred in tube 6?

_______ Explain your answer. ______________________

____

Which pH resulted in maximum lipase activity? ________

Can we determine if fat hydrolysis has occurred in tube 5?

____

In theory, would lipase be active in the mouth? _______

Would it be active in the stomach? _______

Explain your answers. ______________________

____

CHART 4 **Pancreatic Lipase Digestion of Fats and the Action of Bile**

Tube no.	1	2	3	4	5	6
Additives	Lipase Vegetable oil Bile salts pH 7.0 buffer	Lipase Vegetable oil D.I. water pH 7.0 buffer	Lipase D.I. water Bile salts pH 9.0 buffer	D.I. water Vegetable oil Bile salts pH 7.0 buffer	Lipase Vegetable oil Bile salts pH 2.0 buffer	Lipase Vegetable oil Bile salts pH 9.0 buffer
Incubation condition	37°C 60 min	37°C 60 min	37°C 60 min	37°C 60 min	37°C 60 min	37°C 60 min
pH						

Note: D.I. = deionized water

What is the substrate, and what subunit is formed in this experiment? ______________________________

____

8. Click **Tools → Print Data** to print your recorded data.

Physical Processes: Mechanisms of Food Propulsion and Mixing

Although enzyme activity is an essential part of the overall digestion process, food must also be processed physically by churning and chewing and moved by mechanical means along the tract if digestion and absorption are to be completed. Just about any time organs exhibit mobility, muscles are involved, and movements of and in the gastrointestinal tract are no exception. Although we tend to think only of smooth muscles for visceral activities, both skeletal and smooth muscles are necessary in digestion. This fact is demonstrated by the simple trials in the next activity. Obtain the following materials:

- Water pitcher
- Paper cups
- Stethoscope
- Alcohol swabs
- Disposable autoclave bag

ACTIVITY 5

Studying Mechanisms of Food Propulsion and Mixing: Deglutition (Swallowing)

Swallowing, or *deglutition,* which is largely the result of skeletal muscle activity, occurs in two phases: *buccal* (mouth) and *pharyngeal-esophageal.* The initial phase—the buccal—is voluntarily controlled and initiated by the tongue. Once begun, the process continues involuntarily in the pharynx and esophagus, through peristalsis, resulting in the delivery of the swallowed contents to the stomach.

1. While swallowing a mouthful of water from a paper cup, consciously note the movement of your tongue during the process. Record your observations.

____

____

____

2. Repeat the swallowing process while your laboratory partner watches the externally visible movements of your larynx. This movement is more obvious in a male, who has a larger Adam's apple. Record your observations.

____

____

What do these movements accomplish? ______________________________

____

____

3. Your lab partner should clean the ear pieces of a stethoscope with an alcohol swab and don the stethoscope. Then your lab partner should place the diaphragm of the stethoscope on your abdominal wall, approximately 1 inch below the xiphoid process and slightly to the left, to listen for sounds as you again take two or three swallows of water. There should be two audible sounds. The first sound occurs when the water splashes against the gastroesophageal sphincter. The second occurs when the peristaltic wave of the esophagus arrives at the sphincter and the sphincter opens, allowing water to gurgle into the stomach. Determine, as accurately as possible, the time interval between these two sounds and record it below.

Interval between arrival of water at the sphincter and the opening of the sphincter:

_______________ sec

This interval gives a fair indication of the time it takes for the peristaltic wave to travel down the 10-inch-long esophagus. Actually the time interval is slightly less than it seems because pressure causes the sphincter to relax before the peristaltic wave reaches it.

Dispose of the used paper cup in the autoclave bag. ■

Segmentation and Peristalsis

Although several types of movement occur in the digestive tract organs, segmentation and peristalsis are most important as mixing and propulsive mechanisms.

Segmental movements are local constrictions of the organ wall that occur rhythmically. They serve mainly to mix the foodstuffs with digestive juices and to increase the rate of absorption by continually moving different portions of the chyme over adjacent regions of the intestinal wall. However, segmentation is an important means of food propulsion in the small intestine, and slow segmenting movements called haustral contractions are common in the large intestine.

Peristaltic movements are the major means of propelling food through most of the digestive viscera. Essentially they are waves of contraction followed by waves of relaxation that squeeze foodstuffs through the alimentary canal, and they are superimposed on segmental movements.

Histology Review Supplement

For a review of digestive tissue, go to **Exercise 6B: Histology Atlas and Review** on **myA&P** to print out the **Digestive Tissue Review** worksheet.

NAME ______________________________

LAB TIME/DATE ______________________

Chemical and Physical Processes of Digestion: Computer Simulation

Carbohydrate Digestion

The following questions refer to Activity 1: Assessing Starch Digestion by Salivary Amylase.

1. At what pH did you see the highest activity of salivary amylase? ________ Why?

2. How do you know that the amylase did not have any contaminating maltose?

3. What effect did boiling have on enzyme activity? Why?

4. Describe the substrate and the subunit product of amylase.

The following questions refer to Activity 2: Assessing Cellulose Digestion.

5. Does amylase use cellulose as a substrate? Explain.

6. Did freezing have an effect on the activity of amylase? Explain.

7. Do you think that the bacterial suspension contained the enzyme cellulase (an enzyme that digests cellulose)? Why or why not?

8. What is the substrate of peptidase? Explain, based upon your results.

Protein Digestion by Pepsin

The following questions refer to Activity 3: Assessing Protein Digestion by Pepsin.

9. At which pH did you see the highest activity of pepsin? ______ How does this correlate to the location of pepsin in the body? ______________________________

____

10. What effect did boiling have on pepsin? ______________________________

____

11. Was there any digested BAPNA contaminating the pepsin or deionized (DI) water? ______

How can you tell? ______________________________

____

12. What is the substrate in this experiment? ______________________________

What is the usual substrate for pepsin, and what subunits are formed with pepsin activity?

____

____

13. What was the effect of decreasing the incubation time on the optical density results?

____

14. What effect would decreased incubation temperature have on pepsin activity? Why?

____

____

15. What was the significance of using 37°C for the incubation? ______________________________

____

Fat Digestion by Pancreatic Lipase and the Action of Bile

The following questions refer to Activity 4: Assessing Fat Digestion by Pancreatic Lipase and the Action of Bile.

16. Describe the activity of lipase with and without the addition of bile salts. Refer to Chart 4 for pH values. ______

____

17. Is the activity of bile a chemical or a physical process? Explain. ______________________________

____

18. What pH resulted in the maximum pancreatic lipase activity? ______

How does this optimal pH correlate to the enzyme's location in the body? ______

______

19. Explain whether or not we can determine fat hydrolysis in tube 5. Why or why not?

______

______

20. What is the substrate in this experiment? ______

What subunits does lipase form? ______

Physical Process: Mechanisms of Food Propulsion and Mixing

The following questions refer to Activity 5: Studying Mechanisms of Food Propulsion and Mixing: Deglutition (Swallowing).

21. Explain the significance of the movement of the tongue during swallowing. ______

______

22. Describe three events that occur during the pharyngeal-esophageal phase of deglutition. ______

______

______

23. What was the time interval that you recorded between the first and second sound?

______